# USMLE AND COMLEX
# SUCCESS
## SECRETS

Hi Dr. precious Akinsanya,
I wish you all the best in your
medical career.

Dr. Adeleke Adeswemi

10/1/2020

# USMLE AND COMLEX
# SUCCESS
# SECRETS

How Every Medical Student Can Use A Simple Proven Formula to
Score Over 260 on the USMLE and 760 on the COMLEX,
Become the Top Candidate and Match into Top U.S Residency

ADELEKE ADESINA, DO

## Disclaimer

USMLE® and COMLEX® are trademarks of the National Board of Medical Examiners, Inc. ("NBME") and National Board of Osteopathic Medical Examiners, Inc. ("NBOME"). All USMLE and COMLEX examination test items are the exclusive confidential property of the NBME and NBOME. All NBME and NBOME test items are protected by confidentiality agreements with candidates and NBME/NBOME's copyright registration.

No USMLE or COMLEX test item is included within any SMASHUSMLE's test preparation materials, and SMASHUSMLE does not recruit or permit Authors to write test preparation questions based upon actual test items from any USMLE or COMLEX examination. SMASHUSMLE is not affiliated or associated with the NBME or NBOME. The NBME or NBOME does not review, sponsor or endorse any product of Smashusmle Reviews.

**Authors**
**Adeleke T. Adesina, DO**
Emergency Medicine Physician
Department of Emergency Medicine

**Dr. Juan Chango, MD**
Internal Medicine Resident
University of Connecticut

**Farook Wael Taha, DO**
Emergency Medicine Physician
Department of Emergency Medicine

**Contributors**
Fadi, Al- Asadi, MD
Internal Medicine Resident
Mayo Clinic Internal medicine program
Neil Chavarria, MBBS
Prajay Rathore MBBS
Taiwo Ajumobi, D.O
Pediatric Resident
Oklahoma State University, Pediatrics Resident program
Tulsa, OK
Sulaiman I S Abuhaiba, MD, PhD
Clinical Neuroelectrophysiology

Dr. Sabina Ali Khan
Board certified, Pediatric Anesthesiology

Moyosore Awobajo MD
UT San Antonio, Department of Pathology

Ademola Adeseye, MD, MPH
Cardiothoracic Surgery Fellow

vi

# Dedication

*This book is dedicated to Almighty God,*
*the author and finisher of our faith.*

*To my wife, Olufunmilayo Adesina for supporting me*
*through all the tough years of medical school and beyond*
*and believing in my visions to become a doctorpreneur.*

*To my sons, Olamide and Oluwadamola, for always keeping*
*a smile on my face and making me proud of you.*

*And to my dad and mom, thank you for*
*encouraging me to think big and discover my true worth.*

# Contents

## About Smashusmle reviews

This book was written by Dr. Adeleke Adesina and his team at SmashUSMLE Reviews. SmashUSMLE Reviews is the leading USMLE test preparation company that has helped thousands of international medical graduates and medical students pass the USMLE on their next attempt.

The advice shared in this edition comes from over 10 years of experience teaching USMLE and COMLEX prep by Dr. Adesina, a world class instructor who has mentored and coached medical students through his online USMLE prep review course. His mission is to train you to become a better physician through online test preparation for the USMLE.

SmashUSMLE Reviews offers a self-paced USMLE course and 4-week live hybrid USMLE Masterclass for Step 1 and 2CK.

- Over 700 videos, (220 hours) of USMLE Step 1/ 2CK video lectures
- 4-Week live hybrid USMLE Step 1/ 2CK Masterclass
- 2200 USMLE Step 1
- 2100 USMLE 2CK Q-bank
- Yale-G First Aid Crush Step 2CK/ 3
- Instant access to high yield USMLE flashcards
- SMARTMD Study strategies training series
- SmashUSMLE Step 1 lecture notes
- Private Coaching Call
- USMLE prep audiobook
- Detailed 6, 12-week, 6-month Study plan
- Insider secrets to scoring 260 eBook
- Instant access to high yield USMLE flashcards
- USMLE and COMLEX Success Secrets Book
- Exclusive SMARTMD VIP WhatsApp group access
- Daily USMLE Study tips
- 24-hour email support
- USMLE Audio Masterclass
- USMLE Exam Day Rituals eBook
- How to dissect USMLE questions 2hr Webinar
- USMLE Exam Day 2hr Webinar

Sign up today at smashusmle.com to join the course.
You can reach us at admin@smashusmle.com or call (212) 465- 3339

# Here are some of our student testimonials

"I'm Dr. Monica, and I'm a recent student of Dr. Adesina's SmashUSMLE masterclass courses for step one. I recently took his course, and I have to honestly say it was the best decision I could have ever made in my entire life.

After I completed his masterclass, I felt clarity. I understood concepts that I had been struggling with for a really long time, I took my exam and I passed. This was the first time where an instructor actually showed passion for teaching. Someone who actually reached out and gave you personal coaching.

I just want to let you know that if you're contemplating taking his courses, I'm telling you, you need to go and sign up today."

Monica, IMG

USMLE Score 225


Amazing program. It has been very helpful in providing the structure that I need, while allowing for flexibility and self-pacing. I love having access to the video-library and other resources provided both via the Self-paced Lifetime membership and the Masterclasses. Having a personal USMLE coach that can guide and tutor me via Skype sessions is also extremely helpful, and I'm grateful for the support. I am part of the SmartMD WhatsApp group which helps us review/discuss clinical vignettes and ask questions while networking and sharing study tips etc. It's helpful via this group chat to have direct access to Dr. Adesina and his team amongst other student doctors at various levels of training. We're encouraged not just to pick an answer, but also to support why we rule in and/or rule out diagnoses. I appreciate Dr. Adesina and his team for developing this program in a way that's personalized to meet our needs. Fredericka, MD


"I love this review course. I've tried a few others (Kaplan, DIT, USMLErx), and this is the one that stuck out to me the most. Since they are mostly whiteboard lectures, they're straight to the point, simple, easy to understand, and easy to pay attention to. The pacing is great and doesn't feel dry like other review courses. I've also had to contact customer support for a few questions and they were fast and answered everything. They were extremely helpful, I felt like they are not like other companies that are just after money. And unlike courses like Kaplan, the course isn't padded with a ton of extra information, especially with board exams you need to know high yield. SmashUSMLE does a great job of telling you what you need to know. Highly recommended, thank you for the amazing course and I really wish I found out about this sooner. Julie, IMG

"I am a fourth-year student from Trinity medical school in St. Grenadines. I took step 1 and I failed Step 1. I knew I needed to find a coach and a personalized program and I found Smashusmle Reviews. I was paired with a tutor whom I met with once a week and he completely customized a study program for my needs. He gave me so many tips and tricks that I can carry on to my Step 2 & Step 3 studying. My tutor worked with me to get the best resources that were cost effective or free. We also discussed resume building and how to be successful on Step 2 CS and in clinicals. Dr. Adesina was involved and gave me advice before taking the USMLE exam and even called me after I got my result. I truly enjoyed the process of working with my awesome tutor and studying for Step 1.I would highly recommend the Smashusmle tutors! I passed!!! Taylar- USMLE Score 225

# Foreword

*Taking the Boards and getting a residency can be a daunting task. I remember when I was a medical student preparing to take my boards. I felt overwhelmed and remember thinking "It would be so much easier if there was a book or an expert to teach me a systematic approach on how to utilize the highest yielding resources and information available to maximize my board scores". In addition to that, I had to contend with getting the residency of my choice. "How do residencies weigh candidates? How important are board scores? What about the interview??! How do I prepare for that?!!"*

*Dr. Adesina is the founder of Smashusmle reviews and has trained thousands of medical students over the past 10 years. Dr. Adesina and his team have put together an excellent resource for those students preparing for the boards. In an easy to read format, USMLE and COMLEX Success Secrets explains how medical students should prepare for the board exams by using systematic approaches to tackle standardized exams.*

*It gives detailed explanations on how to create a schedule to efficiently study for the boards.*

*Dr. Adesina carefully explains how to easily dissect board exam questions.*

*For Osteopathic students: Should you take the USMLE or just the COMLEX? This book will help you navigate that process.*

*For International medical graduates, this book will guide you through the most important steps to getting into a US medical residency.*

*This book is a must read for every medical student and international medical graduate who wants to learn the secrets to getting high board scores and matching into residency.*

*Robert Savarese, DO*
*Author, OMT Review,*
*Board Certified, Physical Medicine and Rehabilitation,*
*Co-Founder, OMT Review Test Prep, LLC*
*omtreview.com*

"The key to achieving success in medicine is through repetition and mastery."

~Dr. Adeleke Adesina


To me, the ideal doctor would be a man endowed with profound knowledge of life and of the soul, intuitively divining any suffering or disorder of whatever kind, and restoring peace by his mere presence."

~Henri Amiel

# Preface

DEAR READER,

This book was written as a guide for medical students who are preparing for the USMLE Step 1, 2 CK, 3 and COMLEX Level 1, 2 CE, and 3 Board exams. Our goal was to give you a step-wise approach to preparing for these two exams. USMLE and COMLEX (for osteopathic students) are two different examinations, and preparations for these exams are different.

If you are an allopathic or international medical graduate, you need only to focus on the USMLE section. Osteopathic students need to also understand how to study for the COMLEX, so a chapter is dedicated to that exam.

We first describe what the USMLE and COMLEX examinations are and what score ranges students can achieve on these two tests. The book includes a chapter on *First Aid for the USMLE Step 1*, which should be one of the primary sources for your Board preparation. We then discuss the importance of using questions; we highly recommend two of the best question banks on the market: SmashUSMLE and UWorld.

Chapter 6 and 7, the integration and how to dissect USMLE questions chapter, are key to using this book. These chapters demonstrate how students should recognize common patterns with USMLE questions, and how to use a proven technique to approach answering USMLE and COMLEX questions. You should read these chapters to fully understand this process; refer back to it as you proceed with your Board preparation.

We provided a sample Board schedule to serve as a guide during your preparation; use it if it works for you. We offer a system-based learning method to cover the major topics tested on the Boards, according to First Aid for the USMLE Step 1 and Yale G First Aid, Crush USMLE Step 2 CK and 3 books. The book also offers a chapter for osteopathic students who are considering whether or not to take the USMLE Step 1 exam.

For international medical graduates, please read the ultimate survival guide for IMGs chapter. This chapter was written by Dr. Juan Chango, an IMG from Ecuador who went through the rigors of navigating through the ECFMG certification process, passed the USMLE with high scores and matched into internal medicine.

The book ends with a chapter focused primarily on how to stand out amidst the competition and how to be a better clinician.

We have been through the same situation you are in right now, and we are aware of your confusion and anxiety. We have created this book to improve your preparation. We hope this book sheds some light on how to survive the last few months of your Board preparation and helps you achieve the Board score you so wish for.

Confucius once said, *"The journey of a thousand miles begins with a step,"* and your journey is just about to begin.

# Introduction

SINCE THE LAUNCH of the first edition of this book, "How to prepare for the medical boards, secrets to success on the USMLE Step 1 and COMLEX level 1", thousands of students have successfully used this book to pass the USMLE and COMLEX exams. The strategies described in the first edition have been updated to help you succeed based on the formatting of the new exam.

As physician educators at SmashUSMLE reviews, with over 25 years of combined experience from our team, we decided to re-write this edition to help you ace this board exam.

We all have taken the USMLE/COMLEX exam and experienced the dread every medical student feels before and after taking these licensing exams. When it comes to tackling the boards most medical students feel overwhelmed, lost or confused on how to begin their preparation. We realized that most students are overwhelmed with too much resources, or do not know how to utilize the resources and information available to perform very well on these standardized exams. Most students have no systematic approach to preparing for these exams and end up developing anxiety issues over Boards.

We have encountered thousands of international medical graduates, and US medical students who ask for advice about how they should study for their Boards. Dr.Adesina, Dr.Taha and Dr. Chango all scored in the 99th percentile on their USMLE. Dr. Adesina received 17 emergency medicine interviews and matched at St. Luke's University hospital. Dr. Taha received 24 emergency medicine interviews and matched at New York Presbyterian hospital. Dr. Adesina and Dr. Taha are both board certified emergency physicians and shared the best advice to help you succeed in this edition. Dr. Chango, an international medical graduate has written the roadmap to residency section to help all international medical graduates navigate the rigors of surviving the USMLE and matching into residency. If you are reading this book, you probably have the same doubts and fears most students have. Let us start by encouraging you — you <u>will</u> pass this exam! Many students before you have taken the test and succeeded; it is your turn to seize the moment! <u>It is very hard to fail</u>, whether you believe it or not. Even if you have taken the Boards once and did not pass, it was simply because you were either not ready, or you made certain mistakes others have made prior to taking the test. This book is an excellent guide to teach you the correct plan to tackle the USMLE and COMLEX exams, with proven strategies to guide you during your preparation of the boards and beyond.

But do not be discouraged—because you failed once, twice or three times before. This exam does not define you. "What defines you is not what you do when you fail, what defines you is who you are when you rise after failing." (Author unknown)

This is a typical conversation among medical students and international medical graduates: a second-year medical student asks for advice about Board preparation from an upper-classman who just finished taking the exam.

The medical student asks, "How did you study for your boards?" The upper-classman replies: "I did a lot of questions in a Qbank and memorized First Aid for the USMLE Step 1 or 2CK book, Master the boards, or some board review book."

Some students may reply "I used Anki deck flashcards, UWorld, Pathoma, and First Aid for Step 1 or For Step 2 CK/ 3, I just did UWorld Qbank, read Master the boards". For D.O Students, it sounds similar except add OMTReview book by Savarese for OMT portion of the COMLEX to any of these resources and you are good to go.

International medical graduates (IMGs) typically go to USMLE forums, Quora and Reddit for advice and read this same basic advice, without any knowledge of how standardized medical tests like USMLE are structured. They try this basic approach and thousands of these IMGs consistently fail the USMLE every year.

International medical graduates find it difficult to navigate through the complex US health care systems, learn to pass the USMLE and match in U.S residencies.

If this age-old advice is absolutely true, why do 8-10 percent of US allopathic and osteopathic medical students fail the USMLE every year and 30 percent of IMG fail the USMLE yearly?

Are you familiar with this conversation? We bet you are! There is a common theme among medical students advising other medical students about how to prepare for boards while giving the same generalist advice of "Memorize *First Aid, Pathoma and UWorld* and do lots of questions." Maybe you feel like other students are not telling you something.

You have no idea how a student performed on his or her Boards, and no one will tell you either. So, you do not know if he or she did the bare minimum to just pass the test or performed excellently on the exam. You dare not ask students what their Board scores are! (We hope not.) It is a personal thing. Most students only share their scores with a very few people. Do not take this personally either—after you have completed your Boards, you will understand better.

There must be more to the story, right? Yes, you are correct. There is, but no one spends the time to explain it to you; they want you to figure it all out by yourself.

Here are the most common questions that most medical students want to know. Let's take a look at some of them:

How to manage my time when it's time to study for the USMLE?

How should I use "First Aid" or other board prep resources?

How should I study for Step 2 CK, Step 3?

Which USMLE book is the best for USMLE Step 2 CK and 3?

Introduction

Should I start memorizing First Aid immediately?

What approach do I use to answer questions?

How many practice questions should I do to be ready for the USMLE/ COMLEX?

When should I start studying? – beginning of first year, beginning of second year, mid-way second year or wait till 2 months before boards?

How do I create my schedule for the boards?

Should I sign up for a live review or do it myself with online video lectures?

How do I incorporate flashcards into my study routine?

Should I get a study partner or study alone?

For IMGs', how many months will it take to complete each USMLE exam? Should I spend 3-, 6-, 12- or 18 months to study for Boards?

Do I need a USMLE coach to guide?

What should I do if I failed the USMLE before?

Do I have a chance of matching into residency if I failed any of the USMLE exams?

How do I know if I am ready to take the USMLE?

Should I ever push my USMLE date?

How do I avoid burn out when studying for USMLE?

What scores do I need to match into a specialty in medicine?

Where can I get observerships, and/or electives as an IMG?

Do I need tutoring for USMLE?

Which resources can I use to get medical clerkships in the US?

How do I get my Personal statement reviewed before the match?

How do I prepare for the residency interview?

In order to clarify and thoroughly explain the nitty-gritty details that are often unexplained, we have created this book for your benefit. These questions will be answered in detail in this book for you.

So, relax! Instead of panicking, look for the resources, be self-disciplined, settle your mind, plan ahead, and get fired up for the biggest moment of your life. If you are one of those people who wants to excel on this exam, this book was written specially for you.

Read on!

# CHAPTER 1:
# USMLE and COMLEX

BEFORE WE BEGIN discussing the USMLE and COMLEX examinations, let us focus on the main themes we want you to understand before reading this book. As a current US medical student or Caribbean international medical graduate, at no point during medical school should you ignore your coursework and core requirements for the sake of studying for the Boards!

If you are an international medical graduate who has already graduated with an MBBS or MD degree, you can skip the advice below and read the USMLE exam section.

Know that studying for your coursework *is* studying for the Boards. Your medical school is aware that you must perform well on the USMLE/ COMLEX and they spend time covering the curriculum including content tested on the USMLE and COMLEX. Although there are minutiae concepts that are covered during the coursework of the first and second years of medical school that are not tested on the boards, it is your responsibility to study as hard as you can to learn everything taught and test well to pass all your exams. You should know that studies have shown that strong academic performance and financial need may predict Step 1 scores. "Giordano C, Hutchinson D, Peppler R. A Predictive Model for USMLE Step 1 Scores. Muacevic A, Adler JR, eds. *Cureus*. 2016;8(9):e769. doi:10.7759/cureus.769"

Remember, you cannot graduate if you fail your coursework, so it is vital that you spend most of your time ensuring that you pass every class and all exams. Some students focus so much on the boards that they are either barely passing, or failing their coursework. If you are such a student, avoid this mistake and get help so you can focus on your classwork to get through the first two years of medical school.

# The USMLE and COMLEX Exams

USMLE stands for the *United States Medical Licensing Exam*, which every allopathic medical student and international medical graduate in the United States must take in order to be licensed to practice medicine. The passing score for USMLE Step 1 is 194 in 2020, Step 2 CK - 209, and Step 3- 196. As at the time when this edition was published, the average scores on the USMLE are as follows; Step 1- 228 (Standard deviation [SD] 21), Step 2 CK – 242 (SD 17), Step 3 – 225 (15). Scores range from 1 to 300. Check the link for more details: http://www.usmle.org/transcripts/

*Please note: "The USMLE program will change score reporting for Step 1 from a three-digit numeric score to reporting only a pass/fail outcome. A numeric score will continue to be reported for Step 2 Clinical Knowledge (CK) and Step 3. Step 2 Clinical Skills (CS) will continue to be reported as Pass/Fail. This policy will take effect no earlier than January 1, 2022"*

COMLEX is the *Comprehensive Osteopathic Medical Licensing Exam*, required for DOs. Please be aware that **COMLEX is *not* equivalent to the USMLE. These exams are different.** Osteopathic medical students are allowed to sit for the USMLE exam if they wish to. The passing score for COMLEX levels 1, 2 CE and 3 are 400, 400 and 350 respectively.

The average scores for COMLEX levels 1, 2 CE, 3 are between 500 and 550. The scores range from 1- 999. Check the link for more details: https://www.nbome.org/exams-assessments/comlex-usa/comlex-usa-level-1/scores-transcripts/scoring-principles/

There are three parts to the COMLEX series- Level 1, 2 CE (Cognitive evaluation), 2 PE (performance evaluation), and level 3. There are also 3 parts to the USMLE series: Step 1, Step 2 CK (clinical knowledge), Step 2 CS (clinical skills), and Step 3. These three exams are required to become fully licensed as a physician who can prescribe medicine and perform surgery. Every medical student must pass these three exams in order to become licensed as a physician.

So, which of these exams is the most important and why? Many medical students will tell you how extremely important your Step 1 scores are. They are right, in a sense. There is a reason why the emphasis placed on USMLE Step 1 and COMLEX Level 1 by every medical student is three-fold.

First, Step 1 and COMLEX 1 scores are used to screen for candidates that will receive invitations for residency interviews. Some programs are even candid about a "cut-off" value below which an applicant may not be sent an interview invite. Please note that in 2022, USMLE Step 2 CK scores will most likely be the new benchmark residency program directors use to screen applicants.

Second, not all residency training programs are created equal. In the National Resident Matching Program (NRMP) charting outcomes report in 2016, among the US applicants who matched, the average USMLE Step1 score was 233 and the average Step 2 CK score was 245. However, when inspecting the statistics per specialty, the numbers differ. For internal medicine, the average scores of Steps 1 and 2 CK of accepted applicants were 233 and 246, respectively. However, for dermatology, the averages for those same tests were 249 and 257, respectively. Therefore, if you plan on pursuing a residency that requires higher step scores, you may need to dedicate sufficient time and develop a great strategy to answering those questions. (See Charting Outcomes in 2018: https://mk0nrm-p3oyqui6wqfm.kinstacdn.com/wp-content/uploads/2019/10/Charting-Outcomes-in-the-Match-2018_Seniors-1.pdf

Third, these are licensing exams required for you to 1) graduate from medical school, and 2) be able to practice medicine in the United States.

In the United States, medical school is a four-year program that starts with two years of basic and clinical sciences, and finishes with two years of clinical rotations. The basic sciences taught in the first year include clinical biochemistry, anatomy and physiology, histology, embryology, genetics, preventive medicine, biostatistics, epidemiology, microbiology, osteopathic manipulative medicine (OMM, which only applies to DOs), et cetera.

The second year of medical school focuses on clinical medicine, pathology, pharmacology, immunology, geriatrics, pediatrics, psychiatry, and OMM (for DO students). Please note: every medical school curriculum is varied, refer to your medical school for actual classes covered in the first two years of medical school.

After completing the second year and finishing the "basic science foundations" of medicine, most medical schools expect students to take their Step 1 exam. However, some schools pursue a slightly different approach, where students usually finish their clinical rotations in the third year and then take Step 1.

The third and fourth years of medical school involve students rotating in the hospital. This is the time when students get the opportunity to meet and interact with patients; they learn to take histories and perform proper physical exams. After the third year or at the beginning of fourth year, most schools expect students to take the COMLEX Level 2- CE (Cognitive evaluation) / PE (performance evaluation) and/or USMLE Step 2 CK/ CS (clinical knowledge and clinical skills). At the beginning of fourth year, students apply for residency.

Remember when you had to prepare for your MCAT, get good scores, and apply to medical schools? At this point, you are back at the same portal, which leads to a different route. Applications for residency can be very stressful for students, for various reasons. This is the time of your life where you have to make major decisions on what career path you want to embark on in medicine. You have completed all the clinical rotations, but sometimes you are still unsure which area of medicine in which you want to practice. This is normal, many students face this dilemma. You will eventually figure out your passion! By the end of your third-year rotations, you must choose an area of medicine you want to specialize in. This is your career decision point.

As International medical graduates planning to match into residency, you should have completed your USMLE Step 1, 2CK, CS and preferably Step 3, and get your Educational Commission for Foreign Medical Graduates (ECFMG) certification before applying to residency.

After residency applications are submitted by mid-September, students keep refreshing their emails for interview invitations. Therefore, most interviews occur between October and December, with some programs extending their interview season till mid-January.

Upon completing residency interviews, applicants use the NRMP website to rank the programs at which they interviewed in order of their preference (i.e. where they see themselves training during residency). At the same time, residency program directors rank the applicants they interviewed in order of their preference. The deadline for submitting those lists is usually towards the third week of February. Note that, in order to be ranked by the majority programs, you must have taken and received a passing score on the Step 2 CK. After the ranking lists are submitted by both the applicants and the program directors, an algorithm runs the list and attempts to match students to their most preferred program (For a short video on how the algorithm works, visit http://www.nrmp.org/matching-algorithm/). In mid-March, medical students learn whether they matched or not, and if they did, what program they matched to. COMLEX level 3 or USMLE Step 3 is completed during the first year of residency by most US medical students (a.k.a internship).

It is important to obtain a good residency position. What are the requirements to get in? Residency program directors focus on several factors when you apply to their residency programs. Most medical students assume that Step 1 or 2 CK scores are the most important factors that will get them a residency. This idea is not the complete truth. Your Step 1 and 2 CK scores are only one part of the application process. Other requirements, such as clinical rotation grades, your personal statement, letters of recommendation, research and publications, and the interview process all factor into the equation. Therefore, while Step 1 and 2CK scores are important, they are NOT the only factors that determine the competitiveness of your application.

Getting to know the right people is another important piece of the puzzle. If you rotate at a hospital as a fourth-year medical student and work very hard, becoming a solid team member, you can make a strong impression on the attending physician, which might encourage the staff to consider you for a spot in their program. Therefore, the impression you make on your attending physician may allow you to be recognized as a great asset to their program. So, is it all your scores? No! Is it all about who you know? No! It is a combination of everything we mentioned above. Your entire application counts. **Do not ever give up your dreams for whatever specialty you are interested in because of your scores!**

However, Step 1 and 2CK scores do have a strong influence when you apply to highly competitive residencies. Thousands of medical students are competing for the small pool of available spots. The exam scores start to matter. Although a solid USMLE score is not the only thing you need to get into a good residency, it will get you to the door. For example, student A scores 245 on his USMLE or 700 on COMLEX, while student B scores 205 (USMLE) or 500 (COMLEX). If they both want to do plastic surgery, who do you think might get an interview first?

**Here is one big secret for you: every program has a cut off score they use to screen out applications during the residency interview process.** Of course, most programs won't tell you this. Most programs receive on average of 200 to 1000 applications (for high demand/ but not super competitive specialty such as internal medicine). For example, residency program A receives five hundred applications for internal medicine. They only have 10 spots available. They must assign faculty members to interview all potential applicants from September to January. The process is very exhausting for both the student and the faculty. Also, note these are busy academic clinicians who also have clinical work seeing patients and training residents. They have to allocate their time and schedule to accommodate you during your interview. In order to limit endless interviews, how do you think a program screens out applicants? Of course, by arbitrarily selecting a minimum score to eliminate applicants. There may be other factors used also. Let's say program A chooses 215 as their cutoff score, then all applicants below this pool get automatically eliminated, allowing just maybe 100-150 applicants to be interviewed and ranked.

This is how students with the higher scores are more likely to get interviews, especially for highly competitive programs that lay more emphasis on USMLE scores. Also, be aware that by default, if you rotate through a residency program for four to six weeks, you automatically get an interview regardless of your board scores. Although this does not always translate into you matching into the program, some students do. Irrespective of what specialty you are interested in, you should aim for the highest score to make you a strong applicant for any residency of your choice.

In March 2018, the National Resident Matching Program (NRMP) conducted its biennial survey of the directors of all programs participating in the Main Residency Match. The primary purpose of the survey was to shed light on the factors that program directors use to (1) select applicants to interview and (2) rank applicants for the Match.

Beginning with the 2016 survey, program directors were asked to indicate the percentage of interview invitations sent and interviews conducted in certain time periods. They also were asked how often they interviewed and ranked candidates from each applicant group. In addition, program directors rated factors used in assessing residents' success. Beginning with the 2014 survey, program directors have been asked to indicate factors they used in selecting applicants to interview and rank, and rate their importance on a scale of 1 to 5.

Numbers of responses are presented in most of the graphs, and some graphs use data from multiple survey questions. In those cases, different N's are listed. Numbers of applicants ranked and positioned in the Match are extracted from the NRMP database. Graphs are suppressed for questions with fewer than five responses.

This report represents the results by all specialties on selected items from the survey. The NRMP hopes that program directors, medical school officials, and applicants find these data useful as they prepare for and participate in the Main Residency Match.

As you can see, based on 2018 survey, the most important factors in selecting applicants for interviews are 1) USMLE Step 1/COMLEX level

1 score, (2) Letters of recommendation in the specialty, (3) Dean letter, (4) USMLE Step 2CK/COMLEX level 2 CE score, (5) personal statement, (6) Grades in required clerkships, (7) perceived commitment to specialty, and failed attempts in USMLE/COMLEX.

**Figure 1**

**All Specialties**
Percentage of Programs Citing Each Factor And Mean Importance Rating[1] for Each Factor in Selecting Applicants to Interview (N=1,233)

| Factor | Percent Citing Factor | Average Rating |
|---|---|---|
| USMLE Step 1/COMLEX Level 1 score | 94% | 4.1 |
| Letters of recommendation in the specialty | 86% | 4.2 |
| Medical Student Performance Evaluation (MSPE/Dean's Letter) | 81% | 4.0 |
| USMLE Step 2 CK/COMLEX Level 2 CE score | 80% | 4.0 |
| Personal Statement | 78% | 3.7 |
| Grades in required clerkships | 76% | 4.1 |
| Any failed attempt in USMLE/COMLEX | 70% | 4.5 |
| Class ranking/quartile | 70% | 3.9 |
| Perceived commitment to specialty | 69% | 4.3 |
| Personal prior knowledge of the applicant | 68% | 4.2 |
| Grades in clerkship in desired specialty | 67% | 4.3 |
| Audition elective/rotation within your department | 65% | 4.2 |
| Evidence of professionalism and ethics | 65% | 4.5 |
| Leadership qualities | 61% | 4.1 |
| Alpha Omega Alpha (AOA) membership | 60% | 3.9 |
| Perceived interest in program | 59% | 4.1 |
| Other life experience | 58% | 3.8 |
| Passing USMLE Step 2 CS/COMLEX Level 2 PE | 56% | 4.2 |
| Volunteer/extracurricular experiences | 54% | 3.8 |
| Consistency of grades | 54% | 4.0 |
| Lack of gaps in medical education | 53% | 4.0 |
| Awards or special honors in clinical clerkships | 52% | 3.6 |
| Graduate of highly-regarded U.S. medical school | 50% | 3.8 |
| Gold Humanism Honor Society (GHHS) membership | 47% | 3.8 |
| Awards or special honors in clerkship in desired specialty | 46% | 3.8 |
| Demonstrated involvement and interest in research | 41% | 3.7 |
| Visa status* | 40% | 4.1 |
| Applicant was flagged with Match violation by the NRMP | 37% | 4.8 |
| Away rotation in your specialty at another institution | 26% | 3.8 |
| Interest in academic career | 24% | 3.8 |
| Fluency in language spoken by your patient population | 24% | 3.7 |
| Awards or special honors in basic sciences | 22% | 3.3 |
| USMLE/COMLEX Step 3 score | 16% | 3.4 |

[1] Ratings on a scale from 1 (not at all important) to 5 (very important).
* International Medical Graduates only

| Figure 2 | All Specialties<br>Percentage of Programs Citing Each Factor And Mean Importance Rating¹ for Each Factor in Ranking Applicants<br>(N=1,208) | Percent Citing Factor | Average Rating |
|---|---|---|---|
| Interactions with faculty during interview and visit | | 96% | 4.8 |
| Interpersonal skills | | 95% | 4.9 |
| Interactions with housestaff during interview and visit | | 91% | 4.8 |
| Feedback from current residents | | 86% | 4.7 |
| USMLE/COMLEX Step 1 score | | 78% | 4.1 |
| Letters of recommendation in the specialty | | 72% | 4.1 |
| USMLE/COMLEX Step 2 score | | 70% | 4.1 |
| Evidence of professionalism and ethics | | 65% | 4.1 |
| Medical Student Performance Evaluation (MSPE/Dean's Letter) | | 65% | 4.6 |
| Perceived commitment to specialty | | 64% | 4.4 |
| Perceived interest in program | | 63% | 4.2 |
| Leadership qualities | | 60% | 4.2 |
| Class ranking/quartile | | 59% | 4.0 |
| Personal prior knowledge of the applicant | | 58% | 4.3 |
| Audition elective/rotation within your department | | 58% | 4.3 |
| Personal Statement | | 56% | 3.6 |
| Grades in required clerkships | | 54% | 4.1 |
| Passing USMLE Step 2 CS/COMLEX Level 2 PE | | 51% | 4.2 |
| Any failed attempt in USMLE/COMLEX | | 47% | 4.5 |
| Grades in clerkship in desired specialty | | 46% | 4.2 |
| Other life experience | | 45% | 3.8 |
| Alpha Omega Alpha (AOA) membership | | 44% | 3.9 |
| Consistency of grades | | 41% | 4.0 |
| Volunteer/extracurricular experiences | | 40% | 3.8 |
| Lack of gaps in medical education | | 38% | 4.0 |
| Graduate of highly regarded U.S. medical school | | 36% | 3.8 |
| Gold Humanism Honor Society (GHHS) membership | | 36% | 3.9 |
| Awards or special honors in clinical clerkships | | 32% | 3.8 |
| Awards or special honors in clerkship in desired specialty | | 30% | 4.0 |
| Demonstrated involvement and interest in research | | 30% | 3.7 |
| Applicant was flagged with Match violation by the NRMP | | 26% | 4.7 |
| Visa status* | | 25% | 4.0 |
| Other post-interview contact | | 23% | 3.7 |
| Interest in academic career | | 22% | 3.8 |
| Fluency in language spoken by your patient population | | 19% | 4.0 |
| Away rotation in your specialty at another institution | | 17% | 3.9 |
| USMLE/COMLEX Step 3 score | | 16% | 3.6 |
| Second interview/visit | | 14% | 3.6 |
| Awards or special honors in basic sciences | | 14% | 3.4 |

¹ Ratings on a scale from 1 (not at all important) to 5 (very important).
* International Medical Graduates only

Image reference: Figure 1 and 2: Results of the 2018 NRMP Program Director Survey, pages 3 and 4 https://www.nrmp.org/wp-content/uploads/2018/07/NRMP-2018-Program-Director-Survey-for-WWW.pdf

However, the most important factors that residency programs used to rank applicants are: (1) Interactions with faculty during interview and visit, (2) Interpersonal skills (3) Interactions with house staff during interview and visit (4) feedback from current residents (5) USMLE/COMLEX Step 1 score (6) Letters of recommendation in the specialty (7) USMLE/COMLEX Step 2 score.

Getting into residency is not an easy process; the selection process to match into your desired specialty is a combination of so many factors. If you put in the work, you will match. As you continue to read this book, we will guide you through the process from A to Z so you can be a well-prepared applicant for the process and if you follow the steps outlined in this book, you increase your chances of matching into residency.

"The old brick road to the Oz known as residency is riddled with many twists and turns. The process is a test of endurance and strength of will, and chances are you will be a different person at the end of it than who you were before you began your journey." ("USMLE Motivational Message for MDs" YouTube Video," by Dr. Brian Bolante).

# CHAPTER 2:
# USMLE and COMLEX Review Books

WHAT BOOKS ARE top recommended for USMLE and COMLEX?

Every year medical students and international medical graduates ask this age-old question. What books should I buy to study for the USMLE and COMLEX exams?

There are so many books written for the USMLE Step 1 and 2CK and 3 on the market today, but only a few resources are a must have. Other books should be considered supplemental resources to help you review concepts you cannot comprehend. At the end of this book, we listed high yield resources you can use to supplement your knowledge. We will only focus on the top high yield books you must buy before you begin studying for the boards in this chapter.

## The USMLE Step 1 recommended resources:

First Aid for the USMLE Step 1 is a familiar book to every medical student, both internationally and across the entire United States. It is the book of choice for studying for the Boards. We strongly recommend that you (and everyone else) buy this book as early as possible in your medical school experience, if you want to do well on the USMLE/ COMLEX. Do not wait until a month before your Boards to buy this book. And do not buy the book and let it sit around without putting it to good use. Deadly idea …

First Aid for the USMLE Step 1 is not a textbook, as most students often think. We call it a book of facts, covering information from the first two years of medical school. If you open the book itself, it is not readable unless you have previously studied the material. It simply states facts about everything most likely to be tested on the COMLEX or USMLE. It offers effective mnemonics, which can help you retain information using a concise and easy method as you prepare for the exam. Some students find mnemonics helpful, while others do not. If you are a student who loves mnemonics, it will come in handy.

First Aid for the USMLE Step 1 is a comprehensive, high-yield review book that can help you to do well on the exam; we have written this book to help you get the most out of First Aid for the USMLE Step 1, offering you a different perspective on how to approach reading it that allows you to make mental notes and associations that are not emphasized in the book.

One important piece of advice we would like to give you is that you need to actively use First Aid. That is, whatever concept you cover in class, make sure to read about it in First Aid. That will help emphasize the big concepts that you need to be focusing on for your Step 1 or even your class quizzes and exams. Also, whenever you read about a topic in First Aid, you should be actively highlighting information you didn't know or that you feel is important. Additionally, First Aid does not have all the important information. That is why it is updated annually. This also means that, if you come across an important fact that is not mentioned in First Aid, feel free to write it down in the relevant First Aid section. BUT, beware of overwriting additional information. Medical students are type A people who like to record and memorize everything, even if it's not high yield. Resist the urge to do that.

Students are often frustrated about using First Aid, especially international medical graduates who did not study in US medical schools. They complained that they cannot understand the book, or memorize it. At SmashUSMLE reviews, we came up with the solution. We have written a whole book based on First Aid for the USMLE Step 1 with other high yield resources **"SmashUSMLE Step 1 High Yield review book."** The book is the most comprehensive USMLE Step 1 book that actually explains the content in First Aid for the USMLE Step 1 book in detail, and you can get a copy at smashusmle.com.

## Can students memorize all the facts in the First Aid book for the Boards?

No. After studying for the Boards the effective way we will describe, you will be able to understand most of the materials that you need to excel on your Boards.

For USMLE Step 2 CK, Step 3, COMLEX level 2CE or level 3, the book we recommend is **Yale G First Aid CrushUSMLE Step 2Ck and 3.**

This book is the **most comprehensive Step 2 CK and 3 review book** because it covers everything you need to learn for the exam. The good news is you only need one book for USMLE Step 2 CK, 3 or COMLEX level 2CE or 3.

The book is updated frequently by the author, Dr. Yale Gong, a neurology researcher dedicated to helping medical students pass the USMLE with up to date medical content.

The latest edition of "Yale-G First Aid: Crush USMLE Step 2 CK & Step 3" has been significantly updated from Yale-G's previous editions with the author's persistent efforts, based on www.usmle.org*, www.uptodate.com, www.uworld.com, "CMDT," Kaplan's medical books, "FA", and a large volume of supportive feedback from medical students and doctors in the US and around the world. According to such feedback, the book has collected the most up-to-date, comprehensive, and high-yield clinical knowledge for the USMLE Step 2 CK and Step 3 available in the USMLE market. This book can be the equivalent of "First Aid for the USMLE Step 1" for the USMLE Step 2 CK, your ticket to the USMLE and ECFMG Certification! The author's team highly appreciates all responsible/supportive reviews/feedback with reward promise, and strives for monthly updates in the Kindle version to make it better and better.

***Some students opt in to use Master the Boards by Conrad Fisher or First Aid for the USMLE Step 2Ck by Tao Le. These books are good but not comprehensive.***

We want you to realize that you cannot answer all Board questions correctly. So even if you memorize First Aid, you still won't be able to get all the answers correct. The maximum score on the USMLE is 300 and on the COMLEX is 900. We have yet to meet any student who had perfect scores on these board exams.

What you need to know, however, is that a Step 1 score above a 240 (Note in 2022, Step 1 scores will be reported as pass/fail), or Step 2 CK above 240, or a COMLEX score above 600 is considered highly competitive even for the most competitive specialties. Therefore, your goal should be to get a high score but not a perfect score. Doing so requires you to utilize First Aid for the USMLE step 1 very effectively. This will become more evident in the upcoming chapter of this book.

# CHAPTER 3:
# Question Banks

*Mo[...] abo[...] quote*

*"The heights by great men reached and kept were not attained by sudden flight, but they, while their companions slept, were toiling upward in the night".*

Henry Wadsworth Longfellow

THERE ARE MANY USMLE question banks available on the market today, see the back of this book for a complete list of question banks available. However, we will recommend the following question banks: SmashUSMLE review, UWorld, Amboss, and USMLERx. You can purchase any of these question banks online at smashusmle.com, uworld.com, and usmlerx. com, respectively.

For osteopathic medical students, the best COMLEX question banks are OMTReview Qbank (omtreview.com), COMBANK and COMQUEST.

The reason we strongly recommend these question banks is because they simulate the USMLE/COMLEX exam interface, and they are the closest to the real test in terms of question format and content.

Make sure you purchase a 6-month or one-year subscription plan for any or all of those question banks. Always plan for unforeseen emergencies especially if you change your exam date. In that case, you'd still have access to the Qbank for practice.

We understand some people might be opposed to this idea because it is quite expensive. However, we firmly believe it is a worthwhile investment. At Harvard Medical School, medical students are recommended to use a test question bank from the beginning of their first year. To reduce the cost, buy a year's subscription only if you are absolutely sure you will be disciplined enough to use it throughout the year. Some people buy the six-month subscription plan, while others subscribe for thirty days. We are fully aware of the financial burden many students already carry. If you cannot afford to buy the one-year subscription, try to buy the six-month plan and begin studying early. Do whatever works for you, but we advise you to buy it as soon as possible. You will discover our reason as you continue this book.

The second year of medical school is highly intense. It is probably the most challenging, if not the hardest, part of your medical education. This year is so critical because you will learn various aspects of clinical medicine, pathology, and pharmacology in one year. It took the professors teaching these courses an entire career to master the material; and you are expected to memorize, understand, retain, regurgitate, and synthesize all of that information in one year. That is madness, isn't it? Yes, we know—that's just medical school. Doctors are expected to know everything.

We know it is very difficult for most students to adjust to the intensity of medical school. Most students enter medical school with a different perspective toward studying. They suddenly find themselves in the midst of a non-stop flow of information, and they do not know how to deal with it. If you are such a student, read the "how to survive medical school" chapter before continuing.

If you are already a very studious and well-prepared student, a student who has efficiently mastered the best and most efficient way to study any material given to you in a short time—and you still find time to sleep, eat, and exercise—then you are on the right track. Keep up the good work!

Please realize that studying for your second-year classes is equivalent to studying for Boards, since these are the materials you are most likely to be tested on for the exam. Students' coursework performance is the best predictor for their Board scores. Therefore, you shouldn't neglect studying for your second-year exams just so you can prepare for the boards. Master your second-year material first.

Although the second year of medical school does not provide enough time to balance studying for the Boards with your coursework, it is your responsibility to make the time. We discipline ourselves to set aside one hour every night to do Qbank questions. We started this as soon as we started the clinical medicine, pathology, and pharmacology courses. Since these courses are often taught in modules, it correlates well with the Qbank style.

Some medical schools have an integrated curriculum which helps you merge your knowledge of disease processes into one. This is an advantage for you if you attend such schools, as you will be adequately prepared for the USMLE exam.

Another way of doing it would be to use the question banks throughout the day. For instance, while walking to school or if you're in between classes, you can do a few questions on your phone. While taking a break from memorizing the slides for your class, you can work on a few questions. Question: How do I start doing questions when I do not know what I am looking at yet? Answer: That is why the Boards studying is different! As we told you at the beginning, forget everything you know about Board prep.

If you are on the cardiology module at your school, the ideal approach is to start doing ten cardio questions from the question bank every day. Do not underestimate ten questions. It will take you approximately ten to fifteen minutes to complete these ten questions from the question bank. It takes about thirty to forty-five minutes to review the answers for these ten questions. However, taking the test is not what is important. The most important thing is to review every single question and answer from the question bank you are using. Both the right and wrong answers must be reviewed in great detail. This is the best way to learn the material. In order words, preparing this way is the most efficient method of preparing for your actual board exam.

The clinical vignette questions are much harder than you predict. The SmashUSMLE review and UWorld Qbanks are probably some of the most difficult and most valuable question banks you can use to study for the Boards. Although the questions are difficult, they help reinforce the very high-yield concepts for the exam. The Qbank also prepares you for how Board-style questions are often phrased. Therefore, by doing those questions, you are not only learning high-yield concepts, you are developing excellent test-taking strategies that will come in extra handy on the day of the actual test.

Reviewing the explanations to all the questions, the ones you got right and wrong, is both very time-consuming and perhaps a bit painful. It is not an easy process and we know that. But that is the only way you will know exactly what you need to know for the exam, and that is literally the only way to know how to think like the question writers, and therefore, know how to answer those questions. Most students have a habit of taking exams without reviewing the answers. This is not the way to study for Boards. SmashUSMLE review and UWorld Qbanks are excellent tools because they thoroughly explain the reasons why one answer is correct, and the other answers are incorrect. These explanations are often long but very concise. At the end there is an educational objective summary; a short summary of what the test question wants you to know. Make sure you focus on that, as well.

For Osteopathic medical students taking the COMLEX exam, OMTReview question bank is an excellent review as it is written by Dr. Robert Savarese, author of the OMTReview book, best Osteopathic review course for the COMLEX exam. Learn more in the advice for Osteopathic students' chapter.

For international medical graduates who have MBBS, or Caribbean medical students who have very weak basic science knowledge, do not jump into UWorld Qbank or SmashUSMLE Qbank without reviewing your basic science knowledge first. Use a review course such as SmashUSMLE reviews (smashusmle.com), Boards and beyond, USMLERx, Onlinemeded, PASS program or other review courses to boost your medical knowledge. We have noticed a trend among students who buy a USMLE question bank and waste the question bank because they do not know anything and think the question bank will solve their knowledge deficit. Be smart, USMLE question banks are learning tools but only aid students with decent knowledge of basic and clinical sciences.

## Question: How do I know if I am doing well when answering questions?

Answer: Initially, you will perform poorly when you take SmashUSMLE or UWorld Qbank tests. As a medical student, you are not used to getting between 30 and 50 percent on an exam. But with SmashUSMLE or UWorld Qbank, expect to be within that range, especially at the beginning. You do not know most of the material yet; even if you do, you are not familiar with how the concepts are tested in a Board-style clinical vignette format. So, do not feel depressed when your scores are really low. Most students who actually do well on the real exam score an average of 65 percent on SmashUSMLE or UWorld Qbank.

If you are scoring between 40 and 50 percent from the start, you are actually doing really well and getting ready for the test. However, do not focus on your scores. Learn the material, understand the questions, and get used to the style of the exam.

If you are just learning for the first time, for instance US medical students or International medical graduates who are studying to use the

Qbank as a learning tool, you can start doing questions in Timed Tutor mode. That way, you are not focusing on the score; rather, you're going to focus on actually learning how to navigate those vignette-style questions, and most importantly, reading those invaluable explanations.

Toward the end of your Board studies, you should begin to time yourself and mimic real exam conditions as you practice the Qbank. This will allow you to monitor your progress as exam time approaches.

Other question banks currently available are USMLERx, Amboss, Lecturio, Kaplan, Pastest, and Board vitals. However, as you will hear from other senior medical students and perhaps other physicians, do not spread your energy doing questions from different question banks and reading lots of extraneous books. That is counterproductive. You will end up feeling overwhelmed, unhappy, and you will not learn as efficiently. Therefore, we recommend focusing on the important resources you need to succeed. Master them, and you will score well. It is not magic. It's science.

Our simple rule for studying for the Boards is: "Get it wrong now, learn it cold, understand the mechanism, and get a good score when it counts."

## The Five Biggest Mistakes Students Make with Qbanks

1. **Not starting question bank study early.** Contrary to popular belief that just reading your medical textbook first is the key to mastering concepts tested on the USMLE, the opposite could be true. The key to learning how NBME/NBOME board writers create questions is through practicing questions. Start early. During the second year of medical school, start doing 10 questions a day. If you are on a cardiology block, start doing 10 UWorld or SmashUSMLE questions daily. If you attempt 10 questions daily, you will have completed 300 questions in a month! You do not need to focus on biochemistry or epidemiology during a cardiology block. The earlier you start practicing difficult case vignettes in the question bank, the more efficient your question-based studying will be later. If you are an international medical graduate, for your pre-dedicated study period, take your time to brush up on your medical knowledge and use a question bank along with your studying.

2. **Not spending enough time reading the explanation section.**
Students who perform poorly on the USMLE do so primarily because
they do not spend enough time reading and understanding the explanations for each question in the question bank. The purpose of the
question bank is to show you the thought process involved in solving
standard USMLE case vignettes. We hear students complain about
how it takes one hour to complete a 40-question block and three to
four hours to read the explanations. Yes. That is how long it should
take you to read and understand both the correct and incorrect answer
choices. Some students will only read the explanations to the correct
answer choices and educational objective. This is a big mistake. The
incorrect explanations force you learn new information that will be
tested in other concepts later on in the question bank. Take your time
to learn them.

3. **Not annotating First Aid or Yale G First Aid CrushUSMLE step
2CK and 3 with question bank content.** Everyone knows First Aid
is the Bible for Step 1, but a few people know about Yale G First Aid
CrushUSMLE step 2 CK and 3. But have you tried to read the First
Aid for the USMLE Step 1 book by itself? It's not comprehensible.
The reason is because you must flip each page and find where the
question bank concepts come from. Then, annotate and write short
descriptions near the pages for you to understand how it is tested on
the boards. So, do not skip this step; it is the most important part
of your board prep aside from doing questions. Yale G First Aid
CrushUSMLE step 2CK and 3 is a more detailed book, so you can
still use it along with your question bank and add notes to it.

4. **Using the Qbank once.** You must go through one question bank at
least twice to gain mastery of the information. There is an enormous
amount of content in the explanations and no one can grasp all
the knowledge from a question bank on the first try. If you can, do
another additional question bank after completing the first question
bank twice. For example, let's say you did UWorld Qbank twice, do
one round of SmashUSMLE or another question bank. The more
questions you do, the better your scores. Remember, "Repetition is
the mother of all learning, the father of action and architect of all
accomplishment."

5. **Focusing on percentage correct instead of mastery.** Listen,
USMLE question banks are learning tools, not assessment tests.

Students are always confusing this important fact! Some students are more worried about why they are scoring 30% on the SmashUSMLE or UWorld Qbank, rather than what they should be learning for the boards. Do not focus on the percentages of questions you got correct, as it is not the essence of the question bank. It does not matter if you complete the question bank; if you do not learn anything from the question bank, you just wasted the question bank. Even if you are scoring 30-40% correct on the question bank it is irrelevant, as what matters is what you score on the NBME assessment test. This is the most accurate reflec**tion of your actual predictive performance on the real USMLE exam.**

# CHAPTER 4:
# 7 Reasons Why Medical Students Fail USMLE

LET US DISCUSS the top seven reasons why students fail the USMLE exam. The USMLE exam is a nerve-wracking exam that gives many students anxiety. Whether you are a US medical student, a Caribbean IMG or an international medical graduate, it is the most difficult exam you will ever take in your life.

There are over 37,000 students, both US grads and IMG who sit for the USMLE exam every year and are competing for residency spots every year. The euphoric feeling of getting into US medical school quickly vanishes as medical students start their second year and face the reality of taking the USMLE or COMLEX.

In the second year, there is a sense of panic, especially amongst US medical students. We have to go into a panic mode known as step one mania. For international medical graduates, the reality is even worse. IMGs did not train in US medical schools, so they are at a disadvantage to know how to adequately prepare for the USMLE. Thousands of IMGs and US med students fail this exam every year and we will talk about the reasons for these shortcomings.

In the past 10 years, USMLE Step 1 average scores have increased, which has led to anxiety and obsession of medical students to get high USMLE scores. The good news is that USMLE Step 1 scores will be pass/ fail in 2022, but USMLE Step 2 CK scores will now be the new Step 1. We proposed that the new domino effect will be Step 2CK score mania, as students will have to get super high Step 2 CK scores to get into more competitive residencies.

Here is the issue facing medical students: student loans! The average student loan burden is about $200,000 -300,000 and you ask yourself,

"Will I match? Am I going to get a job?" That's what it boils down to, right?

When you are applying for residency, know that your USMLE Step 1 and 2CK scores are important, including letters of recommendation and personal statement to get that interview. You need higher board scores if you want to match into competitive residencies such as Emergency medicine, Radiology, Anesthesia, Ophthalmology, Dermatology and Surgical specialties. For US students, they only need step 1 to get into residency and if you don't do well on step 1, you'll need to do well on step 2CK with higher scores. *(In 2022, program directors will most likely focus on Step 2CK scores)*. Ultimately, residency programs are using these step scores to screen thousands of applications they are getting every year.

So, why do students fail the exam? Well if you look at the statistics, in the US medical schools, about 6-7% of each class every year fails the USMLE. Contrast that to International medical students, where only about 20-30% of students fail the USMLE every year.

Let's talk about the top seven reasons why students fail this exam, so that I can show you what you can do about it, so YOU don't fall into that category.

**Mistake number 1 is attitude**: The attitude towards the step 1 or 2CK exam is the number one reason why students failed the steps. Now, the problem with the attitude these US med students have towards studying for this board exam is that they may feel like "well, I know it's a tough exam but I have not had time to start studying for it yet". So, they put it on the back burner, right? Those students usually have time management problems.

They are still struggling to keep the balance of learning what's being taught in med school and barely having any extra time to do board studying in second year, while most of the top performing students are already in pre-dedicated study period from January, and are using their First Aid book along with class from the beginning of second year.

The students who fail the USMLE are saying things like, I'm just trying to get through all my classes right now" little do they know that they are going to have a big problem down the road. If you start studying at the end of April, when all your classmates have already done 500-1000 questions from their question banks, you have fallen behind and now you are trying to play catchup.

You have about 2400-2600 questions to go through and you want to go through your Qbank at least twice before taking your board exam, right? You may not be able to get through your entire Qbank the first time around in 6 weeks. You can, and it's possible, but you may not be able to complete it the 2nd time, which is going to affect your score on step 1 and will actually put you at risk of failing the board exam.

The same applies for Step 2CK. Most students start doing questions along with their clinical rotations to study for boards and do a short review during their dedicated period.

So, what about international medical students? Well, that's a different story. For IMGs, the biggest problem IMGs have is that they feel that they have too much time, they have this nonchalant attitude towards the USMLE. Some IMGs are overconfident about how to study for the USMLE and end up failing multiple times, while others struggle with procrastination and focus which lengthens the time period they spend studying for the USMLE.

The IMGs from Caribbean island medical school leave after the fifth semester, after passing the NBME exam set by their school, making them eligible to take Step 1. Most Caribbean medical schools use the NBME to screen poor or at-risk medical students from taking the Step 1 exam. Once an IMG passes the NBME to show the school they can at least pass the USMLE, they let you lose to the US or to your country. Then, you have 6 months of prep time or whenever you pass step 1.

There is a major problem with this approach. Most Caribbean medical students do not have the self-discipline to focus on the USMLE by themselves once they leave the academic environment of their medical schools. Also, they lack the motivation to study effectively daily for extensive periods of time, which further leads to forgetting the basic science concepts they have learned in the first five semesters of medical school. Some IMGs have a poor foundation of basic science knowledge and this is a big factor concerning why they fail step 1 exam. The Caribbean medical students who excel are extremely motivated from day 1, and would have excelled anyways if they got into US medical schools.

For Non-US IMGs or older graduates, they often have forgotten most or all the basic science knowledge and tend to struggle to relearn the information again.

Now, some Caribbean medical students who end up failing the steps, might say something like this.

"I have a whole year to study for step 1 or 2 CK". Now, there is a problem with that. Step 1 is a very crucial exam. First Aid, - as it stands in 2020 if you look at the book and you flip it all the way through - is about

650 pages long. That is a lot of information that you've got to cram into your brain. Now, when you're studying for step 1 or 2 CK as an IMG, you don't want to approach this like "I'll get to it when I can," or "I just want to pass the test". No, no, no! That's the wrong mentality and attitude. You have to understand that you also only have a limited amount of scope to cram, memorize, and master all this information. So, what ends up happening as an IMG, is that they start studying, and then take a break. They're not consistent as they study throughout the entire session.

The average IMG spends 12-18 months for Step 1 alone. Some students do it in less time. There are so many factors such as marriage, children, work, no social support, death in the family, lack of money, and poor access to great courses that can prolong an IMG to prepare for the USMLE.

However, here is the right mindset. Slow and steady wins the race. Know yourself and say I will be dedicated for the next 12 months. Even if it takes 3-4 hours a day of consistent studying, it's better than a yoyo approach.

I've got 12 months, I'm going to bury my head in the next 12 months; create an ideal schedule that works for me or get help with a coach to help create a schedule (@smashusmle reviews), study, watch videos, flashcards, do questions, and I am going to stick to the schedule no matter what. I'm also going to take breaks, which is going to help me prepare adequately for this exam. Sometimes students say, "You know what? I need more than 12 months", and that's fine. But, if you have the attitude that you have too much time, what ends up happening is that you are going to start forgetting all the information that you learned at the beginning. Maybe you studied biochemistry like two months ago, right? But by the seventh month, you already forgot the glycolysis pathway, you already forgot the fatty acid chain pathway. What happens is that your knowledge starts high and then starts to drop down as you go further along while studying for the board exam. So that is the first thing I want to share with you guys when it comes to attitude.

**Now, let's talk about mistake number 2.** It is not picking a test date. "What?! What do you mean by not picking a test date? I'm not ready to take the test, why should I pick a test date?" That is the wrong approach. Most students always tell me, "Dr. Adesina, listen, I'm going to pick a test day when I'm ready." That's not how it works. It's reverse psychology. The first thing you want to do in life is 'set a goal'. Because once you set the target, you now have a small time frame to be able to make that target, but if you don't set a goal, if you don't pick a date, regardless of whether you're ready or not, you're going to have this nonchalant attitude that you have too much time. Picking a date gives you a countdown!

So, this is what I tell every student walking up to me and asking me, "Dr. Adesina, so I'm taking my step 1 or step 2 or 3 exam *somewhere around...*" and I say, "I don't want to hear that". PICK A SPECIFIC DATE. If it's Jan 4th, it's Jan 4th. If it's Dec 2nd, it's Dec 2nd. Pick a date regardless of whether you have or have not read a page yet. It doesn't matter! Let's say you decided to pick Dec 10th, just for the sake of argument. And let's say you have six months. Now, what happens is, that allows you to be able to create your schedule and then you can see for yourself how many days you have left to study for this board exam. And then your heart rate starts to go up because every day you wake up, you realize you have one day less until your USMLE board exam. Now, you start studying towards that date. You start your NBMEs and you create your schedule and begin studying.

By the time you take your last NBME two weeks before your actual test date, if you are still scoring below your target score, *then* you can push the date. You can always call the Prometric center or go online and push your test date". You have to pay some fee for it depending on what time you change your date but at least, you are working towards it. So, this prevents you from having that nonchalant, complacent attitude that a lot of students typically have, and allows you to stay focused and laser-intense.

**Let's talk about mistake number three:** Studying for too long. I see this all the time. Student says, "I have been studying for two years for the board exam". And I say, "That's a long time." For example, US medical students typically study for about eight weeks for a dedicated study period. Because what the studies have shown is that, once you cram material in a short amount of time, the longer you wait to review the information, the more you start to forget the information, especially if you're not reapplying it. So, what I tell students is that there is a pre-dedicated study period and then there is a **dedicated study period**. During your pre-dedicated study period is when you amass all that knowledge inside your First aid for the USMLE book or your Step 2 book, and then you do a short rapid review of 6- 8 weeks and take a NBME. And as soon you hit your target score, you sit for the exam and you run. A lot of students start studying, they take much of a break, and then they keep extending the dates and they find themselves forgetting information that they already have learned in the past. That is what happens; you will forget information - it's a lot of information. Step 1 and 2CK and 3. The exam is, at least, 30% memorization,

60% mastery and understanding of basic and clinical science knowledge, and the other 10% requires you to understand the nitty-gritty minutiae concepts. So, don't study for too long. Once you set your date, study as fast as you can, get the information in your brain, and go take the test.

**Now, how about mistake number four?** Using too many resources. I see students all the time; they have First Aid, Anki decks, Pathoma, UWorld, SmashUSLME, and then their friend tells them, "have you seen Amboss?", and then they buy Amboss, and they hear about Lecturio and Kaplan, then they go buy them. They have all these books; videos and they don't know what to do with them. Just because Anki decks works for someone, doesn't mean it may work for you. Just because someone is watching videos, doesn't mean it may work for you. Just because somebody just does question banks, and they say "this question bank is better than that question bank", it may or may not work for you.

It's not about how many resources you have, it's about how you use them. At SmashUSMLE, we actually train students on how to use the resources they have. Regardless of what resources students have, you can go to Smashusmle.com and learn more.

We assign you a personal coach who will meet with you for a discovery call and work with you to show you how to use the resources you have in conjunction with our course effectively.

This is the perfect example: If you buy a brand-new BMW and it's got all these buttons inside of it. If you don't know how to push the buttons or know what those buttons do, what good is it to drive a fancy car? That is exactly what happens to students when they're studying for Board exams. They're overwhelmed while jumping from one resource to another without strategic thinking.

Here is the solution to this madness, at the beginning of your studying, you must have the correct strategy. You have to know yourself, what is my best mode of learning? "Am I a kinesthetic, visual learner, auditory learner? Or a combination of both or all three?" Which means do I learn best by watching a short video of someone teaching what I'm learning, or do I prefer to read on my own, or do I prefer to do questions and watch videos together? Do I like space repetition using flashcards or even Mnemonic? Do I like stories like visual animations and I can recall the meaning of these stories as they apply to medicine?

Which mode allows me to learn the fastest? And once you've identified the best way to learn, use the appropriate resources that match your study skills, that's basically how it works. If you don't do that, you are going to be overly frustrated and overwhelmed. That will lead to you throwing these resources away and eventually failing the board exam.

**Step 5 is 'wasting question banks!'**. Wasting question banks is probably one of the top reasons why students fail the exam. I am sure you have heard this from your friends or read this on USMLE-forums. All you need is just UWorld, First Aid and Pathoma and I got a 260". So, if this was the magic recipe, so simple right? But why are students still failing the boards? Well, there is a reason for that. They don't tell you the full story. They don't teach you how to use the question bank. They don't teach you how to effectively learn from these question banks. So, students go into these question banks, they start selecting answers, they just randomly and nonchalantly read the correct answers and they're like "Oh my God, I only got 20% or 50%!" They're so focused on their percentage score in the question bank. They keep asking themselves, "What percentage score do I need to get in UWorld to get a 260 and pass the exam?"

Then they waste the entire question bank without learning anything. They don't know how to take notes. They don't know the specific strategies that you are supposed to use while studying from the question bank. Here is what you must know: **The question bank is just a learning tool not a practice test.** Students have this notion that using the question bank is for them to be able to just read information and answer questions. No! If you turned that question bank into a book, that is all you need to for that exam. But, you still need to have background knowledge.

For students who have poor basic or clinical science knowledge, use the question bank to challenge your application of the concepts you learn from USMLE video lectures and notes to allow you recognize your knowledge deficits and fill in the gap to see how the concepts will be tested on the actual exam.

For example, if you don't understand endocrine physiology, like the hypopituitary-adrenal axis, where cholesterol is metabolized into aldosterone, cortisol and androgens, guess what? You will always get all these 21-Beta Hydroxylase questions wrong on the board exam.

Once again, question bank is your learning tool, use them wisely.

**Mistake number 6**: Students often shoot for low scores. That's another reason why students fail. When you shoot for lower scores, you are setting yourself up for failure because the amount of work it takes for you to get a high score of 260 is not the same amount of work that it takes to score 205. Students who say "I just want to pass the USMLE," possess the worst attitude you can ever have. Even when USMLE step 1 becomes a pass/fail exam, if you choose to learn just enough to pass step 1, you will struggle to get a high score on USMLE Step 2CK. The reason is that the knowledge builds on each exam and the higher your knowledge base for Step 1, the easier USMLE Step 2 CK is because it's the same concept with more disease diagnosis and management. Back to attitude again when you're studying for this board exam, because if you shoot for a low score you are most likely going to fail the test.

√ **Finally mistake number 7, do not ignore the elephant in the room**. Your NBME score report is the ultimate reflection of whether you're going to do well on the USMLE or not. The reason is - and I've met thousands of students who failed their USMLE and they consistently repeat the same error:

They take their NBME 18, 20, 21, and 22 and their score is below passing. And guess what? They convince themselves that they are ready to take the test and they sit for the board exam thinking they are going to score higher on the exam. No, the NBME assessment test is, by far, the most accurate and the most precise assessment test that determines your knowledge level and whether you are ready to take the USMLE exam. So, I'm begging you while you're reading this book, before you take your USMLE, if your target score is 250 and you're still scoring 205 on your NBMEs, you're not ready to take the test. Don't do it! And if you don't know how to increase your score, reach out to me directly or reach out to our company at smashusmle.com and we will give you a private coach to help guide you and even tutor you to get you a higher score. We have helped thousands of students avoid failing the USMLE, so do not wait, reach out to us for help now.

Do not let overconfidence cause you to fail the USMLE. I coach students and give them the best advice and sometimes they do not listen. I have met IMGs who tell me that they thought they knew what they were doing the first time because they thought were "smart enough" to pass the USMLE. After they fail, they call me to help them. Why do you have to fail the USMLE before reaching out to Smashusmle reviews? Because you thought you had it all figured out? No! What you should have done was come to SmashUSMLE Reviews and we will have shown you how, because your NBME result has already identified that you are weaker in certain areas but you didn't know how to approach that and how to study the right way. That's what we do here in SmashUSMLE. We coach you on how to study the right way. We will get you tutors to be able to get you higher board scores. Not only that, we give you the resources and show you exactly how to use them so that you can get the score you want, regardless of what kind of residency you want to match into. Call now 212-465-3339 or email us admin@smashusmle.com. Or visit us at smashusmle.com to sign up today.

# CHAPTER 5:
# How to use First Aid for the USMLE Step 1 book effectively

YOU ARE DOING questions from SmashUSMLE review, UWorld or Amboss Question bank/ USMLE-Rx; you reviewed the answers. Is that enough? *Absolutely not!* That is just the beginning. To ensure you make the most out of your question banks, here's what you need to do:

1.  **Buy the book**. Go online and buy the book. There are various websites to choose from, such as amazon.com or borders.com. Always buy the most recent edition, which will correct errors from the previous editions. Check out the errors page online, to be sure you have the latest corrections. https://firstaidteam.com/updates-and-corrections/

2.  **Go to a print shop, cut off the book binding, and add a three-hole punch through the book.**

    Insert the pages in a 2.5-inch binder. This will allow you to insert notes and extra materials inside your *First Aid.*

3.  **Add tabs.** Tabs are small plastic holders you can use to demarcate each chapter and section. This helps you easily flip through the book, saving time while looking up indexes and chapters. You can purchase tabs at your local stationery store.

4.  **Use your First Aid.**

    Most students will buy *First Aid for the USMLE Step 1* and immediately start reading the book. Stop! It is *not a book*. Most students have a misconception about review books. *First Aid for the USMLE Step 1* is a collection of random high-yield facts that are commonly tested on the USMLE and COMLEX. Therefore, you need to use another resource to make sense of the facts in First Aid.

    Such resources can be the SmashUSMLE review, UWorld or Kaplan question banks. Review the questions and answers, even for the questions that you answered correctly. This is how you learn how to think like the test question writers. Then, write the important facts and explanations from the question bank on the pages in your *First Aid for the USMLE Step 1* book where that information is given. This is an active learning process. The way you use *First Aid* is by first doing questions. Get involved!

However, one common pitfall is over-annotating your First Aid, which makes it so overwhelming when you come back to take a look at it and study from it. We recommend that you stick to writing down the facts that are high-yield, important, and not mentioned in First Aid. Bottom line: be efficient when it comes to annotating your First Aid.

Warning**: *Do not read*** First Aid for the USMLE Step 1 ***as a book***

Even if you decide to read *First Aid for the USMLE Step 1* first and then do the questions, you will still be scoring within 30% to 40% range on the practice exams. The book does not tell you much, if you do not know how to use it. Until you see how the material is tested in a question format, you have no idea what the facts in the book mean. Here's an example.

## Streptococcus Pneumoniae

| ***Streptococcus Pneumoniae*** | Gram positive, lancet-shaped diplococci. Encapsulated. IgA protease. Optochin sensitive and bile soluble. | Pneumococcus is associated with "rusty" sputum, sepsis in patients with sickle cell disease, and asplenic patients. No virulence without a capsule. |
|---|---|---|
| | Most common cause of: Meningitis, Otitis Media (in children), Pneumonia, Sinusitis, Encapsulated. IgA protease. | MOPS are Most OPtochin sensitive. |

Excerpt-'Streptococcus Pneumoniae' page 13, from First Aid for the USMLE Step 1 2020 © 2020 Tao Le , Vikas Bhushan, Lars Grimm Published by The McGraw-Hill Companies This material is reproduced with permission of The McGraw-Hill Companies.

**The following is a sample question from SmashUSMLE review step 1 question bank, all questions in this book are from SmashUSMLE question bank.**

## Question:

A 10-year-old African American boy presented with cough, a rusty sputum, and fever of 101.4 F. On physical exam he appears pale and lethargic. Vital signs reveal a blood pressure of 90/60 mmHg and warm extremities. Laboratory studies reveal hemoglobin of 7.5 mg/dl. He has a history of painful crises, which are relieved with NSAIDs. What organism is this patient most likely susceptible to?

A. *Staphylococcus aureus*

B. *Toxoplasma gondii*

C. *Listeria monocytogenes*

D. *Streptococcus pneumoniae*

E. *Ricketssia ricketssi*

Correct answer: D. ***Streptococcus pneumoniae***

## Explanation

The patient is African American who is anemic, with a history of painful crises. The Boards expect you to know that he has sickle cell disease and hypotension from sepsis (his blood pressure is low). Since he is 10 years old, you should expect he does not have a functioning spleen, because such patients experience autosplenectomy from extensive hemolysis and splenomegaly by age 5. A patient without a spleen has an increased risk of developing infections from encapsulated organisms such as *Strep. pneumoniae, Neisseria meningitidis, H. influenza, and Klebsiella pneumonia.* When you read the question, always think actively and summarize at the end before looking at the answer choices. An example of such summary can be "a 9-yo AA male with PMHx of pain crises (think: Sickle-Cell Anemia (SCA)) presents with coughing with rusty sputum (buzzword for strep pneumo, which makes sense given SCA and auto splenectomy), fever and hypotension (fever + hypotension = septic shock)." Therefore, the presentation fits with **S. pneumonia bacteremia**

## Educational Objective

Sickle cell anemic patients are susceptible to encapsulated organisms such *as Streptococcus pneumoniae, Neiserria meningitidis, H. influenza and Klebsiella pneumonia.*

**Now you make notations of the objective in your copy of *First Aid*.**

Do you see why "just reading the book" is almost useless? Most of us will read the fact: *Pneumococcus is associated with rusty sputum, sepsis in sickle cell anemia and splenectomy,* but have no idea how it will be tested.

This is why doing questions makes you see how the Boards wants you to understand the material. If you do many practice questions and sample NBME/NBOME questions, you will realize that *BOARDS are not memorization tests.*

### 5. Pick a color.

When you highlight a sentence or phrase in color, it means it is important. Pick your favorite color, perhaps green. *Use this color every time you do questions on your Qbank.* Highlight the facts tested in the SmashUSMLE or UWorld Qbank in your *First Aid*. This approach reinforces the materials every time you open the book. So if something is in green, it is important: *there was a question on it–this is high-yield information.*

## The math.

If you do ten questions every day during your second year (except during exam time), in thirty days, you will have completed three hundred questions. If the semester were four months long, you would have completed approximately twelve hundred questions. Assuming you did not meet your goal at the end of the semester, you still have an opportunity to do so during the winter break, as well as wrap up any remaining questions in modules that you started but did not finish. By springtime, around April, you would probably have completed around two thousand questions. That means you would have completed the Qbank once even before hardcore Board studying begins.

Here's another way to make this happen. You can use your phone to do 5 – 10 questions at a time while you're walking to class, or in between classes. Why? Because that helps make solving those questions a second nature. When you randomly test yourself, you somehow acquire the test-taking skills even more efficiently. By using your phone or iPad, it somehow makes it less of a chore. Also, it may decrease your likelihood of being burnt out before starting your dedicated study time for step. Of course, after you do your 5-10 questions on your phone, you want to make sure to read their explanations and annotate First Aid.

Do you know how that feels? It feels good—you will be ahead of the game. You will have noticed most of the tricks and be familiar with different ways questions can be asked. You will be able to deduce what the exam question intends to test you on, and to a large extent your anxiety level will be reduced. This is simply because you took a whole year to prepare yourself for the COMLEX and USMLE, unlike many other students who just start to jump on the studying bandwagon in March or April. By the time you are almost done with the Qbank, your copy of *First Aid for the USMLE Step 1* should contain a myriad of details and be looking like a textbook that you can easily read and refer to for explanations. You will notice that, by this time of the year, you are already accustomed to your *First Aid for the USMLE Step 1*; it is your personal inclusive review book for the Boards. It becomes your major asset as you prepare for the Boards.

**We repeat:** Do the SmashUSMLE or UWorld Step 1 Qbanks, write in your *First Aid*, and then read it, over and over and over.

**Caveat:** During the time of studying for your Boards, you should be aware that *First Aid for the USMLE Step 1* is not enough!

Although we are recommending that you do BOARDS practice questions during your short winter break, or on weekends, please remember to always maintain a balance between your studies and other life chores and fun hobbies. It is extremely important to avoid getting burnt out early in this process.

*First Aid for the USMLE Step 1* cannot be used alone to study; it is not the only book you need to do well on the test. Even SmashUSMLE or UWorld Qbanks are not enough. The book only contains about 90 percent of the material covered on the Boards. Some of the chapters in the book contain little information, and you will need supplementary materials to enhance your studying. Chapters such as pathology, microbiology, and behavioral science lack sufficient substance for you to fully understand those materials. For instance, reading the microbiology section of *First Aid for the USMLE Step 1* is not enough for you to understand the whole picture. Supplementing it with SmashUSMLE microbiology video lectures, *Microbiology Made Ridiculously Simple book* will give you more information regarding the microorganism's structure, type of endo-or exotoxin released, antibiotic of choice, and pathogenesis of the diseases they cause. Also, if you love visual animated illustrations for learning, Sketchymedical is another resource for microbiology that seems to be popular among medical students.

Likewise, the pathology section is insufficient for the Boards. We cannot overemphasize the importance of reading *Rapid Review for Pathology* by Edward Goljan (see References). Dr. Goljan is an excellent Board review teacher, integrating the material in a concise format to help students understand how the materials will be tested on the exam. **We highly recommend this book for your Board studies.**

Towards the end of studying for Boards, about two days before your exam date, flip through *Rapid Review for Pathology* by Dr. Goljan; review all the side notes and look through all the pathology slides in the book. We found this very helpful for solidifying all the pathology information and recognizing the slides, should they appear on the Board exam.

Pathoma is another excellent video lecture review for the USMLE Step 1 exam. Dr Sattar does an excellent job explaining pathology concepts tested on the USMLE. Pathoma is better utilized as a resource throughout your pre-clinical modules. Make sure to watch the videos and annotate this book with the necessary notes. Reading the book by itself is not sufficient. Visit pathoma.com to buy the course.

Some students prefer *Board Review Series (BRS) Pathology*. Either the Goljan *Pathology* or *BRS Pathology* is a great resource for studying. Note: Goljan has more information in his book and more pathology slides than *BRS Pathology*. Use whichever one you are comfortable with. Another great source for studying pathology is attending Kaplan pathology live lectures by Dr. John Barone. We had a great experience with his lectures; he truly does an excellent job teaching you pathology material that is high yield for Boards. He provides students with awesome mnemonics and a simplified approach to learning difficult concepts. We refer to him as the "epiphany of academia." You will have to purchase Kaplan live class and hope you get him as your pathology professor during the review course.

You might want to review some biochemistry pathways through the SmashUSMLE review lectures. It is an excellent resource for biochemistry for the Boards. If you subscribe to SmashUSMLE review course, the biochemistry videos offered are the best, in our opinion. Dr. Adesina makes you fall in love with biochemistry. He emphasizes all the high-yield points for the National Boards; you will feel very prepared. Check out smashusmle.com to sign up for the course.

Do not underestimate the importance of the behavioral science, epidemiology, and ethics sections. These sections may seem straightforward, but you still need to be familiar with the minutiae, because that's what you're most likely to be tested on. Many students ignore these sections and lose points on the exam. Make sure you read books on behavioral science and biostatistics, if you feel that *First Aid* material is not sufficient.

Here are the books we recommend for biostatistics for the USMLE: USMLE Biostatistics and Epidemiology: USMLE Self-Assessment Series by Tom Heston MD, BRS Behavioral Sciences by Barbara Fadem. By mastering these sections, you can easily boost your score by at least a few points. UWorld also added a new biostatistics question bank to their software; you might want to purchase it. SmashUSMLE reviews has a 5-hour Biostatistics Masterclass that provides a short review and great questions to help you practice. You can improve your score by spending some time on these topics. If you want to invest time to study embryology, we recommend that you practice all the UWorld or SmashUSMLE question banks, after reviewing the section in *First Aid*. The explanations for the answers are more than enough. However, if you still want to study more embryology, you can use other sources to supplement. Check out our High-Yield Resource page for more details on resources.

We were fortunate enough to have the right resources to prepare for Boards. We received a great amount of materials from our upperclassmen, and cannot emphasize enough how important it is for you to do the same. You should make every effort to look for great resources that others have tried and strongly recommended. This will help you greatly during your board preparation process. Again, different resources work for different students, if a resource is not working for you, stop using it and try another one.

As emphasized in this book, the UWorld or SmashUSMLE Question Bank is the best way to prepare for the USMLE. OMTReview question bank is excellent for the COMLEX. Ideally, you should go through the Question Bank twice. The first time, do ten module-specific questions a night, following your second-year schedule. The second time should be at the end of the school year, after you have completed the entire Qbank and *First Aid* at least once. Supplement with other question banks you are comfortable with.

Some students feel discouraged at the beginning of their

10-question-per-day journey. That is normal. We tend to be students who are not used to seeing 30% as our exam scores (at least not before medical school!). One way to combat that is to start doing those 10 questions in Tutor Mode. That way, you actually focus on learning HOW to answer the questions, instead of being held back thinking about your score. You can use this mode for a week or two, and then start doing 5 questions in tutor mode, and another 5 in test mode, and then switch to all test mode. You do NOT want to linger on Tutor mode, because time management is one of the skills you need to master for the Boards. However, if you're completely new to the Board questions, feel free to try our suggested method.

Students who are very efficient with their time may have the UWorld or SmashUSMLE review Qbank completed by the end of their second year (April in most schools). They use the rest of April and some of May to do at least a hundred questions a night to complete the USMLE question bank, which should go faster because they gained a tremendous amount of information from going through UWorld. Then in June, they go through UWorld Qbank the second time in a timed setting, now choosing random questions covering all the topics.

Once you have already reviewed these questions and have written the explanations down, going through UWorld the second time should be quick and easy, and you will definitely score higher because of your efforts. In June, plan to do around two hundred questions a night. That is why it is important to be efficient and to write everything down the first time you go through UWorld Question Bank. The questions you get wrong the second time will point to your areas of weakness and alert you to focus on those areas.

Doing two hundred UWorld questions a night in June means you can complete the Question Bank for the second time by the middle of June. At that point, you should be ready to wrap up Board preparation and go "slay the beast."

If you are struggling to keep up with the school material, **do not risk your education!** Focus on passing every class and exam, because nothing is worse than failing your class—that is to be avoided! You will not be allowed to take the Boards if you fail. So learn the coursework material very well and understand it, and then you won't struggle to try to relearn the material during Board studying time. Doing well in your courses will save you time and effort, thus making the studying process much easier.

For osteopathic students, OMTReview COMLEX question bank,

COMQUEST and COMBANK are resources available to study for the COMLEX. You should make good use of these question banks to help you prepare for the COMLEX-USA Level 1 exam. Although the UWorld and SmashUSMLE USMLE question banks are great resources for their content, they are not the best way to adapt to the style of the questions in COMLEX.

**DO students, please remember—USMLE Step 1 is not the same as COMLEX Level 1, and signing up for both is signing up for two different exams. You can easily see that if you look at NBME/ NBOME sample questions.**

**\*\*Remember, you must do well in your second-year classes. That is why we insist that our technique works best for students who are already comfortable with time management skills and have learned how to survive medical school without falling behind and without being easily overwhelmed.**

# CHAPTER 6:
## The Integration

YOU ARE STUDYING to be a doctor not a test taker. The USMLE exam was designed to test your clinical competency as a future physician who will manage real patients in the office setting or hospital. The U.S medical board is responsible for making sure graduating physicians have the clinical knowledge required for you to practice good medicine and keep the community safe.

That's why the USMLE exam exists. Think of it this way; you will see 280 patients on your actual exam, you are responsible to make the correct diagnoses, treatment plans, surgical management and pharmacological interventions necessary to safely take care of your patients. You must know everything. You will be presented with classic patient presentation of disease, signs and symptoms, physical exam findings, abnormal vital signs, histopathological slides, medical imaging (MRI, CT scans, X-rays, Ultrasounds), Lab results, and medical tests presented as clinical vignettes.

You must recognize all the facts in the questions to make a conclusion and either diagnose a disease, or solve a medical case. Some questions just require you to know an enzyme deficiency causing a disease, or a microorganism causing an infection, or a drug of choice and mechanism of action as well as its side effects, or a contraindication and more.

You must be able to use good clinical reasoning and most importantly, integrate all the basic science and clinical knowledge concepts together to pick the correct answer on the test.

Medicine is a study of human pathophysiological phenomena integrated into one science. In medical school, you learn biochemistry, microbiology, immunology, anatomy and physiology, pathology, pharmacology, and clinical medicine. These classes are taught as separate entities or in integrated modules, and provide students with all the knowledge they need to be able to apply the information in a clinical setting.

For international medical graduates from other countries, your education may vary based on the medical school you attend, and you may not be familiar with the USMLE curriculum used by US medical schools.

However, as most of you know, getting through medical school itself is a hassle. Most students struggle through the rigorous first two years of medical school and emerge confused. Most of us do not have time to think about what we are learning but just try to get through every exam. Dr. Goljan once compared medical students to the cell cycle, constantly in G1-S / G2-M phases due to weekly exams. After exams are over, they resort to their G0 phase, resting until the next exam approaches. This is why some medical students fail to understand that all the information they are being taught is part of a whole! But first you have to learn each aspect as an individual entity. Later down the line, it is up to you to integrate it all together because most medical schools do not do a great job of integrating the material for you.

Basically for the boards, you should learn a different approach for remembering (and understanding) clinical syndromes/situations through connecting all the dots from your previous studying (physiology, pharmacology, anatomy, pathology etc.). See fig. 5.1.

Figure 5.1. Board-like approach for clinical syndromes (on example of Down Syndrome).

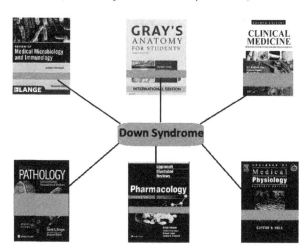

*Source: flixcart.com; blogspot.com; pum.edu.pl; freebooks-forall.xyz; pinterest.com; alibris-static.com.*

Unfortunately, integration of the information is not well taught. Somehow, you are expected to figure that out. You must learn how to see the big picture and think in that perspective. Patients do not present with symptoms and offer written multiple-choice options on their forehead stating the diseases they might have. You are the doctor, and you are supposed to figure that out. If you understand the mechanisms, if you know the "*whys*" and not just the "*whats*", you will be far ahead of the curve. Memorization of facts is not the best way for you to study as a medical student. **When you begin studying for boards, please make sure you focus on understanding mechanisms, mechanisms, mechanisms, and mechanisms! That is the key!**

So, if it is all about the why, shouldn't you be able to simply read the *First Aid for the USMLE Step 1* and do well? As we said before: *no!* That is not true at all. We want you to see the *First Aid for the USMLE Step 1* book as a puzzle. The book contains many hints and facts. At the end, you should be able to put these puzzles together and see the connections throughout the book.

## Dissecting *First Aid for the USMLE* and integrating the concepts

Let us take a look at the book, using the latest edition. The authors correct a few errors and add new content. The book offers advice for medical students at the beginning, and includes other valuable information regarding the Board exam.

The subjects covered in *First Aid* are:

| Basic Sciences | High Yield Organ Systems | |
| --- | --- | --- |
| Public health Sciences | Cardiovascular | Psychiatry |
| Biochemistry and Genetics | Endocrine | Reproductive |
| Pharmacology | Gastrointestinal | Renal |
| Microbiology | Hematology and Oncology | Respiratory |
| Immunology | Musculoskeletal, Skin and Connective tissues | Rapid review |
| Pathology | Neurology and special senses | |

Here are some key issues with *First Aid*. First, many concepts are covered in the course of several chapters, due to their clinical association with various organ systems throughout the book. Here's an example.

In the biochemistry chapter, on pg. 63, autosomal trisomies are discussed in extensive detail. Down syndrome is a perfect example. But pg. 63 does not include everything you need to know about Down syndrome for the Boards. It is also covered on pg. 63, 303, 378, 424, 508, 523, 567, 619, and 674. (Note these pages are based on First aid for the USMLE Step 1 book 2020 edition, these pages will change based on the latest edition of the book)

| | |
|---|---|
| **Down syndrome (trisomy 21)** Findings: intellectual disability, flat facies, prominent epicanthal folds, single palmar crease, incurved 5th finger, gap between 1st 2 toes, duodenal atresia, Hirschsprung disease, congenital heart disease (e.g, ASD), Brushfield spots. Associated with early-onset Alzheimer disease (chromosome 21 codes for amyloid precursor protein), ↑risk of AML/ALL. 95% of cases due to meiotic nondisjunction (↑ with advanced maternal age; from 1:1500 in women < 20 to 1:25 in women > 45 years old) 4% of cases due to unbalanced Robertsonian translocation, most typically between chromosomes 14 and 21. Only 1% of cases are due to post fertilization mitotic error. | Incidence 1:700. **D**rinking age (**21**). Most common viable chromosomal disorder and most common cause of genetic intellectual disability. First-trimester ultrasound commonly shows ↑ Nuchal translucency and hypoplastic nasal bone. Markers for Down syndrome are **HI** up: ↑ **hCG**, ↑ **i**nhibin. The **5 A**'s of Down syndrome: **A**dvanced maternal age **A**tresia (duodenal) **A**trioventricular septal defect **A**lzheimer disease (early onset) **AML/ALL** |

Excerpt-'Down Syndrome Page 63, from First Aid for the USMLE Step 1 2020 © 2020 Tao Le ,Vikas Bhushan, Lars Grimm Published by The McGraw-Hill Companies This material is reproduced with permission of The McGraw-Hill Companies.

Figure 5.2. Prevalence of Down syndrome based on genetic mechanisms.

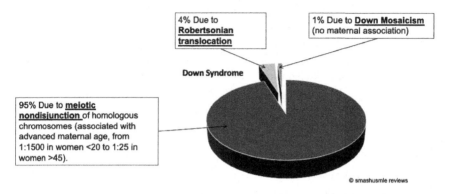

4% Due to **Robertsonian translocation**

1% Due to **Down Mosaicism** (no maternal association)

Down Syndrome

95% Due to **meiotic nondisjunction** of homologous chromosomes (associated with advanced maternal age, from 1:1500 in women <20 to 1:25 in women >45).

© smashusmle reviews

If the syndrome is covered on eight different pages in the book, it must be very important; that means that the national Boards would be very interested in testing it.

Second, connecting the dots is a key. Down syndrome is one disease with several pathological manifestations in different organ systems. How should you understand disease processes for Boards?

(We use Down syndrome as a classical example here, but this can apply to any other disease process).

Down syndrome (trisomy 21) is the most common chromosomal disorder and most common cause of congenital mental retardation.

## Mechanism/pathogenesis

Ninety-five percent of cases are due to ***meiotic non-disjunction*** of homologous chromosomes (associated with advanced maternal age; from 1:1500 in women age < 20 to 1:25 in women age > 45. Four percent can be due to Robertsonian translocation.

## Physical findings

Include flat facies, prominent epicanthal folds, single simian crease, and gaps between the first two toes. (See fig. 5.3).

Figure 5.3. Common physical findings in Down Syndrome.

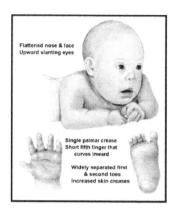

Flattened nose & face
Upward slanting eyes

Single palmar crease
Short fifth finger that
curves inward

Widely separated first
& second toes
Increased skin creases

*** Source: moondragon.org.***

Now that you understand the mechanism, the Boards may test you about every organ system's pathology associated with the disease. Let us break it down by organ systems.

a. **Neurology:** By age 35, a patient with Down syndrome has an increased risk of developing Alzheimer's disease. Refer to pg. 508 (neurology-anatomy and physiology section). **Alzheimer's:** Amyloid precursor protein on chromosome 21 (p-App gene) is associated with Alzheimer's disease. Keep in mind that you probably read page 63 a while ago and may forget that you are reading something similar on page 508.

b. **Cardiology:** The most common congenital heart defects found in a Down syndrome patient are *Atrioventricular Septal Defect (Endocardial Cushion Defect) > Ventricular Septal Defect > Atrial Septal Defect".*

Now, refer to page 303, "Congenital cardiac defect associations." Down syndrome is mentioned again, to remind you of cardiac anomalies associated with Down syndrome.

c. **Gastrointestinal system:** page 378; Duodenal atresia and Hirschsprung's disease are highly associated with Down syndrome.

d. **Hematology and oncology:** page 63 and 424. Down syndrome patients have an increased risk of developing acute lymphoblastic leukemia (ALL).

Figure 5.4. Some physical findings in organ systems in Down syndrome.

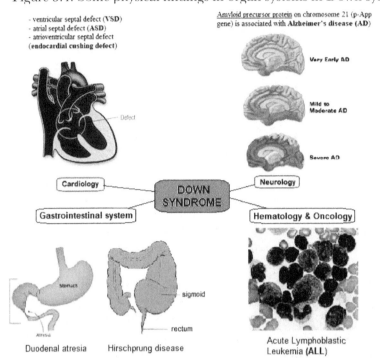

Duodenal atresia    Hirschprung disease

Acute Lymphoblastic
Leukemia (ALL)

*\* Source: MedicineNet.com; atlasgeneticsoncology.org;
blogspot.com; slidesharecdn.com; slideplayer.com.*

## The Big Picture
## Sample SmashUSMLE-style Questions

1.  A neonate was delivered at thirty-eight weeks gestation with no pregnancy complications. The mother did not receive any prenatal care prior to delivery. On physical exam, the physician noted a flat prominent face, a simian crease and epicanthal fold, and a 3/6 loud holosystolic murmur at the left lower sternal border. What is the most likely diagnosis?

A. Trisomy 18
B. Trisomy 13

C. Trisomy 21

D. Fragile X

E. DiGeorge syndrome

**Answer: "C"** - **Trisomy 21**. This is the only disease associated with the physical examination findings of a flat face, prominent epicanthal folds, single simian crease, and gaps between the first two toes.

2.  A neonate was delivered at thirty-eight weeks gestation to a forty-year-old mother with no pregnancy complications. The mother did not receive any prenatal care prior to delivery. On physical exam, the physician noted a flat prominent face, a simian crease and epicanthal fold, and a 3/6 loud holosystolic murmur at the left lower sternal border. Four days after birth the mother of the baby noted bilious vomiting with a distended abdomen. X-ray of the abdomen shows a "double bubble sign." What is the cause of the neonate's abdominal distention?

    A. Meconium ileus

    B. Duodenal atresia

    C. Hirschprungs disease

    D. Constipation

    E. Pyloric stenosis

**Answer: "B"** - **Duodenal atresia** is associated with double bubble sign on an x-ray and is an increased risk in Down syndrome patients.

3.  A neonate was delivered at thirty-eight weeks gestation with no pregnancy complications. The mother did not receive any prenatal care prior to delivery. On physical exam, the physician noted a flat prominent face, a simian crease and epicanthal fold, and a wide gap between the first and second toe. This baby is at risk of what neurologic disease as he gets older?

    A. Pick's disease

    B. Tuberous sclerosis

    C. Alzheimer's disease

    D. Neurofibromatosis type 2

    E. Friedreich's ataxia

**Answer: "C" - Alzheimer's.** Down syndrome patients have an increased risk of developing early onset Alzheimer's later in life.

4. A 38-year-old Caucasian presents to her primary care physician's office at sixteen weeks pregnant. The physician performed ultrasound and noted increased nuchal translucency. What do you expect the result of the pregnancy quad screen to be?

**β-hCG α-fetoprotein Estriol Inhibin A**

A. ↑↓ ↓↑
B. ↓↓ ↓↓
C. ↓↓ ↑↑
D. ↑↓ ↑↑

Key: Up arrow is Increase, Down arrow is decrease.
**Answer: "A"**
Down syndrome quad screen results are: high ®-hCG, high Inhibin A, low alpha-fetoprotein and low estriol. Increased nuchal translucency is a classic finding in a Down syndrome fetus on ultrasound.

5. A 65-year-old Caucasian male presents with fatigue, skin pallor and recurrent gingival bleeding. He denies any trauma or foreign object insertion. On physical exam, it is noted a 3/6 holosystolic murmur at the left lower sternal border other findings are unremarkable. A complete blood count reveals pancytopenia. A bone marrow biopsy is scheduled which revealed a "cytoplasmic needle-like azurophilic granular materials". Which of these would be found upon further investigation?

t(12;21)
t(15;17)
t(8;14)
t(11;22)

**Answer: "B" – t (15;17)**
This patient most likely has AML which is associated with a translocation 15;17, with VSD which are associated in Down Syndrome. The Board exams are trying to move away from key words such as "Auer rods" and would most likely describe it plainly as above.

6.  The patient above is enrolled in an experimental treatment for a new drug which induces differentiation of promyelocytes. This medication has similar properties as which of the following?

Vitamin A

Vitamin C

Vitamin B1

Vitamin E

**Answer: "A"** - **Vitamin A**. The drug of choice for AML(APL) is ATRA, (All trans retinoic acid).

### Example Two

Here is another example of integrated concepts. In *First Aid for the USMLE Step 1,* Hemochromatosis appears on pages 64, 100, 210, 311, 386, 389, and 459. This outlines the association and connections between effects of the disease on various organ systems and this could show up on Board exams.

Hemochromatosis is an autosomal recessive disease in which iron is absorbed beyond the body's needs and there is no saturation point, leading to accumulation of iron in different parts of the body, starting with the liver. The excess iron deposition causes inflammation, fibrosis, and tissue damage. The following are systemic manifestations of the disease.

a. GI (pg. 386 and 389): Liver and pancreas are damaged. Hepatomegaly, liver cirrhosis, causes the typical signs and symptoms of portal hypertension and liver failure, and increased risk of hepatocellular carcinoma. In the pancreas, the damage leads to destruction of the islet cells, resulting in diabetes mellitus (or at least glucose intolerance due to decreased insulin secretion).

b. Cardio (pg. 311): Heart failure due to restrictive cardiomyopathy. The patient will present with signs and symptoms of both left-sided and right-sided heart failure. Conduction defects are also possible.

C. Musculoskeletal (Pg. 459): Arthropathy due to iron being deposited in the joints.

d. Skin (pg. 389): "hyperpigmentation" of the skin.

e. Other: Testicular atrophy and impotence, hypopituitarism, and increased risk of infection by iron-loving bacteria such as *vibrio vulnificus* and *yersinia*. (Other manifestations are available from different review books)

## Sample Board-style Questions

1. A 24-four-year old male presents with polyuria and polydipsia. He mentions that his friends have noticed he is getting tanner. He is also lethargic. Which of the following is likely to help with the diagnosis?

   A) Chest x-ray

   B) Echocardiogram

   C) Kidney biopsy

   D) Liver biopsy

   E) Glucose tolerance test

   **Answer**: **"D"**- Liver biopsy

## Explanation

The question is indirectly asking you what the most likely pathology associated with hemochromatosis is, which is diabetes. The patient has signs of polyuria, polydipsia, and tanning (iron deposition on the skin). Ordering a glucose tolerance test will show elevated blood sugar (hyperglycemia) >126 mg/dl fasting blood sugar. However, his diabetes is secondary to destruction of the pancreas by iron deposition. The best way to diagnose hemochromatosis is a liver biopsy.

2. A thirty-three-year-old Caucasian American presented to his family physician complaining of impotence and loss of libido. He has a past medical history of diabetes, arthritis, congestive heart failure, and hyperpigmentation of his skin. Which of the following lab results of Iron, ferritin, transferrin and TIBC saturation will most likely confirm his diagnosis of hemochromatosis?

   A ↑↓↓↑

   B ↓↓↓↓

   C ↓↓↑↑

   D ↑↑↑↓

   **Correct answer. D.** The patient has hemochromatosis, so you would expect elevated iron levels, ferritin, and transferrin saturation, but low total iron binding capacity.

## Example Three

In *First Aid for the USMLE Step 1* 2019, Turner syndrome (pages 302, 350, 567, 624, 678) is described as a sex chromosomal disorder in females who have XO chromosomes. The characteristic features are short stature, broad chest, ovarian dysgenesis, amenorrhea, preductal coarctation of the aorta, no barr body, horseshoe kidney, cystic hygromas, and lymphedema of the hands and feet.

Figure 5.5. Physical findings in organ systems in Turner syndrome.

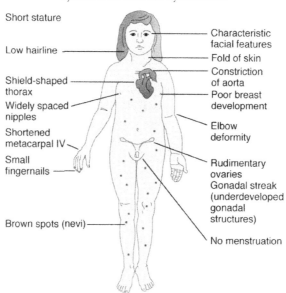

\* Source:
https://www.mun.ca/biology/scarr/MGA2-11-14_Turner.html

Pathophysiology of Turner syndrome is caused by a mitotic error during early development (45XO). These patients have low estrogen, which leads to increase in LH and FSH.

However, learning the above facts is not enough; the way the test examiner will present Turner syndrome will be different. Here are some sample questions.

1.  A twenty-one-year-old female presents to the office, complaining she never had her period. On physical exam, she is fifty-four inches tall

with a broad chest and widely spaced nipples. Her hands and feet appear edematous. What chromosomal finding are you most likely to see in this patient?

A. 44XXY

B. 45XYY

C. 46XX

D. 45XO

E. 47XXX

**Answer: "D".** This is a classic presentation of Turner syndrome. The patient presented with short stature, broad chest, and widely spaced nipples. Her hands and feet appear edematous. Most Turner syndrome patients have 45XO chromosomal abnormalities.

2.  A twenty-one-year-old female presents to the office, complaining she never had her period. On physical exam, she is forty-four inches tall, with a broad chest and widely spaced nipples. Her hands and feet appear edematous. Intravenous pyelogram revealed horseshoe kidney. Which anatomic structure is preventing the kidneys from ascending in this patient?

A. Superior mesenteric artery

B. Celiac artery

C. Inferior vena cava

D. Inferior mesenteric artery

E. External iliac vein

**Answer: "D".** The image shows a bilateral horseshoe kidney, which is common in Turner syndrome patients. The two kidneys are obstructed by the inferior mesenteric artery, which prevents these structures from ascending during development.

3.  A twenty-one-year-old female presents to the office complaining she never had her period. On physical exam, she is forty-four inches tall, with a broad chest and widely spaced nipples. Her hands and feet appear edematous. Her blood pressure in her left arm was 160/95 mmHg and left leg was 90/60 mm Hg, with weak pulses in her legs. What cardiac abnormality do you suspect in this patient?

A. Patent ductus arteriosus

B. VSD

C. Coarctation of the aorta. *pediatric*

D. ASD

E. Tetralogy of Fallot

**Answer: "C".** Coarctation of the aorta is highly associated with Turner syndrome. Such patients also have bicuspid valves, which can result in aortic regurgitation. You can locate this integration in the cardio section of your First Aid, where coarctation of the aorta is discussed.

Can you see how important it is to not only know the pathogenesis of disease processes, but every single association with each disease? There are so many ways the National Boards can test a single concept. As you can see from the test question examples above, learning pathogenesis is not enough; they expect you to know all the associations and possible clinical presentations.

The authors of *First Aid for the USMLE Step 1* do not emphasize the importance of integration when they present the material. They list the associations in different sections of the book; however, in our experience, when you read the book, you miss the trend. It is your responsibility to integrate the facts and connect the dots.

The best resources that actually integrate *First Aid for USMLE Step 1* are either the **SmashUSMLE** or UWorld question bank. The more questions you practice, the more you learn how to integrate the material so you are able to handle two-to three-step thought process questions. As a medical student, you are expected to have the knowledge and be able to apply it to the next step. Not only do you have to commit a lot of the facts to memory, but you have to take it a step further and apply the knowledge to clinical scenarios. Once you master this, you have conquered the art of preparing for the exam. Next, we will discuss the art of taking the test in a more efficient way. In the following chapter, we will discuss strategies and techniques that help you easily answer Board questions.

# CHAPTER 7:
## How to dissect USMLE Questions

### How do I read questions and maximize my time with Board questions?

THE SINGLE MOST important thing to understand about the USMLE is that crushing it is 50% knowledge and 50% test taking strategy. Let's face it. There is a systematic approach for addressing practice questions. Questions are designed so they have a consistent pattern. NBME and NBOME question writers are trained to write USMLE and COMLEX questions with a standard format.

A clinical vignette/scenario is followed by a question stem and then options. However, if you are not aware of these patterns, you will most likely run out of time or not finish each block on your exam day.

Firstly, Read. Every. Word. Before we begin, you need to understand the anatomy of a typical USMLE question.

The stem

**The identifier:** "This is usually the age, gender of the patient, e.g. a 41-year-old Caucasian female presents with ...

**Chief complaint:** What the patient\s primary complaint is, e.g. Chest pain, shortness of breath, diarrhea.

**Key associations.** These are extra data you will be given to make the diagnosis. e.g. "alcoholic, currant jelly sputum, fever, cough."

**Lead in**. "What is the most common cause/management/mechanism of action/treatment."

Options: answer choices

**Distractors:** built in facts to distract you as a test taker. The USMLE is different, but they are not trying to trick you, they are trying to lead you to the correct diagnosis, if you piece together the facts they present in the question. Just know that distractors are built into all questions, then you will be fine. E.g. History of travel, medications, borderline vital signs. If they want to show you a patient with sepsis, they will give you <u>HR 120</u>, <u>BP 82/40</u>, <u>T 103</u>. But they may present distractors with temp 99.3 but it's not a fever. Distractors can be built into questions or placed as "Incorrect answer choices". You must select the best answer when taking the USMLE, but the purpose of incorrect answer choices is for you to pick them rather than the best answer. Each distractor will be picked by some test takers so each option can fool anyone on the exam. Your responsibility is to make sure you do not get confused by the clinical vignette and pick the distracting incorrect answer choices.

The common reason why test takers pick distractors, which can appear to be a partially right answer is from incomplete medical knowledge, inadequate understanding of what concept is being tested, second guessing and faulty reasoning.

Before we begin, we want to emphasize that the exam covers every subject that you have studied in the *First Aid USMLE Step 1*. However, every new question stem is from a different chapter—so how do you narrow your focus without panicking or wondering how to begin to answer a question?

Now let's learn the **EASE-Checkpoint Strategy**

**What does the EASE-Checkpoint study strategy stand for?**

EASE stands for Examine, Associate, Summarize, and Ensure.

Let us do a sample SmashUSMLE question:

## Case 1:

A twelve-year-old African American female presents with chest pain, knee pain and weakness, and shortness of breath. The patient reports she gets painful episodes and sometimes requires hospitalization. She reports having her spleen removed when she was ten because of her sickle cell disease. Lab shows Hb 7.5. **What medication is most likely to increase the concentration of fetal hemoglobin in sickle cell patients?**

A. Amiodarone

B. Acetaminophen

C. Busulfan

D. Hydroxyurea

E. Atenolol

Let's apply the **EASE-checkpoint** strategy technique.

1. **Examine the lead in: Read the last sentence of the clinical vignette first.**

   What medication is most likely to increase the concentration of Fetal Hemoglobin in sickle cell patients? **Correct answer is D. Hydroxyurea**
   This is the lead in the question. In this case, you see how you can just answer the question by reading the lead in only. This is a great strategy to save time on the exam day.
   This is a common theme you may notice when answering USMLE/COMLEX questions. You may not need to read the entire vignette to figure out the answer to the question.

## Case 2:

A four-year-old Caucasian male presents to the clinic with fever of 102° F, cough, and a foul-smelling green mucopurulent discharge for the past three days. His parents noticed his stools have been floating, and he has not been growing well compared to his peers. The mother reports his skin tasted salty. On a physical exam, he shows signs of weakened bones and malnourishment. Lung exam shows decreased breath sounds, rales, increased tactile fremitus, and egophony in the right middle lobe; there is no wheezing. **What organism most likely caused the patient's symptoms?**

    A. *Streptococcus pneumoniae*

    B. *Serratia marcescens*

    C. *Pseudomonas aeruginosa*

    D. *Klebsiella pneumoniae*

    E. *Enterococcus* spp.

## Let's apply the 4-step EASE method to this question

Before we solve this case. You probably read the case from the beginning to the end. Do not do this when doing practice USMLE questions or on the exam day.

**Step 1. Examine the lead in: Read the last sentence of the clinical vignette first.**

What organism most likely caused the patient's symptoms? This is the lead in the question. In this case, we cannot answer the question just by reading the lead in only.

**Examine the answer choices: Take a quick glance at the options first.**

This is extremely important. This allows you to narrow down what the question wants you to know.

A. *Streptococcus pneumoniae*

B. *Serratia marcescens*

C. *Pseudomonas aeruginosa*

D. *Klebsiella pneumoniae*

E. *Enterococcus* spp.

In this case, you can see that the answer choices narrow this down to a microbiology question. Briefly looking over the answer choices ahead of time for a few seconds allows you to focus on microbiology, not something else.

# Step 2: Associate.

Now go back and start reading the entire question stem from the beginning. Select your highlighter tool and start reading and highlighting to extract the **associations,** the identifiers, qualifiers and code switches in the question stem. We use all the information given to us, including associations to arrive at the diagnosis.

If you are using SmashUSMLE Question bank or other question banks, you can highlight words and cross out answers.

This is an important tool that many students do not fully use to their advantage. *Highlighting is critical because it allows you to focus on the main signs and symptoms that the patient in the question presents.*

For example:

A four–year-old Caucasian male presents to the clinic with a fever of 102° F, cough, and foul-smelling green mucopurulent discharge lasting for the past three days. The parents noticed his stool tends to float in the toilet, and he has not been growing well compared to his peers. The mother reports his skin tastes salty. On a physical exam, he shows signs of weakened bones and malnourishment. Lung exam shows decreased breath sounds, rales, increased tactile fremitus, and egophony in right middle lobe; no wheezing is appreciated. What organism is most likely to cause the patient's symptoms?

## Step 3: Summarize the question.

Can you see why highlighting is important? We have highlighted the main signs and symptoms in the question, which allows you to see what is important and ignore the distractors. We can basically summarize the key points of this question as:

"A four–year-old Caucasian male with fever, cough, foul green discharge, steatorrhea, salty skin, failure to thrive, with pneumonia."

What do you think this child has? Cystic fibrosis, of course!

## Step 4: Ensure.

Before you quickly jump to conclusion, ask yourself the following questions.

a. Did I understand what the question writer is asking?

b. Did I use all the information presented in the question to make the logical conclusion and arrive at the correct diagnosis or not?

c. Did I answer the question correctly or am I missing the point?

Now proceed to answer the question.

A four–year-old Caucasian male presents to the clinic with a fever of 102° F, cough, and foul-smelling green mucopurulent discharge lasting for the past three days. The parents noticed his stool tends to float in the toilet, and he has not been growing well compared to his peers. The mother reports his skin tastes salty. On physical examination, he shows signs of weakened bones and malnourishment. Lung exam shows decreased breath sounds, rales, increased tactile fremitus, and egophony in right middle lobe; no wheezing is appreciated. What organism most likely caused the patient's symptoms?

A. *Streptococcus pneumoniae*

B. *Serratia marcescens*

C. *Pseudomonas aeruginosa*

D. *Klebsiella pneumoniae*

E. *Enterococcus* spp.

"A four–year-old Caucasian male with cystic fibrosis presents with fever, cough, foul green discharge, steatorrhea, salty skin, failure to thrive, and has pneumonia. What organism most likely caused the patient's symptoms?"

**Correct answer: C.** *Pseudomonas aeruginosa*

Questions always give you hints and key points to narrow down the disease in question. So, watch carefully for the description of disease processes, because they are literally giving it away. For instance,

- "A four–year-old Caucasian male"— Pay close attention to ethnicity and age of the patient. If ethnicity is mentioned in a question, do not ignore it. It is often a very important clue, due to the association between certain diseases and their prevalence in specific ethnic groups. For example, cystic fibrosis is more common in Caucasians, whereas sickle cell anemia is more prevalent among African Americans.
- "Fever 102° F, cough, foul-smelling green mucopurulent discharge lasting for the past three days…decreased breath sound, rales, increased tactile fremitus, and egophony in right middle lobe" are signs of bacterial pneumonia.
- Steatorrhea indicates the presence of malabsorption and deficiency of the pancreatic enzyme, lipase, which is required for lipid digestion.
- Weakened bones (osteomalacia) is a manifestation of vitamin D deficiency which is in turn due to malabsorption of lipid soluble vitamins.
- Salty skin indicates lack of reabsorption of chloride from sweat.

These represent the clues that are usually given in the question stem. Watch carefully for these descriptions, because they point you in the right direction.

Another example

A 30-year-old woman presents with chest pain for one day. The pain is in the center of her chest and is worse with deep inspiration and coughing. She reports that it improves when she leans forward while sitting on the examination table. An ECG in the office shows ST segment elevation in all leads. **What is the most likely diagnosis?**

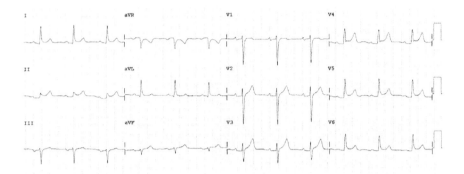

A. Aortic dissection

B. Myocardial infarction

C. Pancreatitis

D. Pericarditis ✓

E. Pulmonary embolism

Let's apply our 4-step EASE method to this question.

## Step 1: Examine the lead in and answer choices.

An ECG in the office shows ST segment elevation in all leads. What is the most likely diagnosis?

You can see that you can easily answer the question if you recognize what the EKG reading is, and glancing at the answers narrows this question to a cardiology answer choice.

## Step 2: Associate-

Highlight to extract the **associations,** the identifiers, qualifiers and code switches in the question stem.

A 30-year-old woman presents with chest pain for one day. The pain is in the center of her chest and is worse with deep inspiration and coughing. She reports that it improves when she leans forward while sitting on the examination table. Patient states she does not take oral contraceptives. An ECG in the office shows ST segment elevation in all leads. What is the most likely diagnosis?

## Step 3: Summarize the case

"30 year-old female with chest pain, worse with inspiration with diffuse ST segment elevation on EKG?"

**Step 4: Ensure.** Make sure your summary matches your differential diagnosis and confirm if your reasoning is in the answer choices. Rule in and rule diagnosis based on the information provided to you in the case.

Correct answer is D. Pericarditis.

You have learnt the EASE method to answering USMLE and COMLEX questions. You must understand the checkpoints inside the standardized board questions. Remember the cell cycle, with M-G1-S-G2 phase.

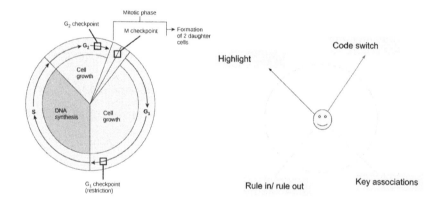

Think of checkpoints as steps inside a question that allow you make sure you are on track with what your reasoning is, to match the desired answer by the exam writer.

**This means, how do you interpret every sentence given to you?**

Be a step ahead - read a sentence and ask yourself, Checkpoint system allows you to rule in and rule out the diagnosis.

- Is there a key association and or code switch?

  o E.g. BP 60/40, this patient is in shock!

- Why is each sentence important or not? Rule in or rule out diagnosis

  o What's the relevance of the Board writer giving me this information e.g. Patient has a history of arthritis, I should assume the patient is automatically taking NSAIDs for pain. May test me on Gastric perforation of the gastroduodenal artery because the patient is having a gastrointestinal bleeding.

- What's my new differential diagnosis? How does the sentence change my differential? Don't change your differential because the last sentence does not meet what your expectations are. E.g. just because they did not give you a bull's eye rash image, does not mean you can rule out Lyme disease.
- Highlight and read with checkpoints, so you don't have to go back and re-read the question again. You just answer and move on!

## What is a Code switch?

Code switches are indirect ways of describing signs, symptoms, abnormal vital signs or lab work to help point you that something is wrong with your patient.

Let's look at some examples. If you are given a patient with;

- RUQ pain with palpation and inspiratory pause→ think Murphy's sign
- Shortness of breath→ think dyspnea
- Potassium of 7.1→ think hyperkalemia
- Heart rate of 125 → think tachycardia
- BP -80/60, HR 140, T 39F, RR- 35 (Pt with pna) - think Septic shock!
- Distended jugular veins, decreased heart sounds, decreased systolic blood pressure (80/40), → think Cardiac tamponade (Becks triad!)

Remember code switches are **NOT** diagnoses (but might suggest them). You will always see these in your USMLE and COMLEX questions, do not ignore them. Use them to guide your diagnosis.

## Finally, you must learn anchoring!

Board exam writers are trained to write questions that are very straightforward and avoid any ambiguity. Each question you are tested on in the actual exam must be a classic presentation of the disease, and the standard of treatment is universally agreed upon in medicine.

This means they are not trying to trick you. You must learn to anchor based on the identifier, chief complaints and qualifiers in your questions. Use symptomatic anchoring to answer all questions and do not come up with your own additional findings that are not presented to you inside the case. For example; if you are given,

- A 2-year-old-boy with wheezing, chest pain and dyspnea. Think (bronchiolitis- from RSV)
- A 17-year-old college male with chest pain, no left lung sounds (think pneumothorax) Spontaneous
- A 32-year-old woman on oral contraceptives, smokes with chest pain, shortness of breath and unilateral right Leg edema (think pulmonary embolism)
- A 42-year-old-man with HIV with chest pain, cough and fever, CD4 count 100- think **Pneumocystis jiroveci**
- A 69-year-old man with a history of diabetes, hypertension, hyperlipidemia presents with chest pain, radiates to the left arm with ST segment elevation in lead II, III, AVF. (Think MI)

In 99% of cases, there is an **identifier and chief complaint + qualifier.** Always anchor on presenting symptoms. Also glance at the answer choices for anchoring.

If you apply the EASE-checkpoint to the question and you still do not understand the concept. Click your best answer and move on.

How do you get good at this? **By practicing as many questions as you can.** Can you see how important doing questions is?

**To watch the EASE method online, visit smashusmle.com.**

The USMLE and COMLEX exams are 8-hour long tests, similar to a marathon. You might have good pace and form for the first few miles but can you keep that up for all 26 miles? Similarly, students can experience mental fatigue hours into a test and then the strategies you've practiced go out the window or certain, otherwise simple facts may elude you.

When you start using the EASE-Checkpoint method, you may feel uneasiness but with time, you will start to see the difference. You will see how easy it is to use and how it will help you solve USMLE questions in ways you have never seen before.

To excel on the board, you must have a solid endurance. So, how do you train for a marathon? You get accustomed to running for hours and hours on end. Essentially, you replicate the conditions during your training so that on race day you will feel and be ready since you have faced similar circumstances before.

In a similar fashion, the best way to prepare for the endurance-aspect of a grueling 8-hour USMLE exam is to do NBME practice tests. Practice exams, such as the NBME self-assessments, are available for purchase online at nbme.org. These assessment tests are a great way to familiarize yourself with the experience of taking the USMLE (as well as gauging your strengths and weaknesses).

However, you can recreate the test-day using SmashUSMLE or UWorld question bank simply by challenging yourself to complete multiple 40-question blocks with minimal breaks in between. At first, you may only be able to finish three or four blocks in a day before you begin to develop headaches and get exhausted. But don't get discouraged! Rome wasn't built in a day, body-builders don't get huge overnight, and marathon runners train for years. Likewise, gaining mental stamina takes time but soon enough you'll surprise yourself by what you are capable of achieving.

## In Summary

**Always, apply the "EASE-move on" method during your practice of USMLE questions. Remember to-**

E-xamine

A-ssociate

S-ummarize

E-nsure

Move on*- I say move on because on the exam day, even if you apply this method, there will be questions you will not know the answer to, make your best educated guess and move on. Do not waste too much time trying to answer these questions. Some of them are experimental questions, make sure you answer every question on the exam. Do not skip any question, you do not get penalized for not answering the questions.

Use your checkpoints- to find associations, identifiers and qualifiers.

Rule in and Rule out diagnosis based on clinical cases based on the facts given to you.

Know your code switches and use symptomatic anchoring.

# Practice! Practice!! Practice!!! To achieve mastery

Learn to distinguish between essential and non-essential information. Understand that all vignettes are reverse-engineered with an important testable concept in mind. Ask yourself "What is the key concept examiner they're trying to get at here?" Don't look at the answer choices until you have given yourself an opportunity to synthesize the vignette and establish a hypothesis or differential diagnosis. Understand that 90% of the time, you have already been taught everything you need to know to answer any question correctly. Focus on what you know and understand, as opposed to that which you do not remember or are uncertain of, or simply do not understand. Think through the set of important concepts you have previously been tested on in the context of your USMLE exam preparation and ask yourself "which answer is most consistent with a key concept I've already been tested on?" Select a single best answer most consistent with your hypothesis or differential diagnosis. Then use the process of elimination as each incorrect answer is incorrect along at least a single dimension of information. E.g., if a 50-year-old smoker with COPD post op day 1 status post knee replacement patient has sudden onset dyspnea, COPD exacerbation is less likely as COPD exacerbations are not sudden in onset. Think about how you thought about questions you got incorrect. What went wrong in your mind? Did you have a lapse of attention? Were you distracted by an irrelevant detail? Did you fail to identify which information was essential? Did you not carefully read the first sentence? I teach all my tutors a list of common cognitive pitfalls to identify in students, how to identify them, and how to give feedback to students on these cognitive errors.

# CHAPTER 8:
## Studying for the Boards

HERE'S A STORY that relates to studying for the Boards and illustrates the maxim, "To fail to prepare is to prepare to fail."

A town crier once came to a small village and warned the people of an impending war that might wipe out their entire population. The town crier said, however, it would be two years before the war began. The people were shocked but replied, "We will be ready in two years." Since it was still two years ahead, they did not have to worry until then. A paraplegic leper overheard the message and decided to start crawling slowly to safety. Two years passed by, and the people forgot. The war came and wiped out the entire population. Only the leper survived.

What is the point of the story? Many students behave like the people of this small village. We all know that we have to take the USMLE or COMLEX. Early Preparation is one the most valuable things any medical student who really wants to perform well on these exams should do.

Image credit: canstockphoto.com

As a student, ever since you learned how to read and write, you are accustomed to studying in a linear fashion. You have attended schools where you were given information that you were instructed to memorize and were told there would be an exam. You did exactly as you were told and you regurgitated the answers back, word for word. You got an A. And people said you were smart. You have done this for as long as you can recall. It always worked. It never failed. Right?

However, *for Boards, it will not work*. We are sorry—we know we just broke your heart. Memorization and regurgitation is the worst approach; it will lead to barely passing, or even failing the test. We call it the "wrong way"! Board exams are not your typical medical school exams, where you stay up all night memorizing every origin and insertion of a muscle or biochemical pathway under the sun. Look at NBME/NBOME sample questions and you will see it is more than memorization. If it was a memorization exam, everyone would score a 275 on USMLE or 790 on COMLEX, and we would all get into dermatology and neurosurgery, if we chose. But this is not the case.

Here is the secret; it is the opposite of how you used to learn. **In-order to do well on Boards, you literally have to move inside the mind of the exam writers and think exactly like them**. You'll want to know how to do that, right? It is a skill that you will acquire after studying the tips we offer in this book.

## The Rules

### 1. Decide and set a goal.

Most of us do not realize that in order to accomplish anything in life, **you must *have goals*.** As a medical student or IMG, ask yourself this question: How well do you want to do on this exam? Do you just want to get passing scores on the USMLE or COMLEX (this will be the case for the USMLE in 2022) or do you want to excel and rock this exam with high scores of 250 for USMLE step 2CK, or 700s on the COMLEX level 2CE? As a human, you have the potential to do anything. Often you think you have reached the limit of how far you can go, but there is room for much more. **We strongly urge you to set realistic and achievable goals.**

We fully understand everyone's goals are different. However, when we embarked on our preparation, we said to ourselves: aim to score over

260 on the USMLE or 700 on the COMLEX exam. That was the *goal!* It sounds like we are high achievers, but we noticed that people who established a high expectation and worked toward it might not necessarily reach that goal, but more often than not, they got close to such a goal. So, aim high, strive for the best, and you will be satisfied with your result.

If your goal is simply to pass the exam, you should aim for it and achieve it. For some, this is a milestone of achievement; for others it may be different. We are by no means telling you what you should do, but rather describing what we decided as a goal. Whatever it is, set your goals, be fervent, and persevere until you achieve it— that will make all the difference.

"Reach for the moon. Even if you miss it, you will land among the stars." ˜Les Brown˜

## 2. Write your goal down.

Most of us have a goal in mind; we only talk about it. But people who write down their goals have a higher chance of achieving them. So, write down your goals in a diary, a paper and place on the wall where you can see it every day. This will serve as a reminder of what your target is and why you should be motivated to achieve it.

## 3. Be disciplined, and have a positive attitude toward your preparation.

Doing well on Boards requires some mental tweaking. Most students are anxious about taking Boards. They panic and are very anxious about the test. The best favor you can do for yourself is to have a positive attitude. Remind yourself daily that you will do well on the exam. Do not associate with friends who are overly anxious and who will raise your blood pressure about taking the exam.

At SmashUSMLE reviews, we have a SMARTMD WhatsApp group for all our medical students where they get a positive environment for learning, daily USMLE exam updates, and positive motivation videos from Dr. Adesina. All our students love the SMARTMD WhatsApp group because of the constant support they receive from Dr. Adesina and his team.

Discipline is one of the most essential tools any physician-to-be should acquire. Be very disciplined, plan your schedule wisely, and spend your time judiciously throughout your second year. This applies to international medical graduates; you should be very disciplined so you can complete your USMLE review. Remember, you do not get a second chance at this, unless you fail.

## 4. Know yourself, start early, and do not procrastinate.

Know yourself. It is simple. If you know you are not a last-minute learner, if you are someone who needs a good amount of time to master any information, then do not fool yourself. Starting early is the right way for you. Even if you are a last-minute learner, someone who can cram in lots of information in a short time, save yourself some anxiety by starting early. You have nothing to lose.

The best advice for you to get your mind ready for this exam is to start early and start small. For international medical graduates (IMG), you have more time than US medical students. You should start preparing for the USMLE as soon as possible. Most IMGs take between 12-18 months to study for USMLE Step 1 alone. You will spend less time studying for Step 2CK, and even less time for Step 3.

### Board Review Courses

There are many courses out there for Boards review. The most well-known ones are SmashUSMLE Reviews, USMLERx, Boards and beyond, Pathoma, Sketchymicro, Physeo, Amboss, Lecturio, PASS Program, and Doctors in Training. Some schools make these courses mandatory for all students; others do not. Do you really need one?

For most U.S Students, your medical school might already have a partnership with a test prep company or you have to choose a program that suits you. If you are a U.S medical student struggling with medical school lectures, get a review course because you are at risk of failing the USMLE or COMLEX exam.

For international medical graduates we strongly recommend you use a test prep course. We recommend SmashUSMLE reviews, UWorld Qbank, or Pathoma. The reason is because most international medical graduates are not familiar with the structure of the USMLE, and often struggle to pass the exam.

IMGs are not well prepared by Caribbean schools to pass the USMLE and often have weak basic science or clinical knowledge which affects their performance on the USMLE exam. For IMGs who have graduated years ago, you have forgotten most concepts you learnt in medical school and need a rapid review course to help you recall and understand what you need to know to excel on the USMLE. If you are an IMG, get started with SmashUSMLE reviews. We can help you pass the boards for sure. We have a self-paced USMLE course or 4-week live hybrid USMLE Masterclass. Learn more at smashusmle.com.

The main benefit of board courses is that they provide structure and discipline for those students who need an online program, or in-person board review program to help them study for the exam. These programs also provide good question banks or review books. Other benefits include the lectures that cover the high-yield topics in each discipline. Please understand these lectures will not cover everything you need to know for the test. There simply is not enough time to squeeze two years' worth of medical school material into a few weeks. If their schedule says three days are assigned for pathology, do *not* put off studying pathology until then, assuming they are going to cover all the material you need to know.

At Smashusmle reviews, we offer a 4-week live hybrid USMLE Masterclass, where you learn high yield review concepts for USMLE Step 1 and 2CK from Dr. Adesina online from the comfort of your home. These USMLE Masterclasses are the best in the industry. Don't take our word for it, check us out at Smashusmle.com.

*If you register for an in-person live USMLE or COMLEX review course, the instructors will pick and choose what they feel is high-yield, based on the sample questions NBME or NBOME put out yearly. Another benefit is that these courses usually provide you books and video lectures to cover most of the material on your Boards. There are companies that offer live in-person courses such as the PASS program by Dr. Francis, Kaplan, USMLEsuccess academy, NYCSPREP, Wolffpacc.*

*For US medical students, is it smart to read all the books and watch all the videos? Probably not, given that most students have about 6 to 8 weeks of dedicated study period for the USMLE or COMLEX. And it should be obvious by the end of your second year of medical school which subjects you are weak at.*

For example, many people feel weak in biochemistry. Well, maybe this is a topic you need to cover entirely, either through the videos or the books. Personally, we believe the videos provided by these review courses are a great study resource instead of reading a whole book, especially because the video will emphasize a few topics over others: for example, which enzymes you need to remember for which pathways in biochemistry. Obviously, if you are strong in a certain topic, do not waste time reviewing it from scratch; instead, jump to the questions and test how well you know it.

If, and only if, you find you are getting many questions wrong in a certain topic you thought you knew—for example, you got all the urea cycle questions wrong—then that is the time to watch the video or read the section on the urea cycle, not the entire biochemistry text.

For international medical graduates, do not follow what US medical students do. This is a big misnomer. U.S medical students take 6-8 weeks of dedicated study period. Most US medical students start their pre-dedicated study period 6 months before boards. US medical students have fresh medical knowledge from the first 2 years of medical school or are currently on clinical rotations with didactics, that's why they can take their USMLE or COMLEX 1 in 6-8 weeks dedicated period.

As an international medical graduate, it depends on what kind of student you are. If you are U.S IMG from a Caribbean medical school and you are strong in your basic sciences, you can complete your USMLE review in three months.

However, if you are a Non-U.S IMG, or US IMG who graduated years ago with weak basic sciences, you will need a much longer time to study for the USMLE exam.

**How do you identify your weak areas before studying for the USMLE?**

Most students do not use objective data to measure their weakest subjects on the USMLE. Students typically guess, or use subjective methods such as their feelings about a particular subject. For example, if you are good at cardiology, you may want to study cardiology first when you create your USMLE schedule. This is wrong!

At SmashUSMLE reviews program, we make sure all our students take an NBME assessment test before studying for the USMLE. We use this 4-hour NBME test result to determine our students' strengths and weaknesses. Then, our USMLE coaches work with you to create your schedule based on your weak subjects first. If you need coaching for USMLE, visit smashusmle.com for more details.

If you are a US medical student in second year, make goals and plan early for how you are going to fit reviewing these topics within your busy second-year schedule. Maybe you will dedicate Sundays to Boards reviews, or maybe you prefer an hour each night. The point is, make use of these resources early, and work on your weak points January through April. Keep in mind, as we've discussed, you should be doing questions every night regardless.

There is no excuse to pick between doing UWorld questions on the topics you are covering in medical school, or reviewing first-year material. You should be able to do both if you plan carefully and study efficiently. We personally did our school studying and UWorld questions about that material every night, and starting in January we dedicated Sundays to Board prep to study and review the material we felt we were weak at. By the middle of April we were almost finished reviewing this material.

For US medical students, we strongly recommend you take a NBME assessment test before your dedicated study period, to also determine your weak areas and create your dedicated study schedule from weakest to strongest subjects.

It's a great feeling to know that your First Aid for the USMLE book has been annotated during your second year, contains everything you need, you have reviewed most of the material, and you still have at least two months. If you achieve that, then in May and June you are mainly doing questions, as well as either watching lectures online or attending the review lectures you feel you can use some extra tips on. Use your dedicated period to complete your first pass on the UWorld or SmashUSMLE Qbank, do a second pass and if not enough, add another pass through another reputable USMLE question bank. That should be enough.

If the review course is mandatory, make good use of it, because it can be a great asset to your studying and Boards preparation. If it is not mandatory, then it is up to you; you know yourself best. If you can find a way to access this information (perhaps through friends or upperclassmen), and you have a good question bank, maybe you will not need it. We will leave it up to you to evaluate your personal situation and needs.

# CHAPTER 9:
## Evidence based Learning Techniques

Effective study strategies for the USMLE and COMLEX

*Repetition is the mother of all learning, the father of action and architect of all accomplishment.*

Zig Ziglar

*The key to high board scores is through mastery.*

Dr. Adesina

IN THIS CHAPTER, I want to discuss the best evidence based learning techniques you can implement while you study in medical school and for the USMLE and COMLEX exams. Please note, everyone studies differently and you should implement the right methods of studying that WORK BEST for you! For example: every technique discussed in this chapter may not necessarily work for you. Take what works for you, apply it and you'll reach that next level of confidence in your study habits.

Let's begin. Studying for the USMLE exam is extremely challenging, however if you use the right study technique, you will be able to study more effectively, spend less time studying, get better scores and have more time to enjoy yourself.

There are two methods of studying. 1. Active learning and 2. Passive learning.

Passive learning is the most common way most medical students choose to study. You simply open a book, read it passively page by page, chapter by chapter, try to memorize the facts on the page and hope to retain the information. You have used this method throughout your education and maybe it has worked for you. This mode of learning is what we all use because it's easier, requires less effort and is more comfortable. This is why most students who try to read First Aid for the USMLE fail to retain any information from the book.

The other form of learning is active learning. This is more challenging, less comfortable but more effective than passive learning.

There are 4 steps to active learning

Steps 1 and 2 are obtaining the information - you will be learning board review information either through video lectures or reading your USMLE review books. To engage in active learning, you must write your own notes by hand using a plain paper or use an ipad pro or surface pro. This method is slower but it forces you to rephrase and organize the information in your own words. Writing compared to typing has been shown to improve retention possibly due to the hand motor coordination required to complete the note taking task.

Most students also use highlighters to highlight text, but how do you use active learning to review the highlights from your textbook: The best way is to summarize what you read into your own words; which will eventually help your recall.

Step 3 and 4 is about reviewing and reinforcing the information. The first step is to identify what is important during your review. Remember, not all information is created equal. You must constantly be sorting information according to the relevance. (that's why review books such as First Aid for the USMLE Step 1 and Yale G First Aid Crush USMLE Step 2 CK and 3 books serve as a blueprint to help you focus only on what is high yield on the USMLE exam. Avoid adding extraneous information from Wikipedia into your books.

Next, organize the information in an easy way that you understand - to implement the active process this is not going to be a copy and regurgitate the information - you will be doing the difficult task of synthesizing the information in your own words, with diagrams or other study aids, e.g. creating your own charts, pathways, redrawing images. If you are studying biochemistry, draw out the glycolysis, kreb cycle and electron transport chain yourself. This will force you to see the connections of each enzyme deficiency in the pathway rather than just passively highlighting it in the textbook.

Finally, you have to memorize the information. In order to memorize, use summary sheets and spaced repetition with Anki flashcards.

What is spaced repetition? **Spaced repetition** is an evidence-based learning technique that is usually performed with flashcards. Newly introduced and more difficult flashcards are shown more frequently, while older and less difficult flashcards are shown less frequently in order to exploit the psychological spacing effect. The use of spaced repetition has been proven to increase the rate of learning.

Most spaced repetition software (SRS) are modeled after the manual style of learning with physical flashcards: items to memorize are entered into the program as question-answer pairs. When a pair is due to be reviewed, the question is displayed on screen, and the user must attempt to answer it. After answering, the user manually reveals the answer and then tells the program (subjectively) how difficult answering was. The program schedules pairs based on spaced repetition algorithms.

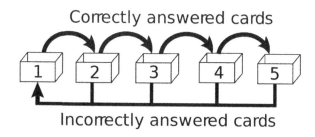

Correctly answered cards

Incorrectly answered cards

In the Leitner system, correctly answered cards are advanced to the next, less frequent box, while incorrectly answered cards return to the first box for more aggressive review and repetition.

There are many spaced repetition software online, but the most widely known is Anki.

Anki flashcards are very popular amongst medical students. The software is free and available on https://ankiweb.net/. The software has a steep learning curve which is why some students hate it, especially if they are not technologically savvy. Once you take your time to learn how the flashcard software works, you can really improve your learning with spaced repetition.

Repetition is key to memorization. Making flashcards is a skill that can be learned. Simply log on YouTube and search "how to use Anki flashcards" and watch the tutorial videos. If you have not used flashcards prior to the time of your dedicated study period, which is 6 weeks for US medical students, do not start using Anki cards then.

We recommend you start using Anki cards from day 1 of medical school.

Get familiar with how to use the software. If you are an international medical graduate, you have more time to study for the USMLE so you should start to incorporate Anki into you studying during your pre-dedicated study period.

The goal of using Anki flashcards is to review each card while studying a particular subject.

After each review, you can increase the interval between them. E.g. you are exposed to the information on day 0, then you see it after 24 hrs., then 72 hrs. etc.

There are lots of free Anki deck flashcards online which you can download and use to study. The most popular decks are First Aid Rapid Review, Brosencephalon - https://www.brosencephalon.com/flashcards. You can download these decks if you are out of time and cannot make your own.

However, we recommend you make your own flashcards. By making your flashcards, rather than downloading someone else's, you engage in active learning. You must review your cards regularly and daily to allow you take advantage of spaced repetition software of Anki decks. Some students may feel like they are sacrificing reviewing old information at the expense of reviewing newer information. That is the point of space repetition. By the time you reach your next subject, the intervals from your previous subject are much longer meaning it takes far less time to maintain the consolidated information, and by time you are finished studying for the USMLE, you will still remember most information.

If you compare this with just passive learning, the large time lapse between the last time you studied the information is much longer and you start to forget the old information anyway.

The reason why spaced repetition works well in Anki deck, is because you use recall rather than recognition. Recognition shows you the right answer and you convince yourself with "I recognize that" whereas recall requires you to extract the information on the go.

We recommend you make your own flashcards with Anki and review them daily. Here are some recommendations on how make your own Anki decks:

1.  Keep decks simple (1 per subject/organ system e.g. cardiology decks) and use tags for systems, mnemonics etc. This will help you waste less time organizing and structuring your decks. Also you get into the habit of reviewing your entire deck of cards.

2.  Understand first, then memorize so you can apply what you learn on test day (makes learning quicker). Do not try to memorize flashcards concepts you do not comprehend, this is poor practice as you are less likely to remember or recall the information on the test day, if you do not have a solid background knowledge.

3.  Lay foundations first: Remember the Pareto principle 80/20 rule: 80% of the effects result from 20% of the causes. Therefore, focus on the highest yielding information in order to optimize your chances of scoring well on the USMLE and learn the basics of the big picture before filling in the details.

4.  Follow the minimum information principle - Make simple cards, they are easy to review and schedule. (don't make complex cards with sub items, make a bunch of separate simple cards for each sub item. This is a big error students' make when making complex flashcards which are more difficult to review and take longer to master. Although making the sub items for each topic you create a flashcard for may make your deck longer, in the long run, you will be able to learn better.

5.  Cloze deletions flashcards are Amazing! (Helps with step 4). These are fill in the blank questions on a flash card. E.g. High Aldosterone

will cause _____ and _____ electrolyte abnormality. (Hypernatremia and hypokalemia).

6. Use images, photos and figures (they are better than a bunch of text. Find even an "unrelated" image that makes you think of the topic and use it on your flashcard - while these may take time, it is worth the time invested. Simply log on google, search an image, then copy and paste it into the flashcard.

You can also block parts of an image and create a flashcard out of it. Download Image

Occlusion Enhanced (download here https://ankiweb.net/shared/info/1374772155)

Image Occlusion lets you create cards that hide parts of an image to test your knowledge of that hidden information. The cards generated by this add-on would be best described as image-based cloze-deletions:

**Front**

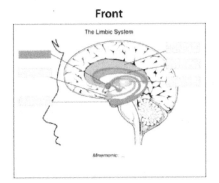

**Back**

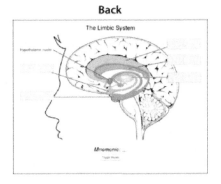

Credit: *Image Occlusion Enhanced* is based on Image Occlusion 2.0 by Tiago Barroso and Simple Picture Occlusion by Steve AW. All credit for the original add-ons goes to their respective authors. *Image Occlusion Enhanced* would not exist without their work.

The best time to review your Anki flashcards are during any small breaks you may have during the day. Do a few flashcards a few minutes a day.

Note, Anki- flashcards should only be used when you have organized the information, understand it deeply and have made connections or simplifications in your head or paper. Anki cards are used to drill in fact information that require memorization rather than conceptual understanding.

Caveat:

Be careful when making Anki flashcards however; you can easily get lost in making too many flashcards and not be able to review them. Only pick topics you have borderline knowledge of and are difficult to master and add them to your Anki deck. This way you can use spaced repetition to your advantage for long term recall.

Another pitfall to avoid: If you've decided that Anki isn't for you, not only might you be making bad cards, you might also be using them incorrectly. The big problem is spending way too much time staring at the same card, and going over it again and again in your head. This is a mistake. It is much more efficient to read a card once, understand it, and move forward. Anki is about active recall. If you're doing too much re-reading of the same card before hitting a button, you're not taking full advantage of the software's ability to facilitate active recall. It's fine to have to review the same card a few times in one session, but if it still doesn't stick, you might not understand the foundational concepts of that card.

Putting a timer add-on so that you only spend a certain amount of time on a card, can help stop this habit and minimize distractions.

As we have discussed in this book, knowledge without application is useless. The USMLE and COMLEX exams are concept based and you are expected to integrate and apply the information you have learned. This is the critical thinking aspect that allows you as a future physician to collect data and make conclusions to make clinical judgement for medical treatment. For the USMLE and COMLEX, you do practice questions in the question bank. This is where all the information you have gathered through active learning come together to allow you to solve problems.

## Now let's talk about your study environment

1.  Location: Where do you study best? Do you prefer coffee shops, library, home? Create your own workspace that suits your learning environment. Use lights, colors, boards, toys, images, that simulate a perfect learning environment.

    a.  For lighting: Use natural light. It has been proven time and time again that natural light is the best solution for reading or studying.

b.  Choose the right color temperature. A good choice would be to opt for a Kelvin scale of around 4000-4500K for a solution similar to natural sunlight.

c.  Use layers of lighting. Use of overhead gentler lighting combined with more focused light of a lamp will make it easier for your eyes while reading, than having one focused light source which may make it too harsh. In light, it is all about balance.

d.  Choose the right lumen output. When looking for a study lamp, you want a high enough lumen to give you the brightness you need for the task at hand. A general rule of thumb is that desk or task lighting should be around 50 lumens per square foot.

e.  Minimize shadows. When reading with a focused and bright task lighting solution, your eyes will have to then adjust to the other lighting levels in the room. If you have a lot of shadows in the space, your eyes will have a harsher contrast to adjust to when you look away from the task lighting. Make sure you remedy this by adding extra lamps as much as possible to avoid eye strain.

2.  Group vs solo studying: Do you like to study by yourself or with others? The best way to benefit adequately from both is to apply a 50/50 or 70/30 plan. In a group study, the rate at which the material is reviewed, is much slower but the main benefit is working through difficult concepts while keeping you motivated and sane. Groups need to be small - 1-2 people. Large groups have more distractions, lower productivity and ever diminishing returns. The benefit of group study is the ability to teach others what you have learned, which allows you to gain mastery of the content itself while helping your classmates. Use a study group whenever you can.

## Note taking strategies for medical school and boards

These are the best methods to take notes in class, during lectures, or from the textbook. With deliberate incorporation of active learning study methods, you can spend less time studying while simultaneously getting better grades. Here's how:

You can do hand writing notes vs laptop note taking. Active learning is king.

Step 1, eliminate distractions, disable all notification, activate airplane mode.

Avoid transcribing - if you are transcribing a lecture, use your own words while transcribing.

Take advantages of images and figures, prioritize incorporating images. When you hand write your own notes, you can draw images yourself. If you are using a laptop to write your notes, you can copy the image into your notes or take photos or screenshots.

Use an ipad pro/ surface pro tablet for note taking; you can draw and annotate. Download Notability or One Note to take notes. The best and most popular note taking method used by medical students is the outline method.

Start with the main point (Myocardial infarction)

If there is sub topic e.g (pathogenesis of MI)

    Symptoms: left sided chest pain radiating to left arm

        -supporting idea e.g EKG findings are ST segment elevation

        II, III, AVF

The outline method is more organized and incredibly easy to use, but it's also easy to misuse.

The first time you take your notes, you are simply trying to understand and organize the information in a way that makes sense to you.

Next step: the key to active learning from the note is not to review the note over and over again. (What you want to do is interacting and reflecting with your notes)

When studying any topic, the first thing to consider is whether the information presented is fact heavy or concept heavy. For fact heavy subjects, there is an immense amount of information to memorize, especially the facts that are difficult to make sense of e.g. HLA-DR5- associated with Hashimoto thyroiditis.

Concept heavy means the difficulty lies in understanding the content and applying the concepts. E.g. Neuroscience (understanding the spinal cord pathways) or cardiology.

However, most subjects have things you need to memorize as well as understand the difficult concepts at the same time. Some will be more dominant in fact and some more dominant in concepts. Understanding how dominant a fact or concept is will help you master the concept effectively.

Finally, use summary sheets. These are condensed notes you take of your notes - basically you are trimming the fat and condensing the information into a more manageable format. Do not simply write smaller, rather make connections you did not realize when you were listening to review video lectures, or synthesize the information in new ways such as in tables or other visuals.

For summary sheet methods to work, the subject must be concept heavy, and don't simply copy your notes, but make it an active learning process by actively seeking to understand, make connections and simplify. This should not be easy or comfortable but that should be expected of any active learning method.

Finally, work on synthesis questions. When you take notes, ask yourself, "What questions can I ask myself to challenge my knowledge on what I just covered?" This will force you to think harder and make connections.

References: spaced repetition, https://en.wikipedia.org/wiki/Spaced_repetition

13 steps to better ANKI flashcards, 7 Evidence based study techniques, Kevin Jubal youtube videos, youtube.com/Medschoolinsiders.

# CHAPTER 10:
## Preparing for the test

Test preparation is another area where students experience difficulty when it is time to study for Boards. We have strongly emphasized the importance of time management from the beginning of this book. Now is the time when you have to be even more disciplined with time management.

Most students register for the exam between May and July of their second year and spend about four to six uninterrupted weeks studying to prepare for Boards. Believe it or not, that is more than enough time to assimilate all the materials and content you need to know to do well on the exam, assuming you have been very efficient and focused during the school year. Honestly, you might just be wasting your time if you spend more than that. If you think you need more time, you are doing something wrong; most likely you did not plan your time well for studying for the exam.

First and foremost: Please **REGISTER EARLY!** Many students procrastinate when it comes to registering early for their exam. Please, we implore you not to be one of those students. You should register as soon as possible to get the best date available.

Rule Number One: Pick a date and ***stick to it!*** We mean it! Pick a date and stick to it. This is very important because you then have a timeline for accomplishing a task. You will begin to work toward completing the task before the time runs out.

Rule Number Two: ***Do not change your exam date except you are not ready!*** Set a target goal for your USMLE and COMLEX prep. If your goal is to pass and you are hitting your target with your NBME assessment tests, go ahead and take the test. If you are scoring below passing scores or your target score, do not take the USMLE, you will fail the test. The students who rush to take the exam when they are not ready end up regretting this decision and having to retake the exam again. At SmashUSMLE reviews, we do not let our students take their USMLE except they are hitting their target scores.

Rule Number Three: Establish a reasonable and strict time schedule. This is the most important aspect of preparing for your exam. A schedule gives you direction as to how you are doing and helps you anticipate how close you are to accomplishing your goal. There are various options when it comes to making a schedule. You can choose a system-based approach or a basic science approach. For instance, a system-based approach focuses on organ systems, cardiology, pulmonary, gastrointestinal, nephrology, et cetera. At the end you can then focus on the basic sciences. The order of the subjects should be based on your weakest to strongest subjects. If you need help to create your USMLE schedule, register online at smashusmle. com and our private coaches/tutors can help you.

We have included in the next section a copy of one of our sample Board prep schedules for your use. If it works for you, great! If not, it can serve as a guide for your personal approach. Every student is different, so we will assume you will do what is best for you.

Rule Number Four: Knowing what material works for you and sticking to it.

The preparation for the USMLE is not quite the same for everyone. There are general principles you should follow, but there should be some slight tweaks depending on the individual.

The first principle is to **know yourself and your target**. What does knowing yourself entail?

For instance, assume there are two students preparing for the test; students A and B. Student A is above the 90th centile in his class, while student B is at the 50th centile. They are both targeting a score of 250 and are using the same material. To achieve the same target score, it is most likely student B will need more time to prepare. Knowing yourself helps you set an appropriate test date to achieve your desired target.

Now that you know your target and how long you need to prepare to achieve it, don't take too long. **Pick a test date and stick to it**. The next principle is how to get there. It is common knowledge that First Aid for step 1 is the go-to book when preparing for the exam. True, it is the most important resource, but not the easiest to use however. First Aid for step 1 is like a zip document and you need other resources to unzip it. In order to understand and appreciate the information in the book, the candidate has to use question banks. At SmashUSMLE reviews, we have written a comprehensive review book; SmashUSMLE Step 1 high Yield Review lecture notes.

These notes explain everything you need to know for the USMLE in detail and you can use it to supplement your medical knowledge while preparing for the USMLE. You can buy a copy at Smashusmle.com.

A faster and more effective method will be to read the first aid once, solve questions and do a second read. This way the candidate saves time and better appreciates the concepts on the second and any subsequent reads.

You've chosen your target; your duration and you know you have to read first aid and solve questions. The next thing is to know which Qbanks to use. UWorld is the go-to Qbank for candidates, and rightly so. However, it is common knowledge that the more questions a candidate solves, the higher the chances of getting a good score, so it is recommended to add other Qbank resources to Uworld. This is when I would recommend **smash USMLE Qbank** as an additional resource. To summarize how effective it is, I would say it has the length of UWorld questions and the awkwardness of NBME questions. That is the nature of questions you mostly see on test day.

Towards the end of your preparation period you might feel you are not ready to take the test. The truth is you are never going to feel ready, but there are some indicators that help you monitor your progress. The most effective are the NBME examinations. The NBMEs are quite predictive of your test day scores. Taking an online NBME exam helps you see where you stand and also addresses your weak areas as well. **Do well not to ignore your weak areas** before the test, and try to go over those areas as the last things you study right before the test. Another indicator of your preparedness is your ability to read first aid for step 1 in a short time without feeling the need to refer to other books for explanations. That means you have grasped the concepts in the book.

# CHAPTER 11:
## How to create your USMLE schedule

DID YOU KNOW that you cannot hit a target you do not have? The Board exam is a marathon and you must prepare for it. You must have a pre-planned study schedule for this exam. The biggest mistake some students make is thinking they can study as they feel on a daily basis. This is a recipe for failure.

To fail to prepare is to prepare to fail. We notice a trend among medical students or International medical graduates looking for someone else's study schedules or online USMLE forums to get a free copy of a premade schedule.

Listen, everyone's schedule is different. You must make your own schedule. You can use a sample schedule as a template to create your own version which we provide for you in this book, or get a USMLE coach to help guide you to create one for you.

In this chapter, we have included sample schedules for USMLE Step 1. This dedicated study schedule is based on First Aid for the USMLE Step 1 book. Our Step 2CK and 3 schedules are based on Yale G First Aid CrushUSMLE Step 2CK and 3. You can download a free copy at smashusmle.com.

For US medical students, we assume you have completed about 800-1000 (50%) USMLE questions prior to the end of your second year. We also expect that you have already annotated in your First Aid book from doing these practice questions. If you are an international medical graduate, your pre-dedicated study period could be between 12-18 months.

Note that if you are a US medical student/international medical graduate studying during your dedicated study period, we recommend a 10-14 hour day study schedule. In order to study effectively, we constructed a fourteen-hour-a-day schedule. The hours are separated into sections and are the same for each day. Fourteen hours might sound a lot, but with frequent breaks and consistent use, you will be accustomed to it by the end of the first week.

There are three blocks in a day that you can allocate for studying. Remember that the average human can only concentrate for forty-five minutes to one hour. Therefore, make it a habit to take ten-minute breaks after every hour of studying. Make sure you take your lunch breaks and use them wisely. Do not prolong your lunch break; make sure you are disciplined with time. When it is 1pm, it is time to end your break and resume studying.

Exercise is an important aspect of your Board study process. You cannot afford to ignore it. During your second break, go for a run, head to the gym, or play some sport. Your body and brain need exercise to function at maximum capacity.

During the breaks, you can be productive and listen to review lectures or review anki deck flashcards.

Sleep. Sleep. Sleep. This is extremely crucial to your health during this time. This is not the time to deprive your body of sleep. Make sure you get at least seven to eight hours of good sleep every night. That will refresh your body and improve your memory function as you study. The reason this is crucial, is because you want your circadian rhythm to be constant throughout your studying period, allowing you to be refreshed the day before the exam. You do not want to burn out before the day of the test.

**The NBME test**

In order to create your own schedule, you must first take an NBME assessment test. Let's talk more about the NBME assessment test.

**How do you create your schedule based on your NBME score report?**

The National Board of Medical Examiners (NBME) is the examination body that offers assessment tests called NBMEs. These NBMEs are USMLE assessment tests that you can purchase online from nbme.org to test your knowledge and preparedness for the USMLE exam. The NBME self-assessment test is the best predictor of your estimated performance on the USMLE. This exam has been taken by thousands of USMLE test takers and do not use it as a practice test. Use this tool to monitor your progress as you continue to study for the exam. Some students say, I'm afraid of taking the NBME because I am not ready to take the exam. " Some say, "I do not think I need to take the NBME. I feel ready for the USMLE, because I have been studying for months".

Do not fall for this trap! You will regret this decision. You must take the NBME exams frequently and if you are getting high scores, you should take the exam. If your scores are too low or below passing score, you are at risk of failing the exam.

This is an example of a NBME score report:

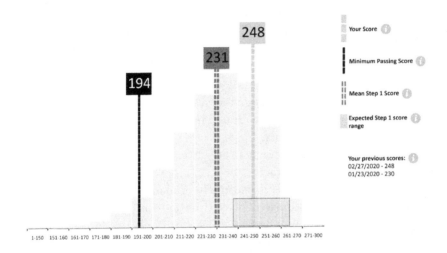

The chart above represents the distribution of scores for recent examinees from US and Canadian medical schools taking Step 1 for the first time. Reported Step 1 scores range from 1-300 with a mean of 231 and a standard deviation of 20.

The Redesigned NBME Self-Assessment score reports (NSAS) intend to help students make accurate conclusions about strengths and areas for improvement so they can focus their study appropriately.

**How can I use the new score report to prepare for USMLE?**

Using the graph on the score report, the NSAS score is shown relative to the distribution of USMLE scores for a recent cohort of examinees from United States and Canadian medical schools taking the USMLE Step for the first time. The minimum passing score and mean score for the national comparison group are also shown on the graph, along with an expected score range for your actual USMLE score. All NSAS scores for exams purchased on or after January 23, 2020, are also listed so examinees can easily track their progress.

## Where can I learn about my strengths and areas for improvement?

The image of the report below helps examinees correctly interpret their strengths and address more challenging areas efficiently on the various content areas. Content areas are grouped by Physician Task, System and Discipline. Content area strengths and areas for improvement are identified relative to your overall performance and relative to the performance of the national USMLE comparison group shown in the graph on page 1 of the report. A range that indicates the percentage of items in each content area on the NBME Self-Assessment and corresponding Step is also provided.

| Performance by Physician Task | | Lower, Same, Higher than Your Overall Performance | | | Lower, Average, Higher than Comparison Group | | |
|---|---|---|---|---|---|---|---|
| | (% Items Per Test) | Lo | S | Hi | Lo | Av | Hi |
| **MK: Applying Foundational Science Concepts** | (55-61%) | | ▨ | | ■ | | |
| PC: Diagnosis | (23-27%) | | ▨ | | ■ | | |
| PC: Principles of Management | (7-10%) | | ▨ | | ■ | | |
| PBLI: Evidence-based Medicine | (4-5%) | | ▨ | | ■ | | |

## What do the grids tell me?

The left grid indicates whether your performance in a content area was lower than, the same as, or higher than your overall performance on the exam. Only clear strengths and areas for improvement will be identified. You will see that your performance is the same as your overall performance for most content areas. The content areas are closely related and performance tends to be consistent across the content areas.

## Performance by Discipline

| | (% Items Per Test) | Lower, Same, Higher than Your Overall Performance | | | Lower, Average, Higher than Comparison Group | | |
|---|---|---|---|---|---|---|---|
| | | Lo | S | HI | Lo | Av | HI |
| Pathology | (41-51%) | | ▨ | | ▨ | | |
| Physiology | (29-30%) | | ▨ | | ▨ | | |
| Pharmacology | (21-22%) | | ▨ | | ▨ | | |
| Microbiology & Immunology | (16-19%) | | ▨ | | ▨ | | |
| **Biochemistry & Nutrition** | (10-15%) | | ▨ | | ▨ | | |
| Gross Anatomy & Embryology | (10-13%) | | ▨ | | ▨ | | |
| Histology & Cell Biology | (10-13%) | | | ▨ | | ▨ | |
| Behavioral Sciences | (10-11%) | | ▨ | | ▨ | | |
| **Genetics** | (5-6%) | | ▨ | | ▨ | | |

The right grid indicates whether your performance in a content area was lower, average, or higher, relative to the average performance of the national USMLE comparison group. Only clear strengths and areas for improvement will be identified. You will see that your performance is in the same category for most content areas. Once again, the content areas are closely related and performance tends to be consistent across the content areas.

## What kind of information does the content area section provide?

You can use the content area section of the report to help guide your preparation for USMLE. In general, it is best to study all content areas as you prepare to take your Step exam, using the percentage of item ranges to help prioritize your study time. Additional focus is warranted for content areas with low performance relative to your overall performance and/or the performance of the USMLE comparison group.

Please note: **Another common misinterpretation was the use of percent correct as an indicator of performance on an NBME self-assessment, across NBME self-assessments, or to compare performance on an NBME self-assessment to another assessment product.** Conclusions cannot be drawn about performance based upon percent correct. The percent correct depends on the difficulty of the set of items on the assessment. The assessment score adjusts for differences in difficulty across the different NSAS forms so that you can compare your scores.

Reference:https://www.nbme.org/sites/default/files/2020-04/ NBME%20Self-Assessments_Score%20Report%20Fact%20Sheet.pdf

Let's use the given sample schedule below. You begin by taking NBME 24 assessment test (visit https://www.nbme.org/ to purchase NBME tests). Review your score report and identify your weak subjects. List them from weakest to strongest. Let's say Microbiology, biochemistry and pharmacokinetics/pharmacodynamics are your weak subjects, start with them and add the rest of the subjects to fill your proposed schedule.

After you have studied for a few weeks, you can retake another NBME and note your performances in all subjects. If you have mastered the concepts in the Microbiology, biochemistry and pharmacokinetics sections, your overall performance should be better.

Here is a sample of a USMLE Step 1 schedule below:

This schedule is broken down into three main tasks per day, labeled with (B1), (B2) and/or (B3). Each of these tasks are expected to take four hours to complete. A short 10-minute break must be taken per hour between these tasks, and oftentimes, the order of completing the tasks is interchangeable. Your daily schedule should be in blocks:

- Block 1- Study (8a-12p)
- Lunch (12p-1p)
- Block 2- Study FA / Qbank review (1p-5p)
- Dinner (5p-6p)
- Block 3 (Qbank Review- 6p-11p)
- Sleep (11p-7a)

| Week # | Sun | Mon | Tue | Wed | Thu | Fri | Sat |
|---|---|---|---|---|---|---|---|
| 1 | (B1) Take NBME 24, review report to identify weak subjects (B2) Review incorrect questions, look up relevant sections in FA and mark new facts into FA (B3) Create your Schedule based on the weakest subject areas on the NBME Report. | (B1) Micro (Bacteriology and Clinical Bacteriology FA p.124-140) (B2) 40 Micro questions with review of questions (B3) 40 Random questions with review of questions | (B1) Review: Micro (Mycology, Parasitology and Virology FA p.151-177) (B2) 40 Micro questions with review of questions (B3) 40 Random questions with review of questions | (B1) Review: Micro (Systems and Antimicrobials) FA p.178-187 (B2) 40 Micro questions with review of questions (B3) 40 Random questions with review of questions | (B1) Review: Pharm-Pharmacokinetics and Pharmacodynamics, Autonomic Drugs, Toxicities and Side effects, Miscellaneous FA 228-249) (B2) 40 Pharm questions with review of questions (B3) 40 Random questions with review of questions | (B1) Review: Biochem (Molecular and Cellular FA p.34-51) (B2) 40 Biochem questions with review of questions (B3) 40 Random questions with review of questions | (B1) Review: Biochem (Lab techniques and Genetics FA p. 52-64) (B2) 40 Biochem questions with review of questions (B3) 40 Random questions with review of questions |

| Week # | Sun | Mon | Tue | Wed | Thu | Fri | Sat |
|---|---|---|---|---|---|---|---|
| 2 | (B1) Review: Biochem [Lab techniques and Genetics FA p. 52-64) (B2) 40 Biochem questions with review of questions (B3) 40 Random questions with review of questions | (B1) Review: Immuno (Lymphoid structures and Lymphocytes FA p.95-103) (B2) Review: Immuno (Immune responses and Immunosuppressants) FA p.104-122) (B2) 40 Immunology questions with review of questions (B3) 40 Random questions with review of questions | (B1) Review: General Pathology (Cell Injury FA p.206-218) (B1) Review: General Pathology (Neoplasia FA p.219-226) (B2) 40 Path questions with review of questions (B3) 40 Random questions with review of questions | (B1) Review: Cardio- Embryology, Anatomy, Phys (FA p.274-293) (B2) 40 Cardio questions with review of questions (B3) 40 Random questions with review of questions | (B1) Review: Cardio Path and Pharm (FA p.294-317) (B2) 40 Cardio questions with review of questions (B3) 40 Random questions with review of questions | (B1) Review: Heme/Onc Anatomy and Phys (FA p.396-403) (B2) 40 Heme/Onc questions with review of questions (B3) 40 Random questions with review of questions | (B1) Review: Heme/Onc Patho and Pharm (FA p. 404-423) (B2) 40 Heme/Onc questions with review of questions (B3) 40 Random questions with review of questions |

| Week # | Sun | Mon | Tue | Wed | Thu | Fri | Sat |
|---|---|---|---|---|---|---|---|
| 3 | (B1) Do NBME 23, reevaluate weak areas based on NBME report (B2) Review incorrect questions, look up relevant sections in FA and mark new facts into FA | (B1) Review: Heme/Onc Path & Pharm FA 423-431) (B2) 40 Heme-onc questions with review of questions (B3) 40 Random questions with review of questions | (B1) Review: Respiratory (Embryo, Anatomy, and Phys) FA.p642-652) (B2) 40 Resp questions with review of questions (B3) 40 Random questions with review of questions | (B1) Review: Respiratory ( Patho, and Pharm) FA.p653-668) (B2) 40 Resp questions with review of questions (B3) 40 Random questions with review of questions | (B1) Review: GI ( Embryo, Anatomy and Phys) FA p.325-369) (B2) 40 GI questions with review of questions (B3) 40 Random questions with review of questions | (B1) Review: GI Pharm and Path) FA p.370-394) (B2) 40 GI questions with review of questions (B3) 40 Random questions with review of questions | (B1) Review: Neuroanatomy, Embryology, and Phys (FA p.474-494) (B2) 40 Neuro questions with review of questions (B3) 40 Random questions with review of questions |
| 4 | (B1) UWorld Sim Form 1, reevaluate weak areas based on test report (B2) Review incorrect questions, look up relevant sections in FA and mark new facts into FA | (B1) Review: Neuro (Neuro-pathology FA p.494-516) (B2) 40 Neuro questions with review of questions (B3) 40 Random questions with review of questions | (B1) Review: Neuro (Ophthalmology and Pharm FA p.517-535) (B2) 40 Neuro questions with review of questions (B3) 40 Random questions with review of questions | (B1) Review Psychiatry Psychology, Path and Pharm FA p.538-560) (B2) 40 Psychiatry questions with review of questions (B3) 40 Random questions with review of questions | (B1) Review: Public Health Science FA p 252-268) (B2) 40 Public Health questions with review of questions (B3) 40 Random questions with review of questions | (B1) Review: Endocrine-Embryology, Anatomy, Physiology-FA p 320-330) (B2) 40 Endocrine questions with review of questions (B3) 40 Random questions with review of questions | (B1) Review: Endocrine Path and Pharm FA p 331-340) (B2) 40 Endocrine questions with review of questions (B3) 40 Random questions with review of questions |

| Week # | Sun | Mon | Tue | Wed | Thu | Fri | Sat |
|---|---|---|---|---|---|---|---|
| 5 | (B1) Do NBME 20 or 200 Qbank questions, review (B2) Review incorrect questions, look up relevant sections in FA and mark new facts into FA | (B1) Review: Renal (Anatomy and Phys) FA p.562-577 (B2) 40 Renal questions with review of questions (B3) 40 Random questions with review of questions | (B1) Review: Renal (Patho and Pharm) FA p.578-592) 2) 40 Renal questions with review of questions (B3) 40 Random questions with review of questions | (B1) Review Reproductive (Embryo, Anatomy and Phys FA p. 594-619) 2) 40 Repro questions with review of questions (B3) 40 Random questions with review of questions | (B1) Review Reproductive (Path and Pharm FA p.620-639) 2) 40 Repro questions with review of questions (B3) 40 Random questions with review of questions | (B1) Review Musculoskeletal- Anatomy, Phys and Path- 434-460 (B2) 40 Musc questions with review of questions (B3) 40 Random questions with review of questions | (B1) Musculoskeletal- Anatomy, Phys and Path- 460-472 (B2) 40 Musc questions with review of questions (B3) 40 Random questions with review of questions |
| 6 | (B1) Do NBME 18 or 200 Qbank questions, review (B2) Review incorrect questions, look up relevant sections in FA and mark new facts into FA | Rapid Review of Weak Subjects in FA Review missed questions in weak subjects again | Rapid Review of Weak Subjects in FA Review missed questions in weak subjects again | Rapid Review of Weak Subjects in FA Review missed questions in weak subjects again | Rapid Review of Weak Subjects in FA Review missed questions in weak subjects again | Rest, watch Netflix. Confirm your ID, buy your snacks, confirm your car is working and get ready to take the exam. Do NOT Read or review anything today! You are done. | Sit for the boards! You did it! Step 1 done. |

## Key (Abbreviations)

B1: Block 1 B2: Block 2 B3: Block 3 , FA (First Aid for the USMLE Step 1)

How should you approach studying for the USMLE subjects? Timed mode or tutor mode? If you are studying during the pre-dedicated study period you can choose tutor mode, but as you progress forward, switch to timed mode only to get into the habit of answering questions in one and half minutes.

Let us talk about the topics you need to cover and how to allocate time to study for these subjects. These are topics you can find in any Board review books.

We would like to emphasize that this is not a perfect schedule and does not necessarily apply to everyone. It is simply a guide. As you will see, some subjects require more time than others. The subject with longer pages requires more time and the subjects/discipline with shorter pages require less time. You might also discover that you cannot complete some organ systems in eight hours of studying *First Aid for the USMLE Step 1*. **Do not panic!** Just postpone the balance till the next day and then complete it, while still following your time schedule.

Should I do the questions random or system based? We recommend that during your first pass through the question bank, you should use systems-based approach learning. Here is how it works. Let's assume your question bank has 200 cardiology questions. You start with 40 cardiology questions a day, set it on time mode in your question bank and complete it by reviewing the correct and incorrect answer choices. Let's say you have three days dedicated to cardiology, you will have completed only 120 questions. You move on to Endocrine and this time, you select both cardiology and Endocrinology. Now, you have a mixed time mode subject-based question review. As you do more questions, the unused cardiology questions will decrease and you will have more Endocrine questions. This method applies to your entire study schedule until you finish your First Aid book, then the rest of the questions will be in mixed mode only.

Note: Your brain needs rest in order to assimilate all the information you have memorized during the day. This is not the time to be staying up all night with coffee in order to read. You need extensive discipline during this time. Try to adhere to your plan as much as possible. Take a break if you need to. Get some sleep if you feel tired. The goal is to learn while your brain is at optimum capacity, not reading while exhausted.

This USMLE schedule is a template for you to begin with; it will serve as a guide for your success. Keep in mind, at this stage, the USMLE or COMLEX is about a month to six weeks away. School is over, and you have all day to study for your Boards.

The key to preparing your day-to-day schedule is to cover the topics in systems using *First Aid for the USMLE Step 1*. Once you have completed your question bank, your First Aid book should be inclusive, containing *all* the information you need.

## Review

Get ready for round two. Rapidly review *First Aid*, read one topic per day. Work on weak subjects, do more flashcards. You can also do another question bank if you have more time. If not, two rounds through one question bank, either UWorld or Smashusmle review is enough.

**Important Note**: Everyone is different. We recommend you read your *First Aid for the USMLE Step 1* twice to reinforce the concepts you have forgotten and to brush up your knowledge of weak subjects. However, some students feel that they are adequately prepared after the first round; they may be concerned about forgetting details as time passes. The decision is ultimately yours; you know yourself best, and you know your strengths and weaknesses. If you plan on going through *First Aid* once, make sure you take the self-assessment exam early in the schedule. Do not take the first assessment exam two days before the exam—bad idea!

## Caveat for International medical graduates:

International medical graduates have more time to prepare for the USMLE. Most IMGs need more time to refresh all the topics they have forgotten since graduating from medical school. At SmashUSMLE reviews, we work with each student to create a study schedule that works for you. Every student is different, and we understand you may be involved in research, have children, and family obligations to attend to while you are also trying to juggle USMLE prep. We have USMLE coaches who will help you create a schedule you will adhere to. While you may spend 12 months studying for the USMLE during your pre-dedicated study period, we recommend no longer than 3 to 4 months of intense preparation for your dedicated study period. You will experience the law of diminishing returns if you choose longer.

You should watch all of our Smashusmle review videos if you are an IMG to maximize your knowledge base while preparing for the USMLE. Also, you should complete at least 2 Qbanks twice (SmashUSMLE and UWorld) before you take your exam. You can download a free copy of USMLE Schedule on smashusmle.com

**On a final note:** Their proximity to the real Board exam in terms of grades and difficulty completely depends on when you take them, and how well prepared you are before you sit for them. For example, if you take the NBME self-assessment exam in April before you start your dedicated study period for the Boards, your score will obviously not reflect your potential grade. You may think it is an impossible exam and freak out— for no reason. If, however, you take your assessment exams in June after you have been studying (doing *First Aid* and questions), then your score should reflect what you may get on the actual exam. These self-assessment tests are similar to the MCAT sample exams you practiced before taking the real MCAT (*any memories* 😊😊). These tests are called self-assessments, because they are supposed to assess your knowledge and preparation for the actual exam.

To summarize, if you want to learn whether you are ready for the real exam, study hard all through and sit for the assessment exam as if you were taking the real exam. At that point, if you do well and you are happy with your score, then proceed and take the exam soon. If you discover that you barely passed with a score you would rather improve on, then be happy that you found out early and think carefully about the best next step. You might consider changing the date of your exam; there is nothing wrong with that, because you have a valid reason. It is better to take the COMLEX and USMLE once and do well, than do poorly or fail it and then take it again. Be aware—some competitive residency programs do not accept applicants who failed the COMLEX and/or USMLE, even if they did great the second time.

# CHAPTER 12:
# The NBMEs and Self-Assessment Tests

**Do not go for your USMLE exam before taking an NBME Self-Assessment Test:**
NBME (National board of medical examiners) is responsible for writing the USMLE exams in addition to shelf tests that can be used for self-assessment. Moreover, the NBME also releases practice exams to help students prepare for their USMLE and shelf exams.

## Currently available NBME self-assessments:

- 6 NBME self-assessments for step 1
- 3 NBME self-assessments for step 2 CK
- 1 NBME self-assessment for step 3
- 26 NBME subject exams for shelf exams

The NBME tracks students' scores and compares them to their actual scores or to a standard normalized group of test takers. Because of their approach, they are now considered the most accurate predictors of your actual performance on the USMLE or shelf-exam score.

For the time being, your step 1 score is very critical in your residency application. However, in 2022 when step 1 becomes a pass or fail exam, it is expected that program directors will shift their focus on step 2 CK scores. Based on this, you should not take your step 1 or step 2 CK exam without having taken at least one NBME self-assessment. Typically, you should take more than one self-assessment to track your progress while preparing for the boards.

An NBME self-assessment test costs $60, whereas subject shelf exams cost $20 each. To sign up for a self-assessment, simply go to the NBME Self-Assessment Services website https://www.mynbme.org/s/login/.

Anyone can register for an **NBME** self-assessment without needing to have registered for the USMLE, an ECFMG certificate for IMGs, or even to have any verifiable form of credentialing.

## Contents of NBME self-assessments:

Each USMLE block has 40 questions and is 1 hour long. NBME self-assessment blocks are longer; however, the self-assessment test as a whole is shorter than the actual USMLE test.

## Comprehensive basic science self-assessment for step 1:

- 200 questions in total, divided in 4 blocks.
- Each block is 1 hour and 15 minutes long.
- On your actual USMLE step 1, you will have 7 blocks that are 1 hour each with a total of 280 questions.

## Comprehensive clinical sciences self-assessment for step 2 CK:

- 184 questions divided by 4 blocks.
- Each block is 1 hour 9 minutes long.
- On your actual USMLE step 2 CK, you will have 8 blocks that are 1 hour each with a total number of questions up to 318.

## Comprehensive clinical medicine self-assessment for step 3:

- 176 questions in total, divided by 5 blocks with 50 to 66 items per block.
- Each block can be up to 45 minutes in duration.
- Your actual USMLE step 3 exam will be done over two days. On day 1, you will get 6 blocks of questions that are 232 in total, and on day 2 you get another 6 blocks of questions that are 180 in total. Day 2 also includes CCS cases.

## Shelf exams:

- Each test has 50 questions.
- The duration of the test is 1 hour 15 minutes.
- Actual shelf exams are 110 questions and 2 hours 45 minutes long.

## Available subjects for NBME shelf exams:

- 4 clinical neurology tests.
- 1 emergency medicine test.
- 2 family medicine tests.
- 4 internal medicine tests.
- 4 obstetrics and gynecology tests.
- 4 pediatrics tests.
- 3 psychiatry tests.
- 4 surgery tests.

## Predictive Value of the NBMEs:

For step 1, two thirds of students will score within 13 points of their NBME if taken one week before the actual exam. For step 2 CK, two thirds of students will score within 15 points of their NBME. There are no predictive scores for step 3 yet.

In reality, if you have a look on Figure 1, you will notice that most students have a USMLE step 1 score that is within 9 points of their NBME. Interestingly, the range of that prediction is 0 to 9 points above the NBME score, implying that students usually do better on their step 1, and NBME underestimates scores.

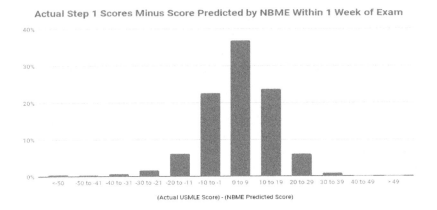

Actual Step 1 Scores Minus Score Predicted by NBME Within 1 Week of Exam

(Actual USMLE Score) - (NBME Predicted Score)

You can take an NBME assessment test to monitor your progress as you study for the USMLE. However, your last NBME test one week before your actual USMLE exam date is the best predictor of your USMLE score. This is because you should have gained enough knowledge necessary to not only pass the USMLE, but get high scores. NBMEs are very accurate and if you fail an NBME assessment, and your exam is within one week, *You Should Postpone your USMLE exam.*

## Prediction value of NBMEs for Step 2 CK:

In Figure 2, you can notice that there is positive skewness to the curve. This means that most students actually score from 0 to 29 points above their predicted score from the NBME on their actual step 2 CK exam. In other words, NBMEs substantially underestimate step 2 CK scores.

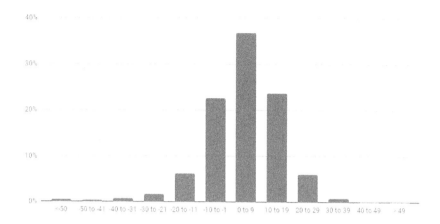

The following table compares between step 1 and step 2 CK NBMEs predicted scores and actual USMLE scores. It shows the likelihood that your final score is equal to, or greater than your last NBME if you take your assessment within 1 week of your actual exam:

|  | Step 1 | Step 2 CK |
| --- | --- | --- |
| Actual score ≥ last NBME | 68% | 77% |
| Actual score more than 10 points higher than NBME | 31% | 50% |
| Actual score more than 20 points higher than NBME | 7% | 23% |

Clearly, it is very unlikely that your actual step 1 score will be 20 points higher than your NBME, but one out of four students will score 20 points higher on their step 2 CK than their NBME.

**Caveat:** NBMEs do over-predict scores for some students and this is seen in up to one third of students. Therefore, if your NBME score is on the borderline, for example your last NBME step 1 or 2 CK score is around the passing score range (198-203), you should not take the actual USMLE exam and you should postpone it, to avoid the risk of failing the USMLE. This is the primary reason thousands of international medical graduates and some US medical students fail the USMLE every year. Do not ignore this advice!

## Why are NBMEs not as accurate in predicting step 2 CK scores as compared to step 1?

There are two possible answers to this question. The first one is based on pure statistics. There are three available NBME assessments for step 2 CK, whereas 6 assessments are available for step 1. When you have a smaller sample, the power of your prediction tool will be compromised.

The other possible answer, which is a bit subjective but still reasonable, is that it has to do with the content of the exam. Step 1 tests your basic science medical knowledge, whereas step 2 CK focuses on problem solving skills, diagnosis, management of diseases, and on how you actually interpret the question. Exams that test your basic knowledge are known to be independent of whether you are having a good day or not. On the other hand, an exam that is up to interpretation as is step 2 CK will depend on whether you had a good-night sleep, relaxed and not stressed. Therefore, the relationship between your NBME and step 2 CK start to become volatile because of these many confounding factors.

## Shelf exam NBMEs and their predictive value:

NBME do not give data on the predictive value of their shelf exams, and from experience we believe that the predictive value of shelf exams is quite low. Shelf exams depend largely on question interpretation and this could explain why NBMEs do not predict shelf exam actual scores. The NBME only has 50 questions for shelf exams, in contrast to more than 200 questions per exam for the USMLE. The small number of questions per exam explains why it has no predictive power.

The NBME has a single step 3 assessment, and without the clinical case simulations, it is unlikely that the NBME will be able to provide any predictive power data for their step 3 assessment.

## If the NBMEs tend to underestimate actual scores, why do some students score dramatically less on the actual exam as compared to their last NBME assessment?

- You should not take an NBME assessment more than once. When you repeat the exam, you reduce its predictive power. Even if you take the exam up to a year before, you will still be able to recall some questions and this will affect your NBME score. Accordingly, this will drastically and adversely affect your predicted step score.
- You should not focus on percentage wrong/correct. The NBME uses a special algorithm to predict your step score and the weight of each question on the NBME is not the same. Because of that, you should not use paper-based NBMEs because again they will not correctly predict your final score.
- Finally, do not guess blindly on your actual exam. Try to read and reason your answer for each question.

## Do NBMEs give explanations for the correct/wrong answers for their assessments?

In April 2020, the NBME started adding explanations to some of their forms. They started with clinical mastery series medicine forms 5 + 6. By the end of 2020, the NBME promises to add explanations for all their assessments.

In the past, the NBME only told students which questions they got wrong without giving any explanations. Subsequently, they started to give the correct answers for the questions they got wrong. Right now, the NBME tells you the correct answer for each question but does not give any explanations further.

Because of this, students might question why they need to review their NBME if they will not get any explanation of why their answer was wrong/right. It has been shown that up to 50% of students' mistakes are due to silly reasons:

- Students might ignore/misinterpret a lab or a physical exam finding. If they get it wrong and then review the question, they will know their mistake.
- Students might not read the question very carefully.

- Students might not understand what the question was actually asking. It was asking them what the next step in management is, and they understood it only means treatment, even though the correct answer was to order a CT for example.

- These mistakes are easy to spot and understand, even if you are not given any explanations by the NBME. Because of that, you should review your NBME after you take it (if you do not plan to re-take the NBME ever again, if you are running out of NBME tests, refrain from memorizing the answer choices because retaking again would not be helpful due to recall bias and invalid higher score)

## Timing modes for the NBMEs:

We advise you to take your NBMEs in standard-paced mode for the exam to have any predictive value. The self-paced mode allows more time per question; however, you lose the predictive power of the assessment which is the actual reason why you are taking the test in the first place! For example, the CBSSA NBME assessment has four sections of 50 questions each, and up to 65 minutes to complete each section in standard-paced mode. In self-paced mode, you have up to 4 hours and 20 minutes to complete each section on that assessment form.

## When should you take your first NBME assessment?

You should take your first NBME before you go through your First Aid/UWorld. You should not start reading First Aid, and then after your first pass you take your first NBME. This is the wrong approach. Do not worry that you might get questions wrong. A low score cannot damage your confidence if you know that you're already going to score bad anyway. You need to take your NBME as early as possible for two extremely important reasons:

1. You need to establish a baseline.
2. You must know how effective your studying is in improving your score and to build the best study schedule based on your strong/weak areas.

If you do not have a baseline, how would you know if you have been studying well or not? Imagine that you took your first NBME and you scored 180. On your second NBME two months later, you scored 220. That is really good progress. On the other hand, if you did not take your first NBME, you would never know if that 220 you got after reading and studying is an improvement or not!

Medical students should take their first NBME long before their dedicated studying period. In fact, we advise medical students to take their first NBME somewhere between their first and second year of medical school. Even if you still did not cover all the topics for the exam in your medical school, remember that step 1 actual exam tests high-yield facts, and not the very small trivial and detailed things that medical schools like to put on their exams.

## What is the predictive value of UWorld Self Assessments (UWSAs)?

USWAs tend to overestimate students' actual scores. However, UWSAs are continuously being updated and we expect that at some point they will be as powerful as the NBMEs in predicting actual step scores.

## How often should you take NBME self-assessments?

For step 1:

- It is recommended to take an NBME every two to four weeks to see if you are making progress in your studying.
- If your timeline allows, it is advisable to take the NBMEs monthly and not every two weeks.
- If your timeline is more than 6 months, you should take an NBME every two months. You do not want to run out of NBMEs before your actual exam because your final NBME within 1 week of your actual test is going to predict your actual exam score, only if this is the first time you take it.

For step 2 CK:

- Take an NBME self-assessment every 1 to 2 months.
- Take subject exams every 1 to 2 weeks.
- DO NOT USE SUBJECT EXAMS TO PREDICT YOUR SCORES. Only use the full NBME self-assessments as predictive tools for your actual step 2 CK score.

There is no single NBME that is known to be more predictive than another. Therefore, we advise you to take the NBMEs in the order you prefer. Remember that the percentage correct is not predictive of your actual score. Each question has its unique weight on the NBME, and each exam has its own scale. Therefore, if you feel like one exam is harder than another, you should not think that this will have any effect on the predictive value of that particular exam.

Based on this, we recommend you take the NBMEs in the numbered order they are available on the website. The NBME assessment with the lowest number is actually the oldest and by the time you reach the final NBME assessment, it is likely that the first NBME you took has been replaced with a new exam. This is good because it means that if you run out of NBMEs, you can retake the first one and be assured that this is actually a new test. The NBME typically releases a new assessment for step 1 every year in March.

## Should you search online forums for NBME questions explanations?

This is not recommended for several reasons. First, you will not take that test again anyway, so there is no point in reading too much in it. Second, remember that most of your mistakes are due to avoidable "silly" mistakes which we mentioned before. If you simply review the exam after you finish, you will catch all these silly mistakes that you made. Finally, remember that the explanations on message boards might actually be wrong!

### When should you retake the NBMEs if you have had a large gap in your exam preparation plan?

- If you needed to delay your dedicated study period for unforeseeable reasons, you might end up with a large gap in your study plan.
- Remember our previous rule; try not to repeat an NBME. If you have taken all the available NBMEs before, try to space them out over time when retaking them.
- If you retake an NBME, even if the last time you took that particular assessment was over a year ago, remember that it is now overestimating your score by up to 20 points!
- If you have taken all the NBMEs and are worried about the

overestimating issue, you might want to try the UWSAs. Even if the UWSAs are known to overestimate your score, they will still have a better predictive value as compared to a repeated NBME.

- If the final NBME that you will take before your actual test has been taken less than 6 months before by you, you should subtract 20 points from your predicted score to know your actual predicted score.

## Should you use online score converters/calculators?

Short answer is a big NO. They are known to be the least accurate in predicting your actual step score. Also, buy the NBME assessment tests and please avoid offline bootlegged NBME practice exams. Remember, there is no point in knowing the percentage of correct/incorrect answers to predict your score, and the NBME has a unique scale for each of their assessments.

Saving money is nice, but DO NOT TRY TO SAVE MONEY WHEN IT COMES TO YOUR USMLE, and potentially your whole career future!

## Last pieces of advice:

- If you are not ready, please postpone your exam. Do not take your actual test and hope for a miracle.
- If the NBME last prediction is that you might fail or score borderline, postpone your actual exam.
- If your school has set an arbitrary deadline for one of the steps, do not be afraid to ask for an extension if you are not ready.
- Do not listen to peer/family pressure even if they keep pushing you to take your test.
- We understand that money is an issue and delaying your exam could/would cost you more money. In the short term, it seems reasonable to lose some money and have a guaranteed future, rather than failing your exam. (Please note, getting into residency after failing the USMLE is very challenging but not impossible, some students still match after multiple attempts to match each year).

# My NBME score is good. But it is not my goal! What should I do?

As I said before, this is a completely personal decision. I would go for the exam; you might prefer to postpone depending on many factors, financial capabilities included. However, I advise you to do the following to make your decision more objective:

- Go to the internet and look for the average USMLE scores by specialty for US students and IMGs at https://www.yousmle.com/average-step-1-step-2-ck-research-by-specialty-imgs/

- If your predicted score is clearly below the average for the desired specialty, have a look on which specialties might accept your predicted score.

  o If these other specialties seem as reasonable options for you, go for your exam.

  o If your predicted score is below your goal, but higher than the average for your desired specialty, go for the exam.

  o If the other specialties can never work for you, postpone your exam.

# Reference:

https://www.yousmle.com/nbme-self-assessments-ulti-mate-guide-usmle-shelf/#Don%E2%80%99t_Take_Your_USMLE_Without_Taking_an_NBME_Self_Assessment

# CHAPTER 13:
# How to study for USMLE step 2 CK, COMLEX 2 CE and step 2 CS

HERE'S WHAT WE'LL cover in this chapter:

- What resources to use for step 2 CK
- What is the best text to use for step 2 CK?
- How to study for step 2 CK
- How to increase your step 2 CK score
- How long to study for step 2 CK
- Step 2 CK study plans from successful test takers
- Sample study plan and study schedule for step 2 CK
- Tips to do well on exam day

You have made it through Step 1 and COMLEX level 1. Guess what! You have already studied the content for step 2CK. The only difference is that you do not know how to manage the diseases you learned in Step 1. USMLE step 1 and COMLEX level focuses heavily on scientific understanding of diseases and mechanisms.

Now, it's time for you to know the best diagnostic test to order, and in what order you must order them. What is the most likely diagnosis of the disease?

What is the most accurate test?

What is the next step in management?

These are the most common types of questions most commonly tested on Step 2 CK or COMLEX level 2 CE.

The strategies for studying for Step 2 is similar to step 1. You should still follow the intensive mastery period schedule.

## What Resources Should I Use For Step 2?

Here, the good news is that there are fewer resources to use for Step 2 compared to step 1. The bad news is that there are fewer resources to use for Step 2 compared to step 1.

## Here are the best Step 2 CK resources we recommend you definitely have when studying for Step 2CK.

## Qbanks:

We recommend you choose the following Qbanks as resources to use for Step 2CK; UWorld, SmashUSMLE, Amboss and USMLERx. Choose one question bank and complete it at least twice before taking your Step 2CK exam.

## Online courses:

For video lecture reviews, we recommend Smashusmle review which has a comprehensive USMLE Step 2ck on-demand video lectures and live hybrid masterclass course covering internal medicine, OB-GYN, Psych, Surgery, Peds, over 1500 high yield step 2CK flashcards, and private one-one-one coaching to teach the right strategies to study for the exam. The flashcards provided on smashusmle.com should be used for the topics you're weak on. If you have a good amount of time before your exam then definitely consider starting them. Check smashusmle.com for more details.

**Onlinemeded**: This is another resource many medical students' use to study for Step 2CK. OME was created by Dr. Dustyn WIlliams and has lots of video lectures, notes, and flashcards for step 2CK. Check online-meded.com.

## In person live reviews:

PASS program by Dr. Francis is another option for students who want to attend live lectures or on-demand lectures. If you prefer this option, visit pass-program.com

**Picmonic**: For students who like pictures or animations to explain concepts, you can check picmonic (picmonic.com) for on demand lectures.

## What Is The Best Book For Step 2 CK?

The best book is **Yale G First Aid CrushUSMLE Step 2CK and 3** by Yale Gong, MD. This golden resource is not well known among medical students, but it is the best and most comprehensive review book you need to crush step 2Ck and 3. The book covers all the high yield concepts on the boards with end of chapter questions. It's about 700 pages and has high yield images at the end.

**Master the boards USMLE Step 2CK** by Conrad Fischer. This book is commonly used by students for step 2Ck but it's not a comprehensive resource. You will need UWorld/ SmashUSMLE Qbank to supplement the missing information in the book.

**USMLE Step 2 Secrets** by Theodore O'Connell MD is a short book for quick review of high yield facts that you can use to supplement your knowledge of high yield concepts. You cannot use it as a primary resource. More for last minute cramming a few days before your Step 2Ck.

## How to study for step 2 CK (Pre- Dedicated period)

For US medical students, you should be using UWorld or SmashUSMLE Qbank along with your third-year clinical rotations to study 10-20 questions a day before your dedicated study period.

For international medical graduates, this is different. Most IMGs need more time to study for Step 2CK. An average IMG may spend between 4-12 months studying for this exam. If you graduated from medical school for more than 1 year, then you will need more time to relearn all the concepts you forgot already.

Step 1: Take an NBME assessment 6, use your scores to determine your weak areas and create your schedule for the pre-dedicated study period. Determine how many hours you have ideally on a daily basis after accounting for all your non-reading activities including daily chores, shopping, child care, eating, and religious activities. Input all these chores into your schedule and then the rest is your dedicated study hours.

Your schedule should be broken down into a combination of reading your Yale G First Aid CrushUSMLE step 2CK and 3 book and doing practice questions. Here is the great news; Your Step 2CK book is readable compared to First Aid for the USMLE Step 1. If you are weak in clinical sciences, you should supplement your Step 2 CK knowledge by watching online video courses. We have over 200 hours of Step 2CK videos on smashusmle.com for your review.

Here is our recommended daily schedule if you are studying for 4-6 months or more:

Assuming you are studying for 8 hours a day. This will work for international medical graduates who have more time to study.

Block 1: 8am-12pm - Read a chapter/section in Yale G book/ Watch video lectures.

Block 2: 12p-1p- lunch.

Block 3: 1p-5p- Qbank review (1 hour to complete 40 UWorld / SmashUSMLE questions and read both explanations of correct and incorrect answers.

Study for 45 minutes and take 15 minutes for every hour you study.

For US medical students on clinical rotations or electives, you can study practice questions of 2-4hours a day while doing your rotations. You still have fresh medical knowledge and do not need to do a complete review.

Here is a screenshot of a sample USMLE Step 2CK six month schedule;

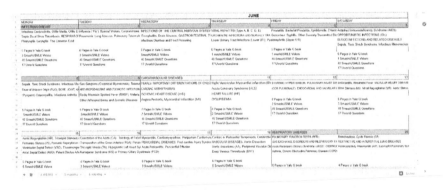

Download a free copy from smashusmle.com

## For dedicated study period

For US medical students, we recommend you choose an easy elective rotation or block 4 weeks off to study for step 2 CK. If you are an international medical graduate, your dedicated period should not be more than

4-6 weeks! Yes. That's it. This is where intensive learning begins and you want to review everything you need to know for the exam.

Step 1: take an NBME assessment test.

## NBME and UWorld Self assessments

Before starting your prep for Step 2Ck, take one NBME self-assessment test and use your results to determine your weak areas. Through this, you can create your schedule for the exam.

-NBME Exams - These questions are literally written by the NBME. Yes, they may not always reflect the question styling, but they will introduce you to concepts and common thought patterns emphasized by the NBME (who also happens to make the test you're going to be taking). You should have a day where you do NBME blocks to evaluate your strengths and weak areas. They have 4 tests for Peds, Surgery, OBGYN, IM, and Neuro with 3 for Psych. If you have a good-sized dedicated period (like 4-5 weeks), I'd do all of them.

Let's talk about practice exams.

Here is the order we recommend taking the NBME exams in;

NBME 6 (Take this day 1 of your dedicated step 2 CK prep phase)

Then UWSA 1 (Take end of week 2)

Then NBME 7 + Old Free 120 (to simulate a full length experience) - Take Week 3

NBME 8 (Take at end of week 4)

UWSA 2 (take at end of week 5)

New Free 120 (the best currently available representation of the real exam). (5 days before your actual exam)

## Caveat:

For NBME 6, pay more attention to your % correct than the actual score. The curve is quite ridiculous. If you start off and are getting around 80ish %, you're in a good situation. NBME 8 and UWSA 2 are the most predictive exams. UWSA 1 for many people is quite the over predictor.

Step 2: Your 6 weeks dedicated study period should be structured this way

Master High-Yield (Week 1 and 2)

Fill in Details (Week 3 and 4)

Master High-Yield (Week 5 and 6)

Now, this method would be done during your dedication. For roughly the first week, your goal is to learn the basics and high yield info that you know will show up. This includes topics the test makers love like cardio, endocrine, GI etc. You will likely see all of these show up on your actual exam.

How you gain this basic knowledge is up to you. We recommend SmashUSMLE reviews videos with Yale G First Aid book, or Onlinemeded videos with Dr. Williams high yield notes. Try to complete this in a short period to give yourself time to fill in the details.

## Week 1 and 2

During the first two weeks, you'll still be doing your UWORLD/ SmashUSMLE questions (pick one). Then your second and third week of your studying is when you increase the amount of questions you do daily (about 80-160 questions a day). During your pre-dedicated period, you will miss questions regarding details you never knew mattered. Well, now it matters. So learn these bits of info.

## Week 3 and 4

One strategy we definitely recommend 6-7 days out, is pounding through large numbers of questions everyday (like 4 blocks of UWorld=160 questions if you can). If you do this, you will not be reading much book content, but rather you will be getting through the questions and reviewing the explanations while correlating it with your Yale G First Aid book. You should be able to do this relatively quickly if your knowledge base has been well shaped at this point.

## Week 5 and 6

During the last 2 weeks, continue doing more questions, review the subjects that you are still weak on and master all the core high yield information commonly tested on the exam. This is the time to raise your confidence going into the exam. You want to feel prepared for it, and trying to memorize detail is likely not going to do it. So, go back to a resource like SmashUSMLE reviews/ OME or Step 2 Secrets and make sure you know the info there cold. The exam won't be stressful then!

## How To Increase Your Step 2 CK Score:

Now you know the best Step 2 CK resources and you understand the general structure. But what can make the difference between an average score and a score that will break the bank?!

The following two strategies will help you decrease mistakes and improve your scores! We recommend making flashcards or using Smashusmle reviews flashcards. When reviewing SmashUSMLE/UWorld Qbank, you should make short and concise flashcards for any question you missed or guessed correctly on. Do your cards the next morning before beginning with a few review cards. This will help you avoid making the same mistakes again on UWORLD and for sure on the real Step 2CK exam.

For example, if you missed a question about endocarditis management, you will write a short sentence about the key concept or try to replicate the vignette. Then write the important info you did not understand before solving the questions.

Caveat: Don't make elaborate flashcards. Don't waste too much time on making the flashcards and have no time to actually study them. Make sure they're in a quick question-and-answer format.

If you don't like flashcards, then try out this next technique: open Microsoft word and create a 2-column table. This is the note-taking method.

| Key fact | Description |
|---|---|
| What is the characteristic murmur in mitral stenosis? | Mid diastolic murmur after an opening snap heard best at apex |

Write your short questions on the left and short answers to the right. Similar to the flashcard method, do this for any question you miss or guess correctly on. Then the following morning go through your notebook and see if you can answer a few pages of missed/guessed questions.

Both of these methods are designed to ensure you don't make the same mistakes again. This is all about preserving the points your hard work has gained and trying to raise your score.

Try these techniques out! They were very helpful and hope it works for you too!

Step 2 CK Study Plans From Successful Test Takers (the 4 week review)

Aside from knowing how to study for Step 2, you should also be acquainted with good Step 2 study plans to guide you in your studying.

# Week 1-2:

### Morning:

- Review Flashcards and Missed Questions
- Block 1 UWorld /SmashUSMLE 40 questions (Random Tutor) -> Review and Make Flashcards
- 7-8 OME Notes or Read Yale G First Aid book (Make Flashcards for Anything you struggle with)
- Block 2 UWorld 40 questions

### Afternoon:

- 40 UWorld questions
- Read Yale G First Aid book/7-8 OME Notes
- 40 UWorld questions
- Read Yale G First Aid book/4-5 OME Notes

Your main goal during these first 2 weeks is to get through all the high-yield info.

Once you understand the key ideas, you can transition close to 100% of your time to questions and really boost your grade!

Take your first NBME 6 at the beginning of Week 1.

Take a UWORLD 1 self-assessment at the end of Week 2 to see where you're really at.

# Week 3:

Increase UWorld questions to 4-5 blocks. You should be almost done reading material (OME or Yale G book) by now. So, continue doing questions and flashcards 100%.

You can replace 1-2 of these days and take NBME 7 (the trickiest one with the steepest score) and ideally NBME 8.

At the end of Week 3, start reading Step 2 Secrets and see how much of the high yield you've retained.

You should also be coming closer to finishing UWORLD at the end of Week 3. Get ready to do your marked questions during Week 4.

## Week 4:

Along with Yale G book, Step 2 Secrets, return to Smashusmle/OME videos and skim the notes and look for any info you've forgotten since you first reviewed the material.

Take UWSA #2 the Monday or Tuesday before your exam date. This should be a good predictor of your final grade.

If you need more practice, take the 120 self-assessment that the test creators provide for free.

The final step is to take the test and kill it! Reward yourself afterwards!

## Tips To Do Well On Exam Day For Step 2 CK:

The last part is all about how to do well on your exam.

## You're Earning Points Not Losing Them:

When we typically test like Step 2 CK, we see every question as an opportunity to lower our grade. This is a common reason why we're always anxious throughout and after the exam. We just focus too much time and energy on what we don't know.

But instead, think about earning points! Think about getting excited about the questions you know well and see your grade getting higher.

If you have a WTF question (which you will) shrug your shoulders, guess, and think that getting it right may only help your score.

This shift in mindset can help you so much during your preparation and test.

You'll feel more confident and not give too much weight to the questions you don't know.

## Plan Out Your Breaks:

The test is long. 9 hours to be exact. So, make sure you have a game plan.

When will you take your breaks? There is a total of 45 minutes (1 hour if you skip the tutorial. Also, any extra time from your blocks will be added (but don't count on this).

During the last few weeks of your prep, try to do a few blocks of UWORLD in a row. When do you find your energy tanking? This is probably a good time to introduce a break during the real exam.

We recommend a 4-7 min break between every section and you will need those breaks! So listen to your body!

Reference: https://themdjourney.com/ ultimate-guide-on-how-to-study-for-step-2-ck-2018/

# Step 2 CS

Most medical schools offer a practice OSCE for all their medical students. This is more than enough for you to prepare for Step 2 CK or Level 2 PE. We also strongly recommend a partner to help you as a standardized patient to study for the exam.

If you are an international student, the challenge is that you did not train in the US medical system. We strongly recommend you take a Step 2 CS course.

Here are the best programs that have helped thousands of IMGs pass the Step 2 CS course.

Goldusmlereview.com is the #1 rated program

http://www.acstep2csprep.com

https://www.c3ny.org

http://www.nycsprep.com

# USMLE Step 3 or COMLEX Level 3

Do a Qbank. You are a resident. You do not have all the luxury time as you were a medical student. You are working 60-80 hours a week.

# CHAPTER 14:
## Advice for osteopathic students

## The Dilemma

THE DILEMMA THAT DO students face is "Do I need to take the USMLE?" The answer to this question is simple yet complicated at the same time. It really depends on the student first and foremost. There are two answers to this question, and of course they contradict each other. One point of view is, why take another difficult test if you are not planning to go to a competitive allopathic residency? Most allopathic programs accept COMLEX anyways. Also, taking the USMLE is more work and stress than simply taking the COMLEX alone, so why bother to pay the extra money (exam cost changes every year, check nbome.org and usmle.org for current pricing) and go through more torture? Some people agree with this view, and others look at it as taking the easy way out.

The other point of view focuses on applying for highly competitive specialties: Emergency medicine, Radiology, Ophthalmology, Anesthesia, Dermatology, and Surgery (known by the widely recognized mnemonic EROADS to riches) residencies. Surgical specialties include neurosurgery, urology, and ear nose and throat (ENT). These residencies are very difficult to obtain. The program directors receive a wide range of excellent applicants with great scores for a limited number of spots. The highly competitive pool of applicants forces the program directors to establish a minimum Board score for selecting the students to interview. Therefore, taking the USMLE can open more doors, since it is a very solid way for the residency directors of allopathic programs to compare you to your fellow MD applicants. **If you're interested in a certain program, the safest thing to do is reach out to the program coordinator and ask if they require USMLE.** You may also want to ask whether they require

DO students take USMLE step 1 scores only or all three boards, USMLE step 1, step 2 CK, and step 2 CS in order to be interviewed and/or ranked for their program. Many Accreditation Councils for Graduate Medical Education (ACGME) program directors may feel more comfortable looking at USMLE scores because it is a good way to compare you to the rest of the applicants.

On a positive note, according to the National Board of Medical Examiners published USMLE performance data, DO applicants who were first time USMLE test takers and took the exam between 2018-January 30th 2019, had the SAME percentage of passing (96%) as their MD applicant counterparts. This signifies that although it may be a difficult task to study for two national licensing exams at once, if one plans wells and uses the appropriate study material, DO medical students are capable of passing the exam at the same rate as their MD counterparts. **However, just like it is important to score as high as possible to be competitive once one begins applying to residency programs with COMLEX scores, it equally important to not only pass the USMLE but to score as high as possible to be competitive to programs that look at either only the USMLE or both COMLEX and USMLE, once one begins applying to residency.** If you fail or barely pass the USMLE exam, it will count against you and hurt your application rather than help it. **For example, if you score a 600 on COMLEX (for the 2017-2018 exam cycle, this score would be at the 68th percentile based on NBOME) and score a 200 on USMLE (during the 2015-2017 exam cycles, this score would be at the 9th percentile based on NBME) your COMLEX score will be overshadowed by your poor performance on USMLE.** Just as taking the USMLE step 1 exam can open doors for you as an osteopathic student; it can also close doors to your application too. **Keep in mind that it's mandatory to report both exams when applying to residency.**

Therefore, the decision is ultimately personal. **It is crucial to know what you are signing up for, when you decide to take the USMLE on top of the COMLEX.** Just realize that signing up for the USMLE has its pros and cons, but it is definitely more work—a lot more work, as you will find out when you begin your journey—than just taking the COMLEX. The best thing to do if you are seriously thinking about taking the USMLE is to actually make up your mind and decide *early*. The sooner the better, because you need to realize the amount of extra work you will need to put in. Begin the process of preparing early. If you decide to take both Board exams, you have to fully understand the repercussions of your decision. It demands twice the amount of work. **If you don't think you'll perform well, then you've already failed. The worst thing you can do is fail an exam. The second worst thing you can do is score well on one exam while bombing the other.**

Our personal point of view is that you have already assumed more than $100,000 in loans; what is an extra $630? Especially if you do not know what field of medicine you are going into. What if you end up falling in love with Anesthesia, Urology, Radiology, or otolaryngology? These are all competitive residencies, so you need your application to stand out. Or what if you realize that you want to be in a certain geographical area for whatever reason: family, spouse, city, life and the program you want requires you taking the USMLE. Personally, we were not sure what we wanted to specialize in, and we wanted to have all the doors open and all options available; hence we took both exams. **It is crucial to know what you are signing up for, though, when you decide to take the USMLE on top of the COMLEX, as emphasized before.**

The biggest mistake DO students make is "giving the USMLE a shot." The USMLE deserves more than just a shot. It is a beast, if we are generous in describing this test. The exam is the worldwide gold standard for all applicants interested in an ACGME residency. It is a very challenging exam, and you must be mentally prepared for it. **Think of USMLE as the deepest trench of the ocean requiring the most in-depth understanding of topics whereas COMLEX tests your breadth of knowledge essentially expecting you to know a little bit about everything.**

Although MD students dread taking the USMLE, they take it once and they run! In the meantime, you as a DO student may accept the challenge of sitting for the eight-hour long exam. Then you return home to continue to study again for the COMLEX. This can either make or break you, because you do not have time to process whether you did well or not on the USMLE. You still have to anticipate sitting for the COMLEX and doing well on it. We say this not to scare you, but just to give you a dose of reality. Remember, *you must pass your COMLEX regardless of how well you perform on the USMLE.* It is a graduation requirement - to pass COMLEX-USA Level 1, 2 COMLEX Exam and Performance Examination (PE).

As an osteopathic student, your main exam is COMLEX, and your priority is to do well on your COMLEX. If you make the choice to sign up for both exams, you need to find the balance to do well on both. Some osteopathic medical students who take the USMLE do not perform as well on the COMLEX, because they studied for both exams using the USMLE question bank and *First Aid for the USMLE* and then added the Osteopathic Manipulative Medicine (OMM) portion of COMLEX to the end of their preparation for COMLEX. *This method may not work.* As we mentioned before, the exams are different and require different approaches to tackle the questions. We highly recommend OMTREVIEW Qbank, COMBANK and COMQUEST to study for COMLEX. Also, you have to study OMM continuously and not leave it until the last few days after the USMLE exam, immediately prior to COMLEX. **Keep in mind that you're an osteopathic medical student and 20-30% of COMLEX questions are OPP related. *Know your OMM.* These questions should be free points. In addition to your question banks, another invaluable resource is OMT Review book 4th Edition by Savarese. In addition, linked to the OMT review book by Savarese is OMTReview COMLEX Qbank created by Dr. Adesina and Dr. Savarese which has over 2500 COMLEX 1 AND 2700 COMLEX LEVEL 2CE practice questions. Check it out at omtreview.com**

The best way to determine if you have a chance of doing well on the USMLE test is to take NBME sample assessment exams online under standardized conditions; whatever score you receive will predict your actual performance on the real exam. So, if you take the USMLE assessment test a week before your USMLE exam and do poorly, rethink your decision about the exam. A poor score will hurt your application and might count against you. **Just because you have signed up and paid to take the exam doesn't mean you have to sit for it. A poor score will hurt you more in the long run than forfeiting $630.**

Residency directors will see your poor USMLE score, and you would have been better off not taking the USMLE, as this may affect your application.

Also, a common scenario is when some students realize in their third year that "oops, I probably should have taken the USMLE." Such students are in a very stressful situation, feeling regret and anxiety as they decide what to do next. We know that third year is *not* a vacation, as many people make it seem. It is an energy-depriving year, and you have COMLEX-Level II USA and COMLEX Physical Exam (PE) to complete at the end of the fourth year. It is hard enough to study for the rotation you are on after a long day of work. (We promise you will miss the first and second years, when you had lectures and went home to review them.) Going to rotations is like going to work, usually from 7 am to 5 pm, or longer if you are on surgery rotation. Imagine adding the stress of preparing for USMLE step 1 in the third year—it is tough. It is not going to be easy to study for such a big exam (USMLE Step 1) in the midst of studying for **COMAT** exams and **COMLEX Level II** exams. Therefore, decide *early* and start preparing *early*—in your second year, not for third year.

If you are planning on taking the USMLE exam, you need to put in 100 percent effort and aim for a strong score. It is not to be taken lightly; it is a serious decision you have to make, preferably early on in your second year. If you sign up for it, put in the hours, studying smart to excel on this exam. If you decide not to take it, just hope that the allopathic residency programs you apply to accept COMLEX scores only.

Here are some questions you should ask yourself before deciding to take the USMLE exam:

- Is my specialty generally known as being "Osteopathic friendly?"
- Does my GPA rank in the top 50 percent of my class?
- Do I have a history of being a strong standardized test taker?
- Will I be applying to competitive residency programs?

If most of your answers here are 'yes', then you may strongly want to consider taking the USMLE. If you find yourself answering 'no,' then you may want to think long and hard about whether the risks of taking the exam outweigh the rewards for you.

## You may need to report your USMLE scores when applying to residency.

Obviously, some students do not need to take the USMLE and do not have to worry about making this decision:

1. Students who know for a fact they want to practice osteopathic manipulative medicine (OMM)
2. Students who want to stay in a system within their osteopathic university hospital
3. Students who do not want to apply to competitive allopathic residencies

4. DO students applying to less competitive residencies or residencies that have a large portion of DO students

Do not listen to anyone who tries to convince you to take the USMLE just to prove your intelligence. The choice is yours. Some students say they wanted to satisfy their ego; that is why they wanted to take the USMLE. But this is not a good reason at all. Other motivational factors should drive you to take the USMLE. Satisfying your ego is simply not enough reason to take such an exam; it can count against you if you do not receive a high score. You need to set a goal; say to yourself that you need to take the USMLE for reasons a, b, and c, and on top of that you will show all the allopathic residency directors that you can do just as well on their exam. This should be the attitude.

## USMLE Recommendations for Osteopathic Students *Only*

These are some reasons you should *not* take the USMLE if you are an osteopathic medical student;

1. I want to show my other MD friends I can do what they can do, or even better.
2. I want to impress my parents and friends because I sat for two Board exams.
3. I just want to take it for the fun of it, to get a feel for what the exam is like.
4. I did not do well on my USMLE assessment test a week before the test. (That is an alarming sign—pay attention.)
5. I am still scoring less than 50 percent on my UWorld or SmashUSMLE question bank in the last week before the exam.
6. I just want to take the exam to pass the test; my score is not important because I am only applying to osteopathic residencies anyway.
7. I want to satisfy my ego.

## Comparing the USMLE and COMLEX

Realize that the USMLE and COMLEX are two different exams and will obviously have two different styles. The best way for students to see the difference is to go to the NBOME and NBME websites and take a look at the sample questions posted, as well as question formats and styles on their website. The links have been provided below.

For USMLE sample questions, refer to the NBME website: **USMLE Step 1 Question Format:** http://www.usmle.org/Examinations/step1/step1_test.html

Read the USMLE **Step 1 Content Description online here:** http://www.usmle.org/Examinations/step1/step1_content.html

For COMLEX style sample questions, refer to the NBOME website: NBOME COMSAE sample question format: http://www.nbome.org/comsaeboi.asp?m=can#format

COMLEX Level Content Description online: http://www.nbome.org/comsaeboi.asp?m=can#content2

For more information about the COMLEX Level I, III and III. Visit www.nbome.org.

As you can see, the styles of both exams are quite different, and doing well on both of them requires you to be able to handle different types of questions. That entails a decent amount of work and effort. **You're studying the same material; the difference lies in how you're applying the information.** Handling both exams is possible, but it must be done in a careful manner to avoid overwhelming yourself and failing both exams. The last thing you need is to do poorly on both exams because you could not manage 100 percent effort on both and settled for 80 percent effort. If you ever feel you are in that position and an exam date is coming up, then maybe you are better off forfeiting the $630 and not sitting for the USMLE. Instead, spend the last few days focusing on the COMLEX. Again, judge your progress by your performance on the assessment exams.

One student may tell you he had more biochemistry on his exam, while another student will tell you she had more neurology on her exam. Please do not listen to anyone who shares such information because they are misleading you. First of all, they should not be discussing the content of the exam, as this violates the terms and conditions of the exam. Secondly, every student's exam is different, and the content of the test varies from one examinee to another. You should study everything you can; prepare for any question that might be posed to you on the actual exam.

Please do not forget to study biostatistics, epidemiology, ethics, and behavioral sciences for both exams; many students push these topics to the end or do not even bother studying them at all. Be careful not to fall into that trap. **This is a potential area where you can earn points on your exam while other students take the hit. Remember that the first question on your exam is worth just as much as the last. Bottom line: it's all about point grabbing.**

Finally, most osteopathic students who take both exams take the USMLE before the COMLEX. The biggest mistake they fall into is scheduling the two exams three days apart. This is not the smartest idea, because you need to physically and emotionally recover from the first test. You need a mental break and you need more time to prepare for the transition between the two exam styles. If you decide to take both, you need to start preparing for both early and equally. That means studying questions from OMTReview, COMBANK or COMQUEST and UWorld/SmashUSMLE together. You should schedule at least seven to ten days between them before you sit for the COMLEX in order to recover from the first exam, get over any emotions, and focus more on last-minute high-yield material that pertains to the second exam. What most people do is take the USMLE first, take the COMLEX next, and then focus on OMM/OPP in the seven to ten days in between. Everyone is different. You might want to leave fewer or more days for whatever reason; again, do what you think is best for you. **Just remember, the USMLE Step 1 and COMLEX Level 1 are two different exams and require different preparations**.

## A. ABOUT THE COMSAEs

The Comprehensive Osteopathic Medical Self-Assessment Examination (COMSAE)s is similar to the NBME's practice exam in that it is the assessment supported by the NBOME (the ones who create the COMLEX Level 1, 2, 3 exams) and can be used to "gauge of the base of knowledge and ability: of an osteopathic medical student".

On the site, NBOME repeatedly states the following: "We encourage the use of COMSAE to analyze and assess strengths and weaknesses in medical knowledge and issues. COMSAE should not be used to predict performance on the COMLEX-USA cognitive exams." This seems contradictory since some Colleges of Osteopathic Medicine (COM) will require a student to score a certain score before the student is allowed by the school to sit down for the COMLEX exam. However, possibly why the NBOME had to put out this statement is because 1) the COMSAE exams themselves may be a few years old and the COMLEX exam itself has different versions and updates. In the score sheet of a COMSAE a person may score "Good performance" range in OMM, but if that version of the COMSAE exam had a lot of Chapman's points and very little questions related to sacral diagnosis, it can be misleading the student's level of preparation regarding the OMM section of the COMLEX exam, especially if on the actual COMLEX exam there are a lot of questions related to sacral diagnosis. This is why it is important to not only use the latest COMSAE exam, but to take multiple COMSAEs so that you have more breadth and depth on the variety of topics that may appear on the COMLEX.

According to an Associate Dean of Assessment at one College of Osteopathic Medicine (COM), from 2016-2018 years, the COMSAE showed a good predictive ability of the COMLEX for first time test scores for the students at the COM. For COMSAE Phase 1 in preparation for COMLEX Level 1, the correlation for those students was ($r = .80$), whereas for COMSAE Phase 2 in preparation for COMLEX Level 2, the correlation for the students at the COM ($r = .70$)*. Knowing this, it should help students understand why some of their classmates have been concerned about the discrepancy between the score on the COMSAE they receive and the actual score a student receives on the COMLEX exam. This correlation is also a reminder of 1) the importance of understanding statistics (you will be tested on statistics on both Level 1 and Level 2 exams) and 2) another reminder that the goal of the COMSAEs is to not be a predictor of a student's score, but to serve as a snapshot sample of the breadth and depth of the COMLEX exam. In other words, use the COMSAEs as a GUIDE. Dr. Adesina has a great strategy on how to use the practice exams as an effective guide to prepare for the exam. Check out smashusmle.com to see these strategies.

Two things of note: 1) Dr. Adesina's presentation is for the NBME practice exam that students studying for the USMLE use, but his suggestions can be related to the COMSAE and how to read a COMSAE test performance analysis. 2) One difference between the COMSAE and NBME is that COMSAE doesn't allow you to know the percent that you got wrong, or allow you to review the questions marked incorrectly. Because of this, it is advised that while taking the COMSAE practice test, each question that you aren't sure of, or a topic area that you realize upon reading a test question, you aren't confident or comfortable with; write a small note to yourself to later on review that topic. By the end of the practice exam, you will then have a list of topics that you should review. Review those topics and then take another COMSAE (once again, writing on a separate piece of paper concepts and questions you didn't understand) There are several COMSAE practice exams, and we advise that you take as many practice tests as possible, making sure to use each test as a guide to help further navigate how to best prepare for the actual exam**.

FOOTNOTE: Please note, the COMSAEs has a standard margin for error. In addition, subsequent scores of the same exam are found to be less predictive. The best thing to do is to use different COMSAE exams to help more accurately and less biasedly gauge knowledge and preparation for the COMLEX exam. Also, when one is taking any COMSAE exam, the student should mimic test settings and have it timed, with no study materials present or used during the duration of the exam in order to ensure the most accurate score.

FOOTNOTE: **Due to the changes to the COMLEX Level 1 and COMLEX Level 2 exams, the previous COMSAEs (any one before 2019) may no longer be a strong indication of the knowledge base necessary in order to appropriately be prepared for the newly updated exam. NBOME has issued new COMSAEs for both Level 1 and Level 2 exams that are now available on their website that better correlate with the new exam. Look for COMSAEs dated after June 2019, as those are the ones that best mirror the most current topics and content being tested on the revised COMLEX exam. If tests before June 2019 are still available, use discretion to use them as possible practice tests. List of topics that are covered on the revised COMLEX Level 1 and Level 2 are in the links below:

Level 1: https://www.nbome.org/exams-assessments/comlex-usa/comlex-usa-level-1/blueprint/

Level 2: https://www.nbome.org/exams-assessments/comlex-usa/comlex-usa-level-2-ce/blueprint/

How to study for COMLEX Level 2 Clinical exam (CE) and Physical Examination (PE)

So, you passed Level 1 exams, passed all of your rotations, passed the COMATS; congratulations! Here is your prize: taking two more national licensing exams that you need to pass in order to graduate and qualify to be ranked by residency programs (we will talk about residency programs [and the merger] a bit later)!!!!

So, at this point, there are two important questions that you should consider and be very reflective in answering for yourself:

(1) Did you like your COMLEX Level 1 Board score?

   a) Was the score in the range of what you predicted for yourself (as soon as you left the exam that day) or within your target scores? If yes, congrats; if no and your score was lower than expected, then what happened/ what can be done to improve test performance (new studying material, new studying strategy, dealing with test anxiety, etc.)?

(2) When would you feel comfortable taking Level 2 (Performance Evaluation; PE and Cognitive Evaluation; CE)

   a) Would you feel comfortable taking it immediately after third year/ rotations ends (usually around mid-June-July) or would you need more time?

      i) Important note: for residency programs; more and more programs like to see all three scores: Level 1, Level 2 PE, and Level 2 CE included in an applicant's residency application as soon as possible and requiring it as a prerequisite for sending an applicant an interview invitation. As of right now, residency programs start receiving applications on September 15th so having the scores back before or by September 15th is ideal. However, it is BEST to take each exam when YOU are READY. Better to have a delayed exam transcript sent to residency programs with a good score than to have horrible exam scores sent to a program on time.

   b) This question is also very important because it will play a role in when you sign up for audition rotations/sub-interns; elective courses, and possibly when you schedule your interviews that residency programs will be emailing you.

    The earlier one reflects and answers these two questions, the more prepared one will be in organizing third year and final year of medical school. In addition, this reflection is important since for the Level 2 PE it takes approximately 2 months to get scores back and 4 weeks to get Level 2 CE back on time. Plus, the earlier one signs up and pays for an exam, the better chance of having the date and time desired.

# Question #3: When should I take Level 2 PE vs. Level 2 CE?

a) It is definitely advisable that one takes time in between the written exam (CE) and standardized patient exam (PE) for two reasons;

    i) You want to avoid test burnout and possibly lower performance on one (or both) exams.

    ii) There are only two testing sites for the COMLEX Level 2PE: Chicago, Illinois and Conshohocken, Pennsylvania. So in addition to paying for the exams, it will be wise to budget and plan for travel time, accommodations and lodging that will be needed.

    However, how much time is taken to sit for the COMLEX Level 2 CE and Level 2 PE off is based on the discretion of the individual and their studying habits. But on average most students take off between 3 days and two weeks.

b) *Which exam to take first, does it matter?* There is no particular order that a student has to take the COMLEX Level 2 CE or PE, as a score on one exam doesn't affect the other. The order of taking the exam is based on the individual's judgement.

c) *Take both COMLEX Level 2 CE/PE AND USMLE Level 2 CS/CK?*

    i) Is it worth it? This question once again is based on a student's judgement. It would be wise for students to meet up with their medical school academic counselors as well as call up program directors at the programs one is interested in submitting residency applications to.

    ii) When reaching out to program directors, you should say (or email) something like this:

d) *"Hi, I am a medical student from an osteopathic medical school who is interested in your program. I have already taken my COMLEX exam(s) and wanted to ask if you require USMLE scores to be submitted to your program in order for you to consider an applicant for an interview. If you do require USMLE scores to be submitted, do you require USMLE step 1 only, step 1 and step 2 (written) only, or all three USMLE steps ( step 1, 2 CK and CS) in order for you to consider interviewing an applicant?"*

Asking these questions should give you the answers you need to mentally (and financially) prepare for these exams. Once again, remember that residency programs want these scores by ideally September 15th, so the earlier you reflect and decide which exams you want to take, the sooner you can start planning how to set up your study schedule so that you are able to study well for all exams. We would advise determining the PERCENTAGE of programs in the geographic region and specialty you are interested in that have a preference of USMLE over COMLEX scores. Spending time, stress and money (close to $2000) to take another set of exams that don't contribute to you graduating from osteopathic medical school is not something to take lightly.

Certain specialties such as Emergency Medicine, Radiology, Ophthalmology, Anesthesiology, Dermatology and Surgical specialties (urology, Neurosurgery, Vascular, and General Surgery) are known to be very competitive (few programs and few seats per program) specialties and most likely a high percentage of programs will strongly recommend students take the USMLE exam; whereas primary care specialties such as family medicine, internal medicine, psychiatry, OB-GYN, pediatrics, etc.; are less likely to have a high percentage of programs recommend taking the USMLE.

## B. COMLEX Level 2 Performance Evaluation (PE)

a) How to study for the COMLEX Level 2 PE: PRACTICE, PRACTICE, PRACTICE

b) This exam is unlike a typical exam in that you are being graded on the ability to ask clinically relevant questions, do a thorough clinically relevant physical examination, come up with clinically reasonable diagnoses and treatment plans for the patient, type up a SOAP note format and discuss with the patient, all while showing compassion and humanism all in 23 minutes. (https://www.nbome.org/exams-assessments/comlex-usa/comlex-usa-level-2-pe/blueprint/). It is a lot! Although the exam is only pass/fail, do not underestimate the exam's performance and the necessity of taking out time to study well for it. Residency programs look unfavorably at candidates who fail a Level 2 PE.

c) One of the most commonly used resources for the COMLEX PE is the: COMBANK PE videos by True Learn (HIGHLY RECOMMENDED; make sure to watch the videos of dos and don'ts regarding each part of the PE exam as well as all the clinical cases and the OMM skills videos) The OMM technique videos in particular not only give you a breakdown of OMT techniques that can be used on each part of the body, but they explain which technique used could get the examinee more points in the OMM section.

Most people are able to get through the numerous videos by sitting and watching them three days straight but use individual discretion when creating your schedule of how to use the videos as a study aid.

d) Another popular resource is books: First Aid for Step 2 Clinical Skills book and JB Review COMLEX Level 2 PE Review guide (equally recommended). The benefit of these books is 1) for students who need help forming clinical relevant differential diagnoses (the Level 2 PE wants a minimum of 3 per case scenario) both books have a list of differential diagnoses and recommended test/labs to order (this was found more in the First Aid book than in the JB Review book) and 2) both books are commonly used as a script for you and a partner to use to role-play and practice patient encounters with.

e) The last resource to use are friends, family, and standardized patients to practice with.

   i) If your school has the resource, sign up for as many practice standardized patients encounters as you can, make sure to check to see if you will be able to view the recording and/or have someone provide you feedback.

   ii) Practice on friends, family, etc.; also practice while being TIMED and with the equipment you will be allowed to use on exam day. Make sure to practice not only doing the clinical encounter and physical exam while timed, but also work on writing up the SOAP note as well as time yourself as you are doing the OMM treatment on the patient (remember, if the patient requires OMT; you are required to perform that treatment within the 15-minute timeframe for the patient encounter given). As much as possible, ask for feedback so that you can improve. Also, don't forget to practice OMM techniques!

## C. COMEX Level 2 Cognitive Evaluation (CE)

There is not much more to say regarding the resources and time planning for taking this written exam.

Based on the reflection questions previously discussed in this chapter, determine which study strategy and study resources: OMTReview, COMBANK, COMQUEST, etc. you would like to use, continue using, or discontinue. If the resource(s) worked well (you got the score you desired/ the score is competitive for the specialty(ies) you are interested in pursuing; then continue using them; if not, change is always a good thing!

    i)   Another new resource you have to help guide your studies is the use of COMAT score breakdowns for each rotation. All of the subjects test each clinical subject COMAT will be testing again in the COMLEX Level 2 CE, so using it would give you a detailed idea of what topics to review. In fact, studies show that the COMATS (especially the IM and EM COMATS) have a correlation (similar to COMSAEs) on Level 2 CE scores (1).

    ii)   Using the COMSAEs provided by NBOME as another study aid is also recommended.

## ABOUT THE RESIDENCY PROGRAM MERGER (Single Graduate Medical Education Accreditation)

Starting July 2019, residency programs which were under the American Osteopathic Association (AOA) are now going to be merged with programs who are under the Accreditation Council for Graduate Medical Education (ACGME). In other words, all residency programs will be regulated by ACGME. How this affects students applying to residency programs is that both DOs and MD medical students will be equally eligible to apply to any residency program of interest.

Before this merger, osteopathic medical students had to choose whether they wanted to apply to solely residency programs that targeted osteopathic medical students (these programs were regulated by AOA) or other programs that didn't specifically target osteopathic medical students (programs regulated by ACGME). Both systems had different application due dates, rank order due dates, and matching into an AOA regulated hospital (which would be revealed to candidates in February) disqualified candidates from matching into an ACGME programs (which isn't revealed until March). Now all programs are now required to have ACGME accreditation no later than June 30th, 2020.

However, what is important to note is how this affects eligibility for residency consideration. Since osteopathic medical students take the COMLEX exams and students granted MD degrees take the USMLE, **it is important to contact residency program coordinators or program directors and ask which exam (or both) will be reviewed for interview consideration. Once again, we would advise determining the PERCENTAGE of programs in specialty, and the geographic region(s) of interest that have a preference of USMLE or COMLEX scores for interview consideration.**

Some residency programs have designated themselves as "Osteopathic Recognition". What this indicates is that a program has met requirements that "demonstrate, through a formal application process, the commitment to teaching and assessing Osteopathic Principles and Practice (OPP) at the graduate medical education level (2)". Examples of these requirements being; a one core osteopathic faculty member, a Director of Osteopathic Education, appropriate number of hours teaching osteopathic principles and practice, teaching facility sites, etc.

The merger will not affect board certification in any specialty, and osteopathic medical students are still eligible to take AOA Board exams in lieu of the non-osteopathic focused (American Board Medical Specialties [ABMS]) Board exams, and osteopathic medical graduates have the option to take either board licensing exam. The merger will not also affect students who match into residency programs in Pennsylvania or Florida (in these two states, osteopathic physicians are required to complete an intern year at an AOA-accredited hospital).

The 2020 Main Residency Match marked the completion of the transition to a single accreditation system and the consolidation to one Match for U.S. DO seniors and graduates. An all-time high 6,581 U.S. DO seniors submitted rank order lists of programs, and the 90.7 percent PGY-1 match rate was the highest ever. (*Results and Data 2020 Main Residency Match*) Contrary to popular beliefs, D.O students had a successful match from the merger, and we anticipate this trend in the foreseeable future.

# CHAPTER 15:
# The Ultimate IMG Roadmap to residency

By Juan Jose Chango Azanza, MD

- Introduction to IMG roadmap to US Medical Residency
- Introduction to ECFMG Certification
- Application for ECFMG Certification
- Application for the USMLE Exams
- Prometric Tutorial – Schedule a USMLE Exam
- How to get U.S. Clinical Experience USCE
- How to get U.S. Clinical Experience USCE
- Cost of applying to Medical Residency
- Getting Letters of Recommendation in ERAS
- Categorical vs Preliminary Residency positions
- How to research the types of programs in FRIEDA
- J1 Vs H1B Visa for Medical Residency
- Medical Residency Interview
- The NRMP MATCH Process
- Statement of Need for J1 Visa – Medical Residency

## IMG Roadmap to U.S. Medical Residency

THE UNITED STATES offers the best medical training programs in the world. A strong academic formation, innovation, technology, research, bedside learning, career development, teaching opportunities, critical clinical thinking skills, and other aptitudes can be obtained by training in a residency program in the United States.

How to get a US Medical Residency is a frequent question among medical students and doctors around the world. Every year, the MATCH results for International Medical Graduates have been improving, and this is a fact that can be verified by checking the statistics presented every year by the NRMP (National Residency Matching Program). If you do not know what is the MATCH or the NRMP organization, please do not worry. Extensive information about this will be described in the following posts. To read more about the statistics of the MATCH, go to the following link:

## NRMP National Residency Matching Program

The road to residency is hard. It requires a lot of preparation and patience. However, there is a huge number of physicians getting into residency programs in the United States every year. There are several factors that influence the chance of being matched into a residency program. We will explain more about these factors and how to make you a stronger applicant.

**These are some useful websites for information about the US Medical Residency process:**

- ECFMG Educational Commission for Foreign Medical Graduates
- USMLE United States Medical Licensing Examination
- USMLE Forums

We would like to share our experiences with you. For this matter, we will gather information regarding the entire process that needs to be done for obtaining the training position of our dreams. The US Medical Residency series will follow a chronological order; from the major steps required for applying to a U.S. medical residency, application for the ECFMG certification, the USMLE exams, and the residency application process.

Most important steps to get a US Medical Residency

1. Take the USMLE Step 1, Step 2 CK, and Step 2 CS exams.
2. Get ECFMG certified.
3. Apply to residency using ERAS.
4. Attend the interview invitations at the residency programs that granted you an opportunity for an interview.

5. Apply for the NRMP MATCH (unless you were offered a pre-match position).
6. Get your results of the MATCH. Usually, the results are released in March every year.

There are other important things that need to be done during or in between these steps. For example, it is important to get clinical experience in the United States and get letters of recommendation from practicing physicians in the United States. More information will be described later about this topic.

## GENERAL DESCRIPTION OF THE MOST IMPORTANT STEPS:

### 1. USMLE Exams:

The United States Medical Licensing Examinations (USMLE) consist of four exams from which 3 of them are mandatory for applying to residency, with the fourth exam (USMLE Step 3 exam) being mandatory only if the applicant is applying for an H1B visa instead of a J1 visa. More information about the visa for medical residency can be obtained here: J1 Vs. H1B Visa for Medical Residency

– **Step 1**: Theoretical exam. It consists of an 8 hour-long exam in which basic sciences such as anatomy, biochemistry, pharmacology, pathology, and others are tested. This exam may be the most challenging for IMG's, mostly if you have graduated or studied basic sciences more than 2 years ago. It is the exam that usually needs the most preparation time as well.

- **Step 2 CK** (Clinical Knowledge): Theoretical exam. It is a more clinical-based exam, in which specialties such as internal medicine, pediatrics, gynecology, cardiology, and others are tested.
- **Step 2 CS** (Clinical Skills): Practical exam. It is a practical simulated exam in which the examinee will need to take care of patients (actors) with medical complaints. The exam closely simulates the environment of the US Healthcare practice. The official language of the exam is English. The most important areas that are evaluated are the test taker communication skills (CIS),

spoken English proficiency (SEP), and the integrated clinical encounter (ICE) which is related with the medical knowledge.

- **Step 3:** Theoretical exam. Not mandatory for the application to residency unless the applicant is pursuing an H1B visa. Some IMG's take this exam before the start of residency, but it can be taken during residency as well.

## 2. ECFMG Certification:

The Educational Commission for Foreign Medical Graduates (ECFMG) is the organization in charge of certifying IMG's. For obtaining this certification, there are 2 major requirements: examinations (USMLE) and medical education verification. **This certificate is not a medical degree, neither does it allow an IMG to practice in the United States.** Instead, it is a certificate that ECFMG provides to allow IMG's to enter into a residency training program certifying that the applicant has undergone all the requirements to do so, and is ready for practicing medicine under supervision. An IMG cannot work in the United States without first training in this country.

In summary, for acquiring the ECFMG Certification, there are 2 fundamental requirements:

1.   Passing the USMLE Step 1, Step 2 CK, and Step 2 CS exams.
2.   Medical education credentials verification.

We will describe more about the application and process to obtain an ECFMG certification in the next sections.

## 3. Apply to residency using <u>ERAS</u>:

Although the ECFMG certification is not mandatory for applying to residency, it is mandatory for starting residency training. The best recommendation is to obtain this certification before the application date. However, it is allowed to apply without it. The application for residency is done using the American Medical Association website called ERAS (Electronic Residency Application System). Every year, the opening date is usually in September.

After applying, the next step is waiting for the invitations for an interview at the programs. The more invitations you get, the better. It is not possible to MATCH into a program without attending an interview.

Next, once the interview session is over, it is necessary to write your Rank Order List (ROL) using the NRMP website. Finally, the MATCH day (generally in March) will let all the applicants know if they have been offered a position by a program on their list.

This summarizes briefly the entire process. It is important to understand that, in the beginning, this process can be overwhelming. However, it is completely possible to do it. We will try to describe as much as possible about the entire path so that you can have a better idea of what is necessary to do. It is also important to understand that all these steps are done one at a time and there is plenty of time to do them if you start early and know what to do.

### Introduction to ECFMG Certification

For International Medical Graduates (IMGs) planning to pursue a medical residency in the United States, the ECFMG (Educational Commission for Foreign Medical Graduates) is crucial and mandatory. Although it is not necessary for applying to residency, most programs prefer it to be held at the time of application by the candidates. It is mandatory to have an ECFMG certificate by the beginning of residency.

ECFMG is the organization in charge of guidance for IMGs in the U.S, acting as Dean's office, regulatory organism, supportive service, and much more. ECFMG becomes the best friend for IMGs. It is in charge of the medical school education credential verification, which encloses grades, hours, curricula, medical degree, and others. ECFMG will also be the organization through which we may apply for the USMLE examinations (except the USMLE Step 3 exam). ECFMG plays a major role during residency for IMGs, mostly for visa sponsorship (J1 visa) unless the applicant was granted an H1B visa by the program. For more information about the difference between the J1 visa and H1B visa for residency, please go to the following link:

## J1 vs. H1B Visa for Medical Residency

Therefore, ECFMG becomes like our medical school or dean during the residency application process. The objective of ECFMG is to get certain that an IMG holds the required accreditation, knowledge, skills, and aptitudes for practicing medicine under supervision (trained in a residency program). The ECFMG certification is not a medical license to practice medicine. The residency programs can check the status of a candidate by asking ECFMG information about their scores and certification by providing the tool called Certification Verification Service or CVS. Perhaps the main objective for an IMG seeking to apply for residency is to get ECFMG certified. For this reason, it is extremely important for IMGs to get familiar with ECFMG. To know everything about the ECFMG certification application and uses, the following link can be used:

https://www.ecfmg.org/resources/publications.html

## Application for ECFMG Certification

As an International Medical Graduate (IMG), in order to apply for a medical residency in the United States, it is essential to apply to the ECFMG (Educational Commission for Foreign Medical Graduates) certification. In previous publications, I have mentioned about ECFMG, and its importance within this process. In this post, I will discuss the steps needed to apply and get this certification that is so important for being able to start residency.

First off, it is crucial to make sure that our medical school in which we are currently studying or have already graduated is listed in the World Directory of Medical Schools (WDOMS). To check this, we can go to the following link and check our school's status, verifying that the school is currently operational:

1. Go to: https://search.wdoms.org/
2. Select your country and the relevant data. For example, the country where I studied Medicine is Ecuador.
3. Click on search. A list of medical schools will appear and we can choose our University (in my case: University of Ibadan).
4. Then after selecting your medical school, the most important thing to confirm is if the school is listed as operational as is shown here.
5. Once we have confirmed that our medical school is listed in the directory and active (operational), we can proceed with the application process.

## Application for the USMLE / ECFMG ID number:

Now, the next thing to do is get this very important ID that will allow us to have our own identity in ECFMG, USMLE, and other organizations in charge of the medical residency process in the United States. It should be regarded that every step from now on is extremely important and we should proceed very carefully. We will need to review the data that we enter because the mistakes we make here will be a headache in the future if a correction is required.

1. Go to the website: https://secure2.ecfmg.org/emain.asp?app=iwa

2. At the bottom of the page, you will find the following phrase: "If you have never been issued to USMLE / ECFMG Identification Number and want to request one, click here." Proceed to select this option.

3. This will take us to a new window where we should read very carefully the ECFMG's indications before proceeding. Please, do not skip this part since it is very important. Once you have read everything, select confirm: "I confirmed that I have read the above information and instructions" and click on Next.

4. In the new window, you will be asked if you have sent an application to ECFMG in the past. If you have done it, it is very important to choose "Yes", because selecting "No" when we have actually done it before, may be considered irregular behavior which could cause us to be permanently excluded from this process. Therefore, select "no" if this is the first time that you are filling an application and then click Next.

5. On the next page, we must write our data:

   1. Last name: Write it exactly as indicated in your official ID which is usually your passport (IMGs). The only acceptable difference here is capitalizations (If we write everything with capital letters or only with the first capital letter, for example).

   2. Rest of the name: That is our names, for example, Juan Pablo, Jose Gabriel. Again exactly as our passport or ID shows.

   3. Date of Birth.

   4. Birth country: Bolivia, for example.

   5. Gender: Optional.

   6. NBME Issued USMLE ID: USMLE identification assigned by NBME, only if you have applied for it previously, usually that is not the case, therefore, simply leave it blank.

   7. US Social Security Number: Fill it out only if you are a United States resident, Green Card holder, or have been granted a social security number generally for work-related reasons. In case you do not have it, leave the field empty.

8. Medical School Country: Select the country where the medical school in which you are currently studying or have graduated from is located.

9. Choose our medical school: When selecting the country, a list of medical schools from the selected country will be displayed. Choose the correct University and the information will automatically appear.

10. Country of Residence: Country of residence (where we currently live).

11. Street Address, line 1: Our address.

12. Email address: This email is very important because it will serve as the primary communication tool for ECFMG to contact us.

13. Verify Email Address: Confirm the email.

14. Telephone number: Phone number.

15. Select that we have entered the information by ourselves and that it is accurate: "I certify that the information in this ECFMG On-Line Authentication Process is true and accurate and provided solely by me". Then click on Next.

16. Verify the data again before sending. Especially the name as shown in our passport. Once everything is reviewed, we can continue and the process is finished for now.

The time it takes for ECFMG to send you your ID is approximately 5 business days. For now, the next step is to wait until you receive the email from USMLE / ECFMG with the ID number with which we can begin the application to the certificate and USMLE exams.

## Application for the ECFMG Certificate:

After obtaining your USMLE/ECFMG ID and password in your email, you can enter the ECFMG website again and start the application. Remember, in case of doubt about how to fill something in your application, do not hesitate to contact ECFMG directly via email or phone call. They are always open to any question that we may have. You can save the application at any time and return later when you are not sure if the data you are entering is accurate. We will proceed as follows:

1. We enter the following website: https://secure2.ecfmg.org/emain.asp?app=iwa

2. Here, it is necessary to enter our ID and password to gain access to our ECFMG account. Most of the application will be made from here in the future.

3. Once inside your account, click on the option: "Submit an application for ECFMG certification".

4. It will send us to an introduction page where we will have to read the instructions and continue.

5. Fill our name (or confirm).

6. Birthdate.

7. Gender.

8. Email or email address

9. Medical Education Status:

   • Choose: Graduate or student.
   • I confirm that I have graduated from medical school.
   • I confirm that the medical school from which I graduated is listed in the World Directory of Medical Schools (World Directory) as meeting eligibility requirements for its students and graduates to apply to ECFMG for ECFMG Certification and examination, and that my graduation year is included in my medical school's World Directory listing. (We confirm that our medical school is on the list of the World Directory of Medical Schools – WDOMS, which we already checked before starting).

10. Then we simply confirm that we agree with everything that ECFMG needs and we move forward.

11. Finally, we will be prompted for the payment section. We can make the payment which in this case is 75 dollars, and we advance to the confirmation page.

12. We will have the opportunity to confirm that everything we have filled is fair. It is very important to review all of our data again.

13. Finally, we have concluded this part of the application. The validation on your ECFMG page is immediate. We will receive an email confirming that our application to the ECFMG certificate has been carried out successfully. The email we will receive is similar to this:

*Dear Doctor:*

*We are pleased to confirm that your Application for ECFMG Certification has been completed and received by ECFMG. A summary of your Application for*

*ECFMG Certification can be accessed using the On-Line Applicant Status and Information System (OASIS), available from the ECFMG website at www.ecfmg. org. You may now proceed with the Interactive Web Applications (IWA) for the USMLE examination (s).*

*Please do not submit inquiries to this mailbox. Messages sent to this e-mail address will not receive responses.*

*Sincerely,*
*Registration and Credentials Services*

Now, on your ECFMG homepage (which appears after entering your username and password) you can start an application for the USMLE exams, during which you will need to do the longest part of this process. It is not difficult to do it and we will guide you in that regard.

## Application for the USMLE Exams

The application for the USMLE exams can be done once we have applied for the ECFMG Certification. Therefore, if we have not done it yet, it is very important to do it before continuing. Please, for more information about the application for the ECFMG Certification, go to the following link:

## Application for the ECFMG Certification

Once ready for the application, we will need to enter our ECFMG account. For that matter, we can go to the page: http://www.ecfmg.org

Then select Online Services, and IWA – Interactive Web Application. We enter our USMLE / ECFMG ID number and password and we will be on our ECFMG account.

### Steps for the application to the USMLE exams:

Now I will explain step by step how to apply for a USMLE exam. I will use Step 1 as an example (the process of applying to the other exams except Step 3 is very similar):

- Under "Begin a new application" we will select "USMLE Step 1, Step 2 CK and/or Step 2 CS".
- A page with policies and instructions will appear. Please read

them carefully and then select the box that indicates you have read and accepted all the aforementioned rules. Then click Next.

- Now we will begin to review each of the necessary items:

1. **Item 1:** Select "NO", unless you have been granted a medical license in the United States in the past (usually not the case).
2. **Item 2:** Choose the exam that you would like to apply for. In our example: Step 1.
3. **Item 3:** Choose your eligibility period, which is the approximate time in which you believe you can take our test. It is very important to plan this time appropriately to avoid having to make changes that cost you more money. The period is three months long, and if you are not able to take the exam in that timeframe for any reason, you can request an extension that adds three months to the initial period requested by paying a fee (currently of 75 dollars).
4. **Item 4:** Select the region where you wish to take the test. To consult the places in the world where the exams are available, please visit the following page: https://securereg3.prometric.com/Dispatch.aspx
5. **Item 5:** Disabilities in case of suffering them.
6. **Item 6:** Names: we must check that our name is correctly written according to our official ID, for example, such as in our passport.
7. **Item 7:** Contact information: Review or enter your address, telephone, and email.
8. **Item 8:** Social security number only if you are a citizen or you have permanent residence, or have obtained one for other reasons. Otherwise the most frequent would be passport number and country, or leave it blank.
9. **Item 9:** Date of birth, city, province or state, country.
10. **Item 10-14:** Gender, your native language, citizenship, passport, and ethnicity data (not mandatory).
11. **Item 15:** Current work or postgraduate training (postgraduate) if applicable. Usually, it is not mandatory to fill this information. Choosing "Not currently employed" is the most usual option.
12. **Item 16:** The ECFMG reporter, which means that we can receive emails about the latest news from ECFMG. It is very important and convenient; thus, it is advisable to choose yes.

13. **Item 17:** Medical education status. Select it properly depending on our specific position. Fundamentally we can pick an option as a student or graduate.

14. **Item 18:** Medical school information: usually we will only need to confirm that the information is correct, otherwise choose from the list.

- **Dates of attendance:** Dates of attendance to medical school. It is essential that the dates are accurate. Write the graduation date and the date on which your medical diploma was issued (Usually they are the same).

- **Title of the medical certificate (degree):** If we are not sure about it, we can refer to the instructions from ECFMG about the title given, depending on each country and University: http://www.ecfmg.org/certification/reference-guide.html. In my medical school, the degree granted is "Physician."

- **Internship:** Enter the dates only if the internship was held before graduation. In my case, I was required to do an internship year before graduation, therefore, it was appropriate to enter the respective dates on the application.

- **Social service / Government:** Rural, community year, or other nomenclature it may have in your country. It should be chosen and described only if it was done before the graduation date or medical certificate delivery. In my case, I did one year of community service in order to get a license and practice medicine in my country. But I did it after my graduation date and the "Not required" option was the better option.

- **Item 19:** Other medical school attended: only if you attended another medical school prior to the school in which you currently study or graduated from.

- **Item 20:** Other institutions: It is not necessary to describe it. Please, properly review the ECFMG instructions. In my case, you may leave it blank, but do it at your own discretion.

- **Item 21:** Clinical clerkships: In my opinion, they are not necessary to describe, but again, it is your decision to fill them with the pertinent information. In my application, I did not fill out this data.

- **Item 22:** Medical diploma: The most important thing here is to select our current state properly, having basically 3 options:

1. I have graduated from medical school and have previously submitted to ECFMG photocopies of my medical diploma. (Graduated and have previously sent copies of your medical diploma to ECFMG).

2. I have graduated from medical school and I am enclosing, with my Certification of Identification Form (Form 186), two photo-copies of the Medical School Release Request (Form 345); two photocopies of my medical diploma with an English translation (if required); and a photograph. If my Form 186 is signed by an autho-rized official of my medical school, the envelope that contains the above-listed documents will be sent to ECFMG directly from the office of that official. (Graduated and you have not yet sent any paper to ECFMG, usually the most common option).

3. I have graduated from my medical school, but my medical diploma has not been issued. With my Certification of Identification Form (Form 186), I am enclosing two photocopies of the Medical School Release Request (Form 345), a letter from my medical school that confirms I have graduated, have met all requirements to receive my medical diploma, and states the date my medical diploma will be issued; with an English translation of the letter (if required); and a photograph. If my Form 186 is signed by an authorized official of my medical school, the envelope containing the above-listed documents will be sent to ECFMG directly from the office of that official. (Graduated but have not yet received your medical certificate).

4. **Name on medical diploma:** Your name on your diploma or medical certificate: Your name must match exactly your passport or ID. Write it exactly as it is on the diploma.

- **Item 23:** Certification by the applicant: Fundamentally after reading and understanding all the indications, we accept the terms and conditions.

Then we will enter the payment area, in which we will need to pay the exam fees, currently (2017) these are the values to pay for the exams:

- **Step 1:** 895 USD.
- **Step 2 CK:** 895 USD.
- **Step 2 CS:** 1550 USD.
- **Step 3:** 845 USD.

## Paperwork:

Now, we will move on to the perhaps more tedious part of the application to our first exam, which is the submission of paper forms to the ECFMG. Please, it is very important that we read clearly the information presented here about the necessary documents to send. It is very detailed and clearly explains what we will need to send. If you are in the same country as your medical school, the paperwork may not be so complicated to do. However, if you are outside of the country (as it was in my case) you will need to follow a series of steps that I will describe later. It should be noted that this form and any other necessary form need to be sent directly from your medical school to ECFMG, and not personally by us.

**20. Paperwork forms:** At the end of the page we will find two options:

1. **Certification of Identification Form (Form 186) – Certification by Medical School Official:** This option may be chosen if we are in the same country as our medical school, since the signatures need to be signed at the same time by the student or graduate and the school official. Please make sure that the official signing is authorized by ECFMG, otherwise, the signature will not be valid and you will need to send the documents again, wasting valuable time and money.

2. **Certification of Identification Form (Form 186) – Certification by Notary Public and Medical School Official:** It is very important that we understand clearly what this option means since it is probably the one that most of us will use if situated outside of the country where our medical school is located, for example, if we are currently in the United States. The process is not difficult, many people are afraid of this part because it seems complicated, but it is not. We will need to have a little patience and understand how it works. These are things to consider:

   - · First, it is important to understand that ECFMG needs to confirm that you signed the forms properly and in person. Since we are far from our University, it is not possible for a school official to be present when we sign the form. Therefore, if you are in the United States, for example, we can go to a notary public - usually located in loan houses (cash loans or credit agencies) - take your ID (passport) and the printed form so that we can sign it in front of that notary public or official. Thus our signature and identity are proven. After doing this, what we will need to do is send the forms to our medical school by mail (regular mail or any other company like FedEx, DHL, or other), so that the authorized official signs the other part of the form. With the school official's signature, the papers are ready to be sent to ECFMG directly from their University (this is extremely important, the medical school should send the papers to ECFMG). That is all.

After choosing our appropriate option as stated in item 22 "Medical Diploma," we can print our Certification of Identification Form (Form 186) that will be brought with us to the school or notary public to be signed.

**In summary,** what will be necessary to send to our medical school and then to ECFMG will be:

1. **Certification of Identification Form (Form 186).** Original form with our photo attached as explained in the form, filled in its entirety and signed on the two parts: A: student, and B: school.

2. **Medical diploma:** Two copies of our **medical diploma** with its respective English translation if it is in another language.

3. **Photo:** A **current color photograph**, passport-sized, full-faced (apart from the one we attached on Form 186).

4. **Form 345** (we have not mentioned it yet). It is a form that we will be allowed to print as well, which is basically an acceptance on our part that ECFMG can obtain information from our medical school. It is very simple to fill out, you will need a photo just like for the Form 186. We can download and print the form directly from here:

5. http://www.ecfmg.org/forms/form345.pdf

6. **Medical school transcript:** Two copies of our "medical school transcript." Please, do not forget to send the translation to English, otherwise, ECFMG will charge you 200 dollars for translating it.

In total, we will **need 3 photos**. These requirements are all that we need for the medical school credential verification and ECFMG certification application. Once your medical school sends all this documentation and is adequate, ECFMG will accept our credentials. Remember to keep track of the status on your ECFMG account since problems may appear on the way.

ECFMG will always contact us to inform how the process is going and if there is any irregularity. When the school sends the Form 186 and it is approved by ECFMG, we will receive an email saying that it has been received, and the validation process of the same takes 3 weeks. The message we receive will be similar to this:

*Dear Doctor:*

*We are pleased to confirm that your Certification of Identification Form (Form 186) has been received by ECFMG. Your USMLE / ECFMG Identification Number is listed in the Subject line of this message. You must use this number in all communications with ECFMG.*

*ECFMG typically processes on-line USMLE applications within 3 weeks of receipt of both the on-line part and the Certification of Identification Form (Form 186). You can track the status of your application by using ECFMG's On-line Applicant Status and Information System (OASIS).*

*Please do not submit inquiries to this mailbox. Messages sent to this email address will not receive responses.*

*Sincerely,*

*Examination and Certification Services*

**Confirmation of acceptance of the From 186:** You should receive a message similar to this one that will confirm the acceptance of your Form 186.

*Dear Doctor:*

*Your Certification of Identification Form submitted (date) has been accepted. This form will remain on file and be valid for a period of five years. The validity dates are as follows: (dates).*

*The Certification of Identification Form is independently of the on-line application. Acceptance of the Certification of Identification Form does not automatically guarantee the acceptance of the application. Once your application has been reviewed, ECFMG will notify you of the outcome of your application.*

*ECFMG typically processes on-line applications within three weeks of the receipt of both the on-line part and the Certification of Identification Form. Processing will now continue on the line part of your application.*

*Sincerely,*

*Examination and Certification Services*

**USMLE Exam application confirmation:** Finally, we will receive an email confirming our acceptance to take the Step 1 test:

*Dear Doctor:*

*The processing of your USMLE Step 1 application is complete. You have been registered for the (specific dates that we chose) eligibility period in the United States and Canada testing region. \*\* Please see BELOW for details on the option to submit a request to have the exam results for this Step 1 withheld from your medical school\*\*.*

*The eligibility period assigned to you for this exam may be different from the one you selected on your application. If you selected an eligibility period that has already begun and your application was not processed in time to assign the eligibility period you selected, you have been assigned the next eligibility period.*

*The National Board of Medical Examiners® (NBME®) will issue your permit, which contains information on contacting Prometric to schedule a testing appointment. (If your assigned eligibility period begins more than six months from now, your permit will be issued approximately six months before the beginning of your assigned eligibility period.) Only electronic permits will be generated for Step 1/Step 2 CK; applicants will access their electronic permits using ECFMG's Interactive Web Application (IWA). You will not receive a paper permit by postal mail. In about one week you will receive another email from ECFMG to notify you that your permit is available. This message will include instructions for accessing the electronic permit using IWA. Although your permit will be issued by NBME, you should contact ECFMG by email at info@ecfmg.org or by phone or fax if you have questions or concerns about this document. You must bring your scheduling permit to the test center on your exam date. If you do not bring your scheduling permit, you will not be allowed to take the exam. Upon accessing your permit, you should check that your name as it appears on the permit is spelled correctly. If the name on your permit is incorrect, you must contact ECFMG immediately. Name changes or corrections to your name must be received and processed by ECFMG no later than seven business days prior to your scheduled testing appointment.*

*If you cannot take a Step during your assigned three-month eligibility period, you may request an extension. There is a fee for this service. You may request an extension on-line using ECFMG's Interactive Web Applications (IWA). For information, access IWA on the ECFMG website.*

*For current information on test centers in your testing region, visit the Prometric website at www.prometric.com or contact Prometric. Practice materials for all Steps and Step Components are available on the USMLE website at www.usmle.org*

*Please refer to the ECFMG Information Booklet and USMLE Bulletin of Information for detailed information on scheduling your testing appointment and taking the exam. Both publications are available on the ECFMG website.*

*INSTRUCTIONS ON HOW TO WITHHOLD YOUR EXAM RESULTS FROM YOUR MEDICAL SCHOOL:*

*ACCESS the IWA home page at www.ecfmg.org under On-line Services. SELECT the exam administration for which you want to withhold your exam results from your medical school under "Request to Withhold Exam Results". Be sure you read and understand the conditions before you authorize ECFMG to withhold your exam results.*

*Sincerely,*

*Registration and Certification Services*

Please, track the progress and be sure to receive these emails. If you don't after a while, contact ECFMG to check what has occurred. In about a week after receiving the acceptance for the USMLE exam application, we will receive the email that indicates that our "Scheduling permit" is available on our ECFMG page. With it, we can go to Prometric which is the page where we will reserve the date for our test. The email that you should receive is similar to this one:

*Name: Your name.*

*USMLE ID: Your ID number.*

*Your STEP 1 SCHEDULING PERMIT IS NOW AVAILABLE on the ECFMG Interactive Web Applications (IWA) website.*

*YOU MUST PRINT YOUR SCHEDULING PERMIT AND BRING IT WITH YOU TO THE TEST CENTER ON YOUR SCHEDULED DATE. You will not be able to take the test if you do not bring your Scheduling Permit to the test center. Note: You will NOT receive an orange Scheduling Permit for this exam in the mail.*

*To access your Scheduling Permit, go to IWA at https://iwa2.ecfmg.org, login, and select "Print / Reprint your USMLE Step 1 Scheduling Permit." Your permission will open in a new browser window. Use your browser's "Print" function to print the permit.*

*If you have any questions, contact ECFMG Applicant Information Services at info@ecfmg.org or call (215) 386-5900.*

*Sincerely,*

*ECFMG*

Once you have received your "Scheduling Permit," you have officially finished the application part in ECFMG for the ECFMG exams. The next thing to do is to schedule your exam using the Prometric.com website. In the next publication, I will continue to explain this topic in detail and how to book our test date step by step.

I would like to emphasize that our Form 186 – Certification of Identification Form, will be valid for the next 5 years. Therefore, when we apply for the next USMLE examinations, this procedure will no longer be necessary to be repeated since this form will continue being valid.

**Prometric Tutorial – Schedule a USMLE Exam**

In this tutorial **"Prometric Tutorial – Schedule a USMLE Exam"**, I will describe how to reserve our USMLE test date. In order to do it, first, we need to obtain our "Scheduling Permit". If we have not yet obtained it, please go to the Medical Residency in the United States section where you will find all the necessary information, or go to the following link:

## Application for the USMLE exams

ECFMG and NBME are the organizations responsible for providing our "Scheduling Permit" or permission to reserve the exam, but the reservation is made with another organization called PROMETRIC. Prometric is a company that has tons of test centers throughout the world and offers standardized test structures for different organizations, one of them being USMLE. To make the reservation, it is necessary to go to the following page:

https://www.prometric.com/en-us/Pages/home.aspx

- Here, we will search for our exam. We will be asked to enter who is our exam sponsor. Here we will write USMLE and click on "GO":
- Then we choose **USMLE – United States Medical Licensing Exams.**
- The other option: **USMLE – United States Medical Licensing Exams – Practice session**, is used to reserve a practice session on Prometric to simulate the exam environment by doing the free 150 questions that are also available on the practice materials section of USMLE. It is very helpful to get familiar with the test environment. It is highly recommended to try it.
- We choose from the list, the exam that we want to reserve. In this case, we will do it for Step 1 but the same process will be followed for our Step 2 CK and Step 3 exams.
- The next thing will be to choose the region where you want to take

the exam. If you are in the United States, we select the country United States and the state: for example New York.

- Now, the page will show us some options to choose. I would like to recommend to you **first before choosing the date of the exam,** to look for **available places in your city** and the **available dates** so when we apply we will know what to choose and we will have more options. For this, we will select: "Search for availability". Introduce the address and we will get a list of available places. We can see the available dates and the addresses of the centers. It is very important to choose a nearby center so that on the day of the exam we do not need to commute too far, which may increase our anxiety and affect our performance. We will be able to consult by month what the available dates are. It is fundamental to reserve our exams in advance because the dates are occupied quickly. Usually, it is recommended to schedule at least 2 to 3 months before the exam date we would like.

- When we have chosen the date and place for the exam, we can go on and schedule it. Directly from the page where we consult the available dates, we will find a link that says: "Schedule an appointment" and we can click on it. Otherwise, we perform the steps mentioned above and when the list appears, we choose an option gotten from the "Search for availability" option and select "Schedule an appointment."

- It is necessary to carefully read the instructions provided by Prometric and select "next". On the next page, we accept the Prometric policies, by clicking on "I agree".

- Then on the next page, we will be asked for our "Scheduling Number" which we can find in our "Scheduling Permit". That is why it is necessary before choosing the date to have our scheduling permit. We write our number and the first four letters of our last name and click on "next".

- In appointment selection as we did before, we searched for our address the center, date, and time desired.

- Finally, most new pages will be important information to read and understand. At the end, we will have the option to verify that everything is appropriate and we have selected correctly depending on our preferences for the exam's options. After we have confirmed the date, we will get a confirmation email with all this information and with the necessary instructions for our exam day.

## The email will look like this:

*Subject: Confirmation of computer-based Step 1 – United States Medical Licensing Examination*

*Your appointment for the computer-based Step 1 – United States Medical Licensing Examination is confirmed. Please find the confirmation details that follow:*

*Confirmation: 00000000*

*Program: STEP1*

*Exam Code: STEP1*

*Step 1 – United States Medical Licensing Examination*

*Exam Date: ——*

*Exam Time: 08:00*

*Prometric Test Center: # 0000*

*IDENTIFICATION POLICY*

*You must bring your Scheduling Permit and proper identification with you to be admitted to the exam. Review your Scheduling Permit for complete details. \* This email is NOT your Scheduling Permit.*

*You may access your Scheduling Permit from your account on your registration entity's (NBME, ECFMG, or FSMB) website. We strongly encourage you to print your Scheduling Permit at least several days in advance of your scheduled test date, to avoid any problems accessing or printing your permit on test day.*

*You can print your Scheduling Permit or present it electronically (e.g., via Smartphone). If on the day of your exam, you are unable to access it electronically for any reason, you must present a paper copy.*

*RESCHEDULE / CANCEL POLICY*

*If you need to change (e.g., reschedule, cancel, change test center location) your appointment, you must go to www.prometric.com/USMLE or call the Prometric Regional Registration Center (RRC) on your Scheduling Permit. If you reschedule, your rescheduled test date (s) must fall within your assigned eligibility period. If you are unable to take the test within your eligibility period, contact your registration entity to inquire about a one-time eligibility period extension. A fee is charged for this service, and some restrictions may apply.*

*The date that you change your appointment, using local time of the RRC, will determine if you pay an appointment change fee and the amount of this fee:*

*– If you change your appointment 31 or more days before (but not including) the first day of your scheduled test date, there is no fee.*

*– If you change your appointment less than 31 days but more than 5 days before (but not including) the first day of your scheduled test date, the fee is $ 50 US Dollars (USD).*

*– If you change your appointment 5 or less days before (but not including) the first day of your scheduled test date, the fee is $ 114.00 USD for domestic U.S.A. and Canada, $ 276.00 USD for International Zone 1, $ 314.00 for International Zone 2, or $ 506.00 USD for International Zone 3.*

*SPECIAL NOTE ABOUT CANCELLED OR MISSED APPOINTMENTS: If you cancel your appointment within 30 days or do not appear on your scheduled test date, you must call the RRC as directed on your Scheduling Permit and pay the appropriate fee to reinstate your eligibility record, before you can schedule a new appointment. You will not be able to perform any transactions via the web.*

*If you do not take the test within your original or extended eligibility period and wish to take it in the future, you must reapply by submitting a new application and fee.*

*If you fail or do not complete your exam and want to retake it, you must reapply by submitting a new application and fee. Retest policies are available in the USMLE Bulletin of Information at www.usmle.org.*

*ADDITIONAL INFORMATION*

*– TEST DAY ARRIVAL: Report to the test center 30 minutes before your scheduled appointment for check-in procedures. If you arrive later than your scheduled appointment, you may not be admitted. If you arrive more than 30 minutes after your scheduled appointment, you will not be admitted to the testing center.*

*– BIOMETRIC CHECK-IN: The USMLE exams include biometrics as part of the testing experience. In many locations, examinees will provide their finger-print during check-in, breaks, and check-out for identification purposes. To learn more about biometrics, please visit the USMLE website at http://www.usmle.org/frequently-asked-questions/#becs.*

*– EARPLUGS: Though the test center provides noise-reducing headphones, you are encouraged to bring your own soft-foam earplugs (subject to inspection).*

*– TEST CENTER REGULATIONS: For a full listing of Prometric Testing Center Regulations and other FAQs, please visit the Prometric website at http://www.prometric.com/TestTakers/FAQs/default.htm.*

*– TEST CENTER AVAILABILITY: In the event that the test center becomes unavailable on your scheduled test date, we will try to notify you in advance and schedule for a different time and / or center. However, on occasion, we may need to reschedule your appointment at the last minute. We encourage you to check your*

*voicemail and email prior to leaving for your appointment on test day, particularly during inclement weather. You may also call the test center to check for weather-related closings.*

*BIOMETRIC CONSENT*

*You have agreed to the Biometric Consent for this appointment. For additional information, please refer to the following webpage.*

*http://www.prometric.com/biometricconsent*

*Sincerely,*

**North America**

*Prometric*

Here we are clearly told about what we need to know about the day of the exam and what we will need to take. It is very important that we are well-informed for the exam, and for that, we must read the pertinent information in the pages of USMLE, ECFMG, Prometric.

Finally, it is very helpful to see the instructional video of the exam facilitated by Prometric.

Watch video here: https://vimeo.com/190759122

Having done these steps, we will have our date confirmed. We will receive an email reminder of the examination by Prometric one week before the exam. Now, the most important thing to do is study hard and prepare well for our exam. Trust yourself because it is possible to shine in these tests. The amount of effort put in these exams will be reflected in your scores. High scores can open the doors to your dreams.

## Application for the USMLE Step 3 exam

The USMLE Step 3 exam is the final of the USMLE examination series required to practice medicine without supervision in the United States. The "application for the USMLE Step 3 exam" is slightly different from the application for the other steps. In this post, I will describe how to apply to this exam step by step. In order to understand more about the exam, please, review the following useful links with important information required to know about the exam:

## USMLE Step 3 exam
## Federation of State Medical Boards FSMB Step 3 exam

Review the requirements necessary for applying and confirm that you meet all of them. It is expected for IMG's to have the ECFMG certification. Please, check the requirements for the USMLE Step 3 exam here.

# HOW TO APPLY FOR THE USMLE STEP 3 EXAM:

The Federation of State Medical Boards FSMB requires the following for submitting an application and the required documents:

1. *Create an account and submit your application with proper payment.*

2. *Your application fee must be paid by American Express, MasterCard or Visa. The Step 3 fee is non-refundable and non-transferable from one eligibility period to another or from one application to another.*

3. *Provide an email address: This is the primary means for us to communicate with you regarding your application and will be used to notify you of your application status. Please provide an email address that will accept an email from* **usmle@fsmb.org***.*

4. *Print and mail a completed, notarized Certification of Identity form (be sure to attach a photograph). Your CID will not be approved if there is any information missing or if a photograph is not attached; in such cases you will be required to submit a new CID form.*

5. **Your registration will be completed within 5-7 business days after we 1) receive your online application (with fees) and CID and 2) verify you meet all eligibility requirements.** *We will email you when your application is approved.*

6. *Use the* **Step 3 Candidate website** *to monitor the status of your Step 3 application, to check the availability of your scheduling permit and score report, and to schedule your exam. Scheduling permits are not available more than 6 months prior to the start of your eligibility period.*

7. *At the end of your Step 3 online application process you will be asked if you would like to create an FCVS profile using your Step 3 information; this is optional. If you are applying for licensure with a board that is an accepting or requiring board of a FCVS profile, it may be beneficial to create your profile now.* **Learn more about FCVS***.*

# TUTORIAL – APPLICATION FOR THE USMLE STEP 3 STEP BY STEP:

### Overall steps to apply for the USMLE Step 3 exam:

1.  Create an account in the Federation of State Medical Boards website.
2.  Online application.
3.  Paper application (Certification of Identification Form CID).
4.  Exam scheduling through Prometric.

# 1. CREATE AN ACCOUNT IN THE FEDERATION OF STATE MEDICAL BOARDS WEBSITE:

1.  Go to the FSMB website and click the "sign in" button.
2.  Create an account. There are four steps for creating your account. First, you will be asked to provide your medical degree (MD or DO), first and last names. Please, do it accurately following your ID document like your passport.
3.  The second step is writing your date of birth, identification type (the last 4 digits of your social security number if available, or your USMLE ID which is the most common option), and email address. The email address will be used for any future communication with the FSMB.
4.  In the third step, you will be asked to create a username and password. You will also need to select a security question.
5.  The fourth step is to agree with the end user license agreement. Accept the terms and click on create an account. You will see a message indicating that your account has been created. You will receive a confirmation email as well. There will be a button with the word 'continue' that will take you to the online application website.

# 2. ONLINE APPLICATION FOR THE USMLE STEP 3 EXAM:

The message "Before getting started" will appear. Please, check that you are completely eligible for the exam before applying, and check the USMLE Step 3 bulletin of information too. They are both provided in this window.

1. **Eligibility period:** Click on "continue" and you will start the online application. The first step will be the eligibility period. As with the USMLE Step 1 and 2 CK exams, you will have the option of a three-month eligibility period to choose. This period can be extended for 3 months more in case of need, with the payment of a fee. Once you have selected your eligibility period, click continue.

2. **Personal information:**

   1. **Name:** Verify your name accuracy. Select your current legal name.

   2. **Identification:** Select your gender, date of birth, birth country, birth state, birth city, NPI (National provider identifier for doctors in the United States), enter your USMLE ID number, and last 4 digits of your social security number. This is simple information to fill out. Please, be careful with the accuracy of the information provided.

   3. **Address:** Indicate your current address.

   4. **Phone number:** Select the phone number type, number, and extension if applicable.

   5. **Email address:** Provide an email address that will be used for all the communications between FSMB and you.

   6. **Test accommodations:** Indicate if you need such accommodations due to disability. Select if you accept to release your score information to the major health organizations and schools in the United States. Please, fill out your demographic information as well such as ethnicity and native language.

7. **Medical school:** Select the country, state, and school type. In the next window, indicate the start and end dates, and check the option if you have graduated from this school.

8. **ECFMG/Fifth pathway:** Indicate graduation type (ECFMG certified is the most common option), ECFMG ID number, and the certification date. If you are not sure about this information, log in into your OASIS/ECFMG account and check under ECFMG certification dates.

9. **Accredited training:** Add an option if you have done a postgraduate training program. If not leave it blank. Then indicate what the specialty in which you are interested is.

10. **Licensure history:** Add information here if you have been granted a medical license in the United States.

11. **Certification of Identification Form (CID):** This is a very important step. We will need to print this form, which is very simple. You will have a link for downloading it in this window. Fill it out, put a current photo on it, and sign it in front of a public notary so that it gets certified. Next, mail it to the address indicated at the bottom of the page. After receiving this form, FSMB will verify and validate your application. It is mandatory to do this in order to complete the application.

12. **Review and submit:** Review that all the information is accurate and submit your application.

13. **Payment:** You will be directed to the payment portal in which you can pay the exam fee by credit or debit card. The 2017 fee is 850 dollars.

14. **Confirmation:** Finally, you will see a confirmation message stating that you will receive an email confirmation within the next 3-4 days once the processing of the application has begun.

The email with the confirmation that the application has been received will come in about 3-4 business days. However, remember that the CID form is necessary for the application to be complete. After FSMB has gotten the physical CID form, the processing should take 2-3 days to be complete. You will receive a confirmation email and it will state that your scheduling permit should be ready in about 2-3 days after. Finally, you will get the email that says that your scheduling permit is ready and you can check it on the applicant website of FSMB. You will be able to open your scheduling permit using the applicant website of FSMB from that moment forward. You can use the following link for that:

https://apps.nbme.org/fsmbexamstatus/prod/jsp/login.jsp

Enter your credentials on this website and you will see your dashboard. Select print my scheduling permit and you will have access to it for saving and printing it.

The last step is to schedule our exam. For that matter, we can follow the same process that we did for scheduling our Step 1 and Step 2 CK exams. For more information about this, please check the following link:

## Prometric Tutorial – Schedule a USMLE Exam
## How to get U.S. Clinical Experience USCE

The preparation for applying to a medical residency in the United States should ideally start early. The ideal plan should be to apply for clinical experiences before graduating as a physician in your home country. The reason why this is important is mostly because it is easier to get valuable clinical experiences before graduating, since you can apply through your medical school to certain places that accept international students. This would give you the opportunity of traveling to the United States to get this clinical experience (US Clinical Experience USCE). Having done clinical electives, or being experienced in a health care institution in the United States is very important for applying to your residence of choice. Another advantage of applying before graduation is that the done electives would be part of your curricula.

Another important reason to perform these rotations before the graduation date is that most hospitals do not accept graduate physicians for clinical experiences (electives) due to important issues such as legal liability and others. This suggests that, although it is not impossible, it becomes more difficult to get such experiences for a graduate physician, and to register for these rotations, the application needs to be done by your medical school in most cases.

To learn more about clinical rotations for international students in U.S. hospitals, you can perform a Google search with queries such as:

• Clinical electives in the US for international students.

• Clinical clerkship for international students in the US.

You can also get a lot of information about the subject in places like:
– http://www.usmle-forums.com

There is a lot of information on this subject, so it is advisable to carry out an investigation of the hospitals that offer electives as well as certain private companies that can also help you get clinical experiences.

In case of being a graduate physician (the most common example) without clinical experience in the United States, there are several ways to obtain clinical experience. However, the options are limited, because as mentioned before, most hospitals do not accept medical graduates in their rotations.

The options for international physicians (International Medical Graduates – IMGs) basically consist of:

1. **Observations:** Experiences in which a practicing attending physician is observed (shadowing).

2. **Research (Research experience):** Usually in a research laboratory or directly in a hospital.

3. **Externships:** Experiences similar to observations but with more exposure and contact with patients (hands on experience), today these are a bit more complicated to get.

To obtain any of these opportunities, there is not a single way to do it. It depends mostly on yourself. For example: with a known doctor that allows us to make an observation, writing emails to different hospitals requesting clinical experiences, through private companies that they are in charge of directly assigning the rotations with the disadvantage of being highly expensive, by using your friends or close contacts. Again, the ways are variable and it depends on how much you look for them.

For more information, please refer to the following links:

- Ace.md- https://www.ace.md/find-american-medical-rotations
- Foreign medical graduate portal: https://fmgportal.com/
- USMLE Sarthi: usmlesarthi.com
- https://www.kaptest.com/blog/residency-secrets/2012/10/09/how-to-find-usce-united-states-clinical-experience/
- https://www.kaptest.com/blog/residency-secrets/2016/06/01/the-imgs-guide-to-finding-us-clinical-experience/
- http://www.usmlematch.com/us_clinical_experienced.htm
- http://medclerkships.com/explaining-clerkships-observer-ships-externships/

Even though it is difficult to find a meaningful experience, it is not impossible to get. Contact programs such as Cleveland Clinic, MD Anderson, and others that allow observers or electives in their institutions. Some of them require you to have at least one USMLE exam done, but it depends on the program.

## Application for Medical Residency via ERAS

The process of applying for residency in the United States is the final step of that long and arduous road to get that training position of our dreams. In this post, I will explain the confusing process of "Application for Medical Residency via ERAS" for International Medical Graduates

(IMGs). Definitely, this is not the final step we will need to make in our careers, but it is one of the major ones. Ideally, before applying we should try to finish our USMLE examinations, ECFMG certification (if applicable), the United States clinical experience (USCE), letters of recommendation (LoRs), personal statement, and others I will explain in detail later on.

It is crucial to understand the application process from the official resources such as:

- USMLE United States Medical Licensing Examinations
- ECFMG Educational Commission for Foreign Medical Graduates
- Association of American Medical Colleges AAMC

## ERAS Residency Process

It is very important to get familiar with the ERAS user guide for residency: Download it: my eras residency user guide (https://ecuadoctors. com/wp-content/uploads/2017/06/myerasresidencyuserguide.pdf)

First of all, it is vital to recognize the timeline for the entire process so that we can do everything promptly. Every year, the Association of American Medical Colleges (AAMC) publishes the timeline for the next season. This timeline can be used to plan ahead and start preparing the necessary documentation and requirements for applying. Here we can visualize the timeline for the ERAS 2018 season:

As we can note, the process is very long and takes months. Even though it seems that we will have a lot of time for preparing, please, try to start as early as possible because "time sure flies". **The overall process for applying can be summarized in the following steps:**

1. **ERAS Token request (ECFMG).**
2. **Filling the ERAS application.**
3. **ERAS application submission.**
4. **NRMP application.**

## 1. ECFMG ERAS Token request.

The token is a 14-digit code that will allow us to enter in the ERAS application program before September 6th (when ERAS opens the application date for ACGME accredited programs). The reason why we should ask for this token is that the application may take a while to fill out and prepare. Having the chance to enter in this program and start preparing our data is very convenient. Asking for it is quite simple and can be done on the ECFMG website. The main steps are as follows:

- Go to ecfmg.org
- Enter in your ECFMG – OASIS website.
- Inside the OASIS dashboard, go to the left column and select the option at the bottom called "ERAS support services".
- In the next page, we select "ERAS Token request" and select the one that we need: residency or fellowship token.
- Read carefully the indications in the next page, and after you have fully understood them, we select 'confirm' and we will get the code which we can copy and paste in our AAMC account.
- Next, we open our AAMC account and it will show an option that says: "register token". In case we do not have one, we can create it easily on the AAMC website: Association of American Medical Colleges AAMC.
- Paste the token code in your account. Again, read carefully the politics and protocols of AAMC and ERAS. Once we have done it, click "I agree" and it will give you access to start filling your application.

## 2. MyERAS: Filling the application and submitting the supporting documents.

After getting access to the ERAS application AAMC website, we can start preparing our application. On the website dashboard, we will see a list of items to complete. We must remember that the data we are entering for now is preliminary, therefore, it will not be sent to the programs until we click the "verify and apply" option. Feel free to write your information as best as you can knowing that you will be able to change whatever is necessary. The "verify and apply" option will be available to select only when the application season is opened by ERAS (usually on September 6). The main three parts of the "Application to Medical Residency via ERAS" are:

## a) **Application:**

1. Personal information.
2. Biographic information.
3. Education.
4. Experience.
5. Licensure.
6. Publications.

## b) **Documents:**

1. Letters of recommendation (LOR's).
2. Personal Statement.
3. Medical School Transcript.
4. Medical School Performance Evaluation (formerly called "Dean's letter").
5. ECFMG Status report.
6. Photo.

## c) **Programs:**

1. Search for programs
2. Saved programs.
3. Programs applied to.

Disclaimer: Before continuing, please use this information as a guide for your application preparation. In case of doubt, contact ERAS or ECFMG directly to assure that the data you are entering is accurate. We cannot take responsibility for the inadequate data entry that can occur, since every application is unique and personal.

# a) APPLICATION: How to fill out application step by step:

## 1. Personal information:

It is very important to review carefully all the data that we enter in the application.

- **First name:** Type your name exactly as written in your official and current ID. The same name should be the one registered in your important records like ECFMG and AAMC accounts. Usually, it should be the name exactly as it appears in our official ID, for example, a passport.
- **Middle name:** If applicable.
- **Last name:** Same as the first name indications.
- **Suffix:** Choose the one that you feel is adequate for you, even though we can leave it without modification.
- **Preferred name:** Optional for helping programs to know how you would like to be addressed.
- **Last 4 digits of SSN:** If applicable.
- **Email:** Generally, it will be already written since we created an AAMC account before with our email, but we can change it if we feel it is necessary. It is important to choose an email account that is readily accessible for us.
- **Address:** Our current address.
- **Permanent mailing address:** Choose yes if it is the same as your current address, otherwise indicate what your permanent residence address is.
- **Citizenship information:** Select the citizenship and visa status if applicable.
- **Visa sponsorship needed:** Indicate the type of visa you would like to get for your residency. We can choose from two options: J1 (student exchange visa) or H1B visa (work visa). If we are interested in either of the two types of visa, select both of them. Remember that, in order to be eligible for an H1B visa, the USMLE Step 3 exam must have been taken (the timeline is variable depending on the program preference).

- **If residing in the United States or Canada:** Indicate the state or province.
- **Information about the MATCH:** Select "**I plan to participate in the NRMP match**". It is very important to understand that the application for the NRMP MATCH Residency season is separate from the ERAS application which is the one that we are describing. The explanation about the application to NRMP will be described in this post afterward. Once we have our NRMP ID after registering for the MATCH, we will come back to type our provided ID. It is fine to leave it blank, and something even more important to consider is that **it is not mandatory to have the NRMP ID in order to apply to the programs in September using the ERAS common application website.** We can update this information after the application, since the NRMP registration opens on September 15 at 12:00 pm. If you are applying as a couple, please indicate that here as well.
- **Urology MATCH:** enter your AUA Member number.
- **USMLE/ECFMG ID number:** Our ECFMG ID, which is the one we have used for applying to the USMLE exams and ECFMG certification.
- **ACLS, BLS, PALS certification:** If applicable.
- **AOA or Gold Humanism Honor Society:** If applicable.

## 2. Biographic information:

- **Gender:** Select if you desire to, since it is not mandatory.
- **Birthplace:** City and country.
- **Birthdate:** month/day/year.
- **Self-identity:** We can select the ethnicity we believe we belong to. Not mandatory.
- **Language fluency:** We can select the option that suits the actual English proficiency more from the options provided: basic, regular, good, advanced, and native. It is better to be sincere about our English proficiency, since it will be proven during the interviews. We should also indicate our primary language, selecting it and choosing the option "native".
- **Military service obligation or deferment:** Yes or no.

- **Hobbies & Interests:** Perhaps the more important part of this section, since it is the one that can describe us outside of the medical world. It is very important to write something interesting about yourself. Be creative. This section can help you to make a difference with other candidates. The character limit is 510.

# 3. Education:

- **Higher education:** For International Medical Graduates, the adequate option will be none, unless you have been trained in a fellowship or done a higher education degree. Our previous degrees before medical school are not the same as in the United States system, this is the reason why it is better to leave this blank (this is explained in the ERAS residency guide.
- **Medical education:** Choose the country and name of our medical school and the medical degree obtained. Sometimes, the medical degree that you obtained is not listed exactly as the option that ERAS provides to you, therefore, it is important to contact ECFMG if this occurs. In my case, my medical degree is described as "Physician" which is not listed. ECFMG indicated to me that I could choose the more similar one that I could find, which was "Physician Surgeon" that is a common medical degree granted in South American medical schools. We must indicate the date of graduation and attendance dates to the school.
- **Membership in Honorary/Professional Societies:** When applicable.
- **Medical School Awards:** If you received an award while being in your medical school you can describe it here. In my case, my medical school does not grant such awards so I left that information blank.
- **Other awards/accomplishments:** Here we can describe the awards that we earned in the medical school, practice, and extra-curricular activities like sports.

# 4. Experience:

Basically, there are two types of experience that can be described in this section: training and experience.

- **Training:** D.O. Internship, D.O. Residency, D.O. Fellowship, M.D. Residency or M.D. Fellowship qualifies as a training experience. Most IMGs will leave this section blank unless such preparation was done. In the case that you do have a previous residency training, for example, it is crucial to describe it here.
- **Experience:** This is where we can describe the educational and work experiences as "work experiences," and voluntary or extra-curricular activities as "volunteer experience." We can describe observations, externships and other types of clinical experiences as "work experience" (as described in the ERAS residency guide).
- **Was your medical education/training extended or interrupted?** : As applicable.

## 5. Licensure:

- **State medical license:** In the case that we have been granted a medical license in the United States, we can describe that here. The most common answer here for IMGs would be none.
- **"Additional questions:"** Answer them as applicable.

## 6. Publications:

- If you have done research and have been published, or been in the middle of a research project, you can describe it here.
- You can check the following link for a good explanation about how to fill this part. It is recommended that you also consult your professors, mentors, tutors, or any other individual that can guide you.

### Student doctor forum – ERAS publications

Now we have concluded the "application" section. It is simple to fill, and the more important aspect to consider while filling this part, is to be accurate about the data entered. We will be able to edit this information later until we "verify and apply" to the programs.

## b) DOCUMENTS:

The important documents that we will need for the ERAS application are:

- **Letters of recommendation.** For more information go to https://ecuadoctors.com/how-to-ask-and-upload-a-letter-of-recommendation-for-eras/.
- **Personal Statement.**
- **USMLE transcript:** The only thing that we need to do is select "authorize release" in the documents section in ERAS. It will be automatically delivered to the programs by ECFMG.
- **Medical school transcript:** There are two options to send it:

1. **Upload it yourself:** Go to the ECFMG OASIS website and proceed to ERAS support services. Then, select "upload" and select "transcript." Then read the directions carefully. Select the file from your computer that has the specifications described and click upload.

2. **Upload by ECFMG:** Request ECFMG to send a copy of the medical school transcript sent by your medical school to ECFMG when you applied for a USMLE exam. This can be done at the ECFMG OASIS website too. Select ERAS Support Services and click "Request for Transcript Transfer from ECFMG Certification." Read the indications and click "submit a request".

- **Medical School Performance Evaluation (MSPE):** For more information go to https://ecuadoctors.com/medical-school-performance-evaluation-mspe/.
- **ECFMG Status report:** This is an automatic verification that is done by ECFMG without any necessary action.
- **Photo:** For more information, please go to https://ecuadoctors.com/eras-residency-application-photo/.

After having uploaded the documents, the next important thing is to assign to the programs the documents that require manual assignment. I will describe this in the "ERAS application submission section." Do not forget in the "additional documents" section of the "documents section" to click in the question: Will you be using an MSPE/Medical School Transcript this season? Once you click on it, a pop out will appear and you can select yes to both and click ok.

## c) PROGRAMS:

Before proceeding, there are two more important steps for applying to the residency programs, which are:

1. **Search for programs:** We can do it by selecting the specialty of interest or by introducing the accreditation ID of the program.

2. **Saved programs:** After you have finished searching for programs and saved all the ones you would like to apply, you can go to saved programs and check them.

To research for programs, we can use the **FREIDA AAMC** program, the official website of the program, or any other source of information. The application to the programs will be described in the "ERAS application submission section."

Although the **FRIEDA AAMC** online platform is used by most US and international medical graduate to research residency programs to apply to, it is very important for international medical graduates to learn the right way to apply to residency.

Most international medical graduates apply blindly to 100-150 residency programs every year and get a few interviews. This is a smart strategy. The truth is, there are International medical graduate friendly residencies and there are residencies that do not review or accept IMGs.

If you are an IMG and you blindly apply without doing proper research, you are simply wasting money.

This is why I recommend, **MATCH A RESIDENT** (www.matcharesident.com). This company was created by Dr. Zach. Match-a-resident has created an artificial intelligence platform that allows international medical graduates to apply by entering their USMLE scores, clinical observerships and other data that allows your profile to match with programs that are more likely to increase your chances of getting an interview.

Match A Resident is the #1 choice for the International Medical Graduate (IMG) residency applicants. The unique platform helps you apply smart by generating the most compatible and up-to-date Customized Residency Programs List in any of the 18 most popular specialties for IMGs.

Image credit: matcharesident.com

Why should you use their service?

1. If you are an US International Medical Graduate (US IMG) or Non-US International Medical Graduate (Non-US IMG), it's important to know which programs are IMG friendly to target your applications.

2. Each Specialty List is created from your Applicant Criteria and based on the most relevant professional credentials for IMG candidates such as USMLE scores, Visas, time since graduation, and more.

3. You get access to interview Link (I-Link) which shows members the residency programs that include interview feedback or previously scheduled interviews from candidates with applicant criteria similar to your own.

4. You can use their interview schedule tool which allows you to keep track of your interview dates by adding them to your Interview event schedule

5. You can filter each program by multiple USMLE attempts, missing USMLE exam scores, ECFMG Certification, etc.

6. you get a compatibility score that allows narrow down your selection to the most compatible programs in your customized List.

Image credit: matcharesident.com

Using Match-a-resident is a smarter way for IMGs to apply to residency therefore increasing your chances of getting the right program. Visit matcharesident.com to get started.

Now that you know which programs to apply to; these are the important documents that are required for the ERAS application. You can find more information on this website about the documents, how to get them, and how to upload them in ERAS.

## 3. ERAS application submission.

Once we have finished filling our application, uploading the supporting documents, and selecting the programs that we wish to apply for, the next step is the actual application. ERAS allows the application to be sent beginning on September 6, however, September 15 will be the date that the applications will be stamped and sent to the programs regardless if you applied earlier.

The recommended order for the following steps in the application is:

1. **Assign documents.**
2. **Certify and submit your application (irreversible).**
3. **Apply to programs (payment).**

The final step is the application per se. The first two steps can be done alternatively, but the third will be the last one always.

# 1. ASSIGN DOCUMENTS TO THE PROGRAMS

The documents that need to be assigned to the programs are:

- **Personal Statement:** We can write several depending on how many specialties and programs we would like to apply to.
- Letters of recommendation.
- USMLE transcript.
- Photo.

There are a few documents that we need to assign manually to the programs. Overall, it is easy to do it. The process of assignation is the same for all, except the letters of recommendation. When opening our MyERAS dashboard we can see the documents section. After they were uploaded, we can select the bottom at the side of the document name and select assign (see the picture below):

After picking assign, a pop out will appear and indicate the list of programs that we have saved. Select the small bottom option for choosing all the programs and select confirm. That is it.

For the letters of recommendation, we will need to do the same steps, with the difference that there is no option to select all the programs and we will need to pick one by one. We can assign the letters of recommendation depending on the specialty and programs if we have chosen to customize the personal statement for the specific specialty or program. After selecting them, click confirm and that is all.

# 2. CERTIFY AND SUBMIT YOUR APPLICATION

Once you are completely sure that all the information of the "application" section in ERAS is complete and accurate, you can select, verify and apply. To do that, simply enter in the application section and go to the end of the column where it says "verify and submit." After you have certified and submitted your application, a message like this will appear:

*Once you have certified and submitted your application, it will be irrevocably locked and no changes will be permitted. Your application, once certified and submitted, is provided to all programs to which you apply during this ERAS season. Please take the additional time to proofread your application for any errors or omissions.*

Finally, you will be able to print an application and CV copy of the submitted information in the application section.

## 3. APPLY TO THE SAVED PROGRAMS

To send the application and finish the whole process, we must apply and pay the ERAS fees. For doing it, proceed with the following steps:

1. Go to the programs section, and select "saved programs."
2. Click the small square to select all the programs and then go to the upper right corner of your screen where it says "apply/preview invoice."
3. You will see an invoice showing you the total payment needed to be done. Continue and enter your payment information, and after the payment has been approved, a window saying that the payment was done will appear.

You will also receive an email with the payment confirmation, and you can check the payment history in the "programs section."

Once the payment has been approved, you will receive a final email confirming the payment was processed and approved. That is all. Now you have finished your "Application to Medical Residency in ERAS."

## 4. NRMP MATCH Registration – National Resident Matching Program or "MATCH"

Remember, it is NOT mandatory to apply to NRMP for sending the applications through ERAS, it can be done later when the MATCH is opened. The application date for the NRMP Match **opens on September 15 at 12 pm EDT**. It is very important to follow the calendars for the NRMP and ERAS deadlines. To review the NRMP MATCH calendar, please go to this link:

## NRMP – National Resident Matching Program Calendar

For applying to the NRMP MATCH, please follow these steps:

1. Go to NRMP – National Resident Matching Program.
2. Select login/register, or directly choose register to the "Main MATCH."
3. Fill all the required basic information about you and your medical school until NRMP asks you to create a username and password for your account.
4. Continue and enter in your account in the following window with the data just created. You will see the notice for the NRMP policies.

5. After reading everything, click "I accept."
6. In the next window, you will see the fees and payments needed. Select next and you will be asked to provide your payment information.
7. After the payment was made, you will observe a summary of the payment and an option for printing it which is recommended.

That is everything you need to do for registering for the MATCH at NRMP. Now, please don't forget to come back to your ERAS account and go to the personal information part (which is the only part of the application that can be changed after the application is done). In the "MATCH information" option of the personal information, type your NRMP ID and then click on "save my personal information". This is necessary because programs need the NRMP ID to rank you after the interviews.

## Cost of applying to Medical Residency

The "Cost of applying to Medical Residency" is a very important topic to know before the application. The most important variable to consider which is "how many programs are we planning to apply" will affect the cost.

It is very difficult and unclear how many programs IMGs should apply to, therefore, it is imperative that we assess our own possibilities based on our background, USMLE scores, letters of recommendation, and clinical experience in the United States. The number of programs that an IMG should apply for is not a settled rule. In my experience, it seems that most IMGs may apply around 100 to 200 programs. But again, there's no such thing as a rule of how many programs to apply.

There are several things to consider in your budget regarding the expenses of the application. However, the cost directly related to this process is described in the following table:

## COST OF APPLYING TO RESIDENCY 2018 (IMG's)

| RESIDENCY COSTS | 100 programs | 120 programs | 150 programs | 175 programs | 200 programs |
|---|---|---|---|---|---|
| ERAS Token | 115 | 115 | 115 | 115 | 115 |
| USMLE transcript | 80 | 80 | 80 | 80 | 80 |
| Standart registration to NRMP | 75 | 75 | 75 | 75 | 75 |
| Application to programs | | | | | |
| 1. First 10 | 99 | 99 | 99 | 99 | 99 |
| 2. 10-20 (13 each) | 130 | 130 | 130 | 130 | 130 |
| 3. 21-30 (17 each) | 170 | 170 | 170 | 170 | 170 |
| 4. 31 and more (26 each) | 1820 | 2340 | 3120 | 3770 | 4420 |
| | | | | | |
| TOTAL | 2489 | 3009 | 3789 | 4439 | 5089 |

As you can note, the cost varies mostly depending on the number of programs that you wish to apply. Therefore, this table can help you plan ahead your budget, or can help you understand your chances of application if your budget is already settled and fixed. The ERAS token is the only fee not mandatory to pay. However, getting your token for the residency season and preparing your application early is highly recommended.

## ERAS Residency Application photo

One of the most neglected aspects of the application for medical residency and fellowship is the photograph. The ERAS Residency Application photo can be a key component of our applications. Here are several reasons why:

1. **"First impressions always matter".** Regardless of the field, a professional picture can make a very good first impression about yourself. Some people may ask why. As an example, think about the selection process done in many companies or institutions nowadays. It is believed that approximately 40 % of employers use social media sites to screen and recruit potential candidates, and they strongly agree that a professional looking picture can aid to boost a candidate's chances of being considered for the job. Now, even though residency programs may not look into your social media profiles due to lack of time (some may do it), they will definitely see your photograph as a gate to your personality.

2. **It can show your determination.** A high-definition photo, in which the candidate is wearing professional clothes, and is well-groomed. Having an expression that shows empathy and happiness of applying for his or her dream job will reveal that you are really serious about your goals and dreams. On the other hand, the opposite of this will probably denote that you don't care much about it. You probably worked hard and struggled to be where you are now, therefore, keep up the good work and don't give up yet. "There's one more round to go".

3. **It can display your personality.** Your photo will be used by programs to identify you and your personality. If you are a very kind and cheerful person, you should try to show it. But if you show something completely different in a bad picture with a bad expression, they may never get to know how great you are. The specifications in ERAS state: "natural expression", don't confuse that with a "serious expression". You can try a nice and natural smile (not fake). Try to demonstrate yourself in a picture. Remember, your picture may be the only thing that they'll see because if it's not good enough, they might not grant you an interview to see you being much better than that boring and poor picture.

4. **Reminder after the interviews.** Names are really difficult to remember, and it's more difficult when we come from all over the world with our "difficult names". However, a picture can say a thousand words, and in this case, it can help them to remember you after the interview. If you are smiley and cheerful, and your picture shows that, they will say: "I remember that person and that personality".

5. **It looks really cool.** Let's accept it, we all like to have a nice picture about ourselves.

A good picture can really make the difference. The best option should be using a professional photo service that can offer a high-definition digital image. There are several ways to do it. The choice depends on your budget. Some services can be very expensive (200-300 dollars) but they offer the best quality. Others may be cheaper options that can also provide good quality photography. Finally, you can also try to do it by yourself, but to do so you will need to have a good camera, an excellent background, and good illumination.

Professional services can offer to take the photography, prepare your set appropriately, choose the correct background color, give clothing tips, and others. Although this service can be expensive, we should remember that we have spent so much effort and money to be in this moment. In this level of competitiveness, the little details can make a difference. Some of the professional service options can be found online doing a Google search "ERAS application photo":

- City headshots NY
- Beaupix headshots NY
- JC Penney portraits (my choice)

## ERAS photo format requirements:

- It must be in the Joint Photographic Experts Group (JPEG) format.
- The maximum file size accepted is 100 KB.
- It must be no larger than 2.5 by 3.5 inches in size (which is a tiny size and very difficult to maintain a high quality).
- It must be a clear, full front view of your head and shoulders. Your face should be in the middle of the photograph, and your expression should be natural with your eyes open and looking directly ahead.

Some of the professional services may offer within the package to format the picture for the ERAS requirements. In case that they don't, you will receive a high-definition image that is way too big (size in pixels or inches) and heavy (usually more than 1 MB, which is too heavy for the ERAS requirement). Trying to format these images can be very frustrating and difficult. This is why I would like to discuss that in a greater detail.

## How to format your photography for the ERAS residency application

I would like to explain two ways to do it. The decision depends on which operating system you have: windows vs. mac.

## Formatting option for Windows users only:

The easiest way to do it is by using a program called "paint net". This is not the paint program that comes with windows. We will need to download it first on the internet and then use it. This is what we will need to do:

1. Download paint net: https://www.getpaint.net/. When you open this link, the developer's website will appear. Click the option "get it now" at the upper right corner of your screen.

2. Install the app. Follow the usual steps for installing any program in windows.

3. After you have finished installing the app, go to your photography file and with a right-click choose "open with" and then paint net.

4. Once your image is opened, go to "image" in the upper toolbar and select "resize".

5. Now you just need to change the following settings:

6. Resolution: write 150 pixels per inch – PPI.

7. Print size: write in width 2.5 inches and then the height will get resized automatically. However, if the height is more than 3.4 inches you can try doing the exact opposite; this means writing first the height as 3.5 and then verifying that the width is not bigger than 2.5 inches.

8. Once you have done these changes, click ok and then go to file and "save as" in the toolbar. After you select the destination where you want to save your file inside your computer, you will be asked about the quality of the picture. What I suggest doing is selecting the one that makes the file size to be less than 100 KB that will accomplish the ERAS requirement.

You can note that in this picture above, the file size is 58.3 which is adequate for the ERAS application.

## Formatting option for Windows and Mac users:

The other option can be achieved by using Photoshop. These are the steps to follow:

1. Open your picture using Photoshop.

2. Go to the toolbar and select image and then image size.

3. Choose the width as 2.5 inches and then the height will get resized automatically. However, if the height is more than 3.4 inches you can try doing the exact opposite; this means writing first the height as 3.5 and then verify that the width is not bigger than 2.5 inches.

4. Select the resolution as 150 PPI (pixels per inch).

5. Select the resample option as "bicubic for reduction" and click ok.

6. Then go to file and "save as", select the file location and click save.

7. A pop-up will appear making you select the quality of the picture. Select the one that makes the file size to be lower than 100 kb.

Here you can note that in the above picture, under "previsualizar" or preview in English, the file size is 83 kb which is fine because it is less than the 100 kb required.

This is an easier and better option for formatting your picture. It is really hard to have an outstanding quality for this size and weight of the file, however, you can achieve a good quality doing this process that I have already described.

## How to upload your photo in ERAS (ECFMG for IMG's):

1. Go to ecfmg.org. and open your oasis account.

2. Once inside of your account, go to the left column of options and select the one from the bottom called "ERAS support service".

3. Click upload and select photograph.

4. Read the information carefully, and after you have finished, pick "choose file" and select the correct file from your computer.

5. Click on upload file, and after you have done it a message will appear saying that the photo has been uploaded. It'll take a few hours to days to be uploaded in your ERAS application. If the upload process fails, there may be something wrong with your photo. In that case, verify that the photograph you chose was the correct one and the formatting is adequate.

## Medical School Performance Evaluation (MSPE)

One of the key documents to apply for a U.S. residency position through ERAS (Electronic Residency Application Service) is the **Medical School Performance Evaluation (MSPE)** or formerly called **"Dean's Letter"**.

## Why is the MSPE important for the application?

The MSPE allows the program directors and members to know the performance of a graduate during his or her studies in the medical school. It constitutes valuable and objective information, since it will show the academic performance, experiences, awards and other accomplishments of a graduate with respect to his or her peers. This is very important to understand. The comparison with other students is the most important part of the MSPE since it provides objective and tangible data about the participant. This is why an MSPE should have as much feasible information as possible, like charts, graphs, tables and/or any other source of information.

To know more about the MSPE you can check the following link from the Association of American Medical Colleges (AAMC):

## AAMC MSPE

The aim of the AAMC is to standardize the MSPE for all the medical schools, so that it would not matter which one wrote the MSPE, it would still have more important information that would allow the comparison with others as well.

**Recommended Structure of the MSPE (AAMC) pdf:**
**School of Medicine**
**Date**
**Identifying information**

- Student's information: legal name and ID.
- Medical school information: name, location, and any other pertinent identifying information.

## Noteworthy or unique characteristics

Provide a maximum of three characteristics highlighting the most salient noteworthy traits of the student. This section should be presented as a bulleted list. Each characteristic should be described in 2 sentences or less. Information about any significant challenges or hardships encountered by the student during medical school may be included.

- Characteristic number one.
- Characteristic number two.
- Characteristic number three.

## Academic History

| | |
|---|---|
| Date of Initial Matriculation in Medical School | |
| Date of Expected Graduation from Medical School | |
| Please explain any extensions, leave(s), gap(s), or break(s) in the student's educational program below: | |
| Information about the student's prior, current, or expected enrollment in, and the month and year of the student's expected graduation from dual, joint or combined degree programs. | |
| Was the student required to repeat or otherwise remediate any course work during their medical education? If yes, please explain. | |
| Was the student the recipient of any adverse action(s) by the medical school or its parent institution? | |

## Academic progress

## Professional Performance

Describe how the medical school defines professionalism and what it assesses in students. Whenever possible, areas of strength and weakness should be addressed.

## Preclinical Coursework

If preclinical courses are graded as Pass/Fail, the MSPE should convey that the student has met all requirements. Whenever possible, areas of strength and weakness should be addressed.

## Clerkships (in chronological order)

The components of each clerkship grade and the weight of each component (for example, % clinical assessment, % shelf exam, % case write-up, % OSCE, etc.) should be included to better inform program directors on performance. Whenever possible, areas of strength and weakness should be addressed. Clerkship evaluations are a crucial piece of information for program directors and are considered by many to be the most important section of the MSPE in determining applicants for interview selection and rank order list.

NOTE: The graphs included in this template are meant **only** as examples. Schools should use their own grading systems or schemes in their graphs depicting comparative student performance.

**Tables should follow next. This is very important.**

## Summary

The Task Force recommends providing a summative assessment, based on the school's evaluation system of the student's comparative performance in medical school, relative to their peers. Schools should include information about any school-specific categories used in differentiating levels of student performance. This may - though does not have to - include graphic representation of the student's performance relative to their class overall>

Sincerely,

Name.

Title.

## Medical school information

For additional information about the School of Medicine, please see: <website> or <appendix>.

The MSPE should be asked to your medical school usually by yourself. The best way to do it should be by a written petition. The difficulty depends on your medical school experience granting this letter. If they have done it frequently in the past, you can be confident that they will not need much information from you than a written petition. If your school is not experienced, it will be recommended that you send them the petition and all the guidelines mentioned in this post, so that they become confident with the instructions and objectives of the MSPE.

Try to work together with the personnel from your medical school since it can be challenging to write such an important letter for the first time. After they have finished a draft, there are some recommendations to follow:

## MEDICAL SCHOOL PERFORMANCE EVALUATION (MSPE) FORMATING:

If you follow the recommendations mentioned before, your letter should be adequate for presentation to ECFMG or ERAS. However, there are some tips needed to be considered before uploading the MSPE:

1. The document must be in Portable Document Format (PDF) and unlocked.
2. The maximum file size accepted is 1,200 KB; the maximum image size accepted is 300 dots per inch (dpi).
3. The dimensions of each page cannot exceed 8.5 by 14 inches.
4. All pages of the document must be scanned in as one file. **Do not upload pages separately. Do not include any other document besides the MSPE letter, like your medical diploma, CV, etc.**

If the file that your medical school prepared is too big or heavy in size, thereby being inadequate for upload in ECFMG, please consider using this link for compressing your file:

http://www.ilovepdf.com/compress_pdf

(To review MSPE samples that are adequate and therefore can be used as a template, please, check AAMC website)

## HOW TO UPLOAD THE MSPE IN ECFMG/ERAS:

To upload your MSPE in ECFMG and therefore ERAS, please follow the next steps:

1. Go to ECFMG website.
2. Click on online services in the menu bar and then click on OASIS and go to OASIS options.
3. Once in the ECFMG/OASIS dashboard, select ERAS support services in the left lateral column.
4. Then click "upload" and select "upload MSPE."
5. Read the instructions carefully before uploading your document.
6. Select "Choose file" and search for the file in your computer or system.
7. Finally, click "upload file" and it will be done.

ECFMG will verify your MSPE in 5 business days approximately. After the verification has been completed you will see the MSPE uploaded in your ERAS application, which means that you will not need to do any other further action. Sometimes the MSPE gets rejected, one of the main causes being copyright and plagiarism. Your letter should follow a template, but should not be a copy of somebody else's MSPE.

### How to ask and upload a Letter of Recommendation in ERAS

The Letters of Recommendation (LORs) are an important part of the application to Residency through the **Electronic Residency Application Service (ERAS).** Therefore, knowing **"How to ask and upload a Letter of Recommendation in ERAS"** is critical in order to accomplish this requirement. As in other jobs and careers, for Medical Residency these letters of recommendation play a substantial role in providing valuable information to the programs that we apply. Therefore, these letters can be really helpful or harmful in our application.

# WHAT MAKES A LETTER OF RECOMMENDATION "STRONG"

The best letters are the ones that describe the best of you, showing that you will be unique and valuable for the aimed program. They will discard the existence of a red flag or concerns about you. It should make you look like a top student. The more personal it gets, the stronger it will be.

## What makes a poor letter of recommendation.

### Characteristics of Poor Letters

- Lack direction and focus
- Not addressed to anyone specific
- Doesn't indicate why the student is a worthy candidate.
- Written half-heartedly
- The author obviously does not know the applicant well.
- Vague and non-specific

Check out University of Illinois – College of Medicine Advice about letters of recommendation

Visit http://www.med.illinois.edu/facultydev/letterofref/ for more information

You can also review the ECFMG information regarding letters of recommendation in the Certificate Holders Office ECHO resources:

ECFMG ECHO Asking for a letter of recommendation: http://www.ecfmg.org/echo/asking-for-lor.html

# HOW TO ASK FOR A LETTER OF RECOMMENDATION:

Making a good decision about our letters of recommendation is very important, thus we need to consider first whom we should choose as the potential author. It is clear that LORs written by U.S. based Doctors are more valuable than International writers. This indicates that seeking for a clinical experience in the U.S. is not only important for learning, but also can give us the opportunity to earn these important documents.

Perhaps the most important thing to remember when selecting a probable writer is "how much does that person really know from us". The ideal person that we can approach and ask to write a letter of recommendation should have the following characteristics:

- Well respected.
- The title or department of the author is important as well. Program Directors are the stronger authors.
- Specialty-focused letter of recommendation.
- Knows you well enough to write something good about yourself. The more they speak about you describing "personal or specific" qualities that they identified in you, the better.
- Mid to late-career faculty member.

In the case that such a person is not available for us, we can ask another author that we contacted through our educational or clinical background. Usually, in this case, multiple letter writers can help to cover all the important parts of our experience. It can become quite difficult to find the LOR author. However, there are options that we can try like clinical or research experiences that allow you to contact them.

## WHEN TO ASK FOR A LETTER OF RECOMMENDATION

The answer to this question is "as soon as possible". We must consider that the Physicians that will write our letters are very busy with their activities. Composing a letter of recommendation is not an easy task, they will need to spend a considerable amount of time preparing the letter for us. If we already spent the necessary time for them to get to know you well, you may ask the letter right away. If for some reason they have not uploaded the letter in a reasonable amount of time, you can write them a polite letter or email asking them to upload the letter. Remember that, an author has the choice of revoking or not writing an LOR if they consider not doing so. That means that we should always maintain a good relationship with our letter writer, even though they have not uploaded our important documents on time.

When obtaining an LOR through a clinical experience, the recommended time to ask for the letter will be at the end of the rotation. That way, we will ensure that the writer will have the necessary knowledge about ourselves for writing an excellent letter.

# HOW TO ASK A LETTER OF RECOMMENDATION

The best way to ask will be doing it in person. An email, mail letter or phone call is not appropriate. Try to set up a meeting in which you can ask for it in a professional and polite manner. Don't be late for the meeting. Bring a copy of your CV and personal statement with you so that you can facilitate the process. Remark the preferences that you have about the letter. For example, if you would like the letter to be written in a specific time, facilitate a timeline for the author. Inform him or her about your choice of waiving or not your rights to review the letter. Remember to clarify when you will deliver the information about the letter, like the ERAS-obtained request for the letter of recommendation.

In overall, be sincere and clear about the entire process so that the writer can feel comfortable. There are no rules about how many letters of recommendation are necessary for applying for Residency since every program has its own requirements. You can research the participating programs in the season in the AAMC FREIDA application.

## AAMC FREIDA Residency & Fellowship Database

# HOW TO ADD A LETTER OF RECOMMENDATION IN THE ERAS APPLICATION

In our myERAS application dashboard, we will see a "documents" section. We click on the letters of recommendation option and then the "add new" button. Once we do this, we will see the following window:

## Categorical vs. Preliminary Residency positions

After finishing medical school, the U.S and IMG doctors may seek specialty training. This can be obtained majorly through the NRMP-MATCH process. Understanding the difference between Categorical vs. Preliminary Residency positions, transitional year and so on is very important.

The nomenclature used to refer to the year of residency one is coursing is as follows:

1. **PGY-1:** Post graduate year 1, where regardless of the specialty the trainee is called "intern".

194

2. **PGY-2:** Post graduate year 2.
3. **PGY-3:** Post graduate year 3.
4. And so on.

## The concepts to understand are:

- **Categorical position**: Offers a full-length residency training position. Thus, if you accomplish the required goals throughout your residency, you will graduate. Internal Medicine, for example, is a three-year long training program, thus, you will get three years of training with a Categorical position.
- **PGY-1 positions:** Consist typically of one year of training necessary for entry into more advanced specialties like Anesthesiology, Ophthalmology, Radiation Oncology, etc. There are 2 types of PGY-1 positions:

1. **PGY-1 Transitional year position**: An intern year that offers a global training before the specialty of choice. The graduate rotates in both clinical and surgical areas acquiring good experience in basic sciences, clinical and surgical procedures. A transitional year can also be called a "Global year".

2. **PGY-1 Preliminary position:** Offers a partial length residency training position. Therefore, usually offers 1 year of training prior to entering into an advanced training program. The difference with transitional year position is that the preliminary position is divided into clinical (Internal Medicine) or surgical (General Surgery). The choice between clinical or surgical preliminary year depends on one's desired specialty.

To know more about which one fits our needs, it is very important for us to check the information of the programs in that specialty and what requirements they ask for.

Sometimes applicants choose to apply to categorical positions and preliminary positions in order to have a backup plan. In case that they are not accepted into a categorical position, they can do a preliminary year that can help to boost their application for the next NRMP-MATCH year.

# CATEGORICAL INTERNAL MEDICINE VS PRIMARY CARE INTERNAL MEDICINE

The ERAS website will show you categorical positions as Internal Medicine, or Primary Care when you research Internal Medicine programs with the FREIDA database.

It is crucial to understand the difference between them and which one is a better fit for us.

- **Categorical Internal Medicine:** Traditional training with more focus on the in-patient setting. After completion one is able to get certified by the American Boards of Internal Medicine (ABIM).

- **Primary Care Internal Medicine:** Focused more on the outpatient setting and in primary care, but with the same in-patient training as the traditional program. Most of the primary care programs state that there's no difference in the in-patient training of both positions. Thus, during the hospital stay there's no way to differentiate between what resident is in the primary care or categorical track. At the end, you can get certified in Internal Medicine by the ABIM as well.

Some people worry about the chance of getting fellowship after finishing a primary care track training program. We have reviewed a few programs and they state that there is no major difference in applicants whether they had a traditional or primary care training.

It is the applicant's responsibility to research appropriately the programs to apply and check the specific requirements of each program.

# HOW TO RESEARCH THE TYPES OF PROGRAMS IN FREIDA:

FREIDA Database

## 1. Transitional year positions:

We can research this type of position on FREIDA looking directly for transitional year positions. Remember this is a "global" year training.

## 2. Preliminary positions:

First search for your specialty of interest: Internal Medicine or Surgery. Then, in the options list, you will find the programs and positions they offer as "categorical or preliminary". You can choose the one you are looking for.

## 3. Categorical positions:

The same as preliminary positions. Search for your specialty of interest and then choose the available options.

- In the LoR Author Name: we will write the name of the writer, for example, Dr. Joe Davis.
- In the LoR Author Title/Department: we will describe the position of the Author. We should ask the writer to specify what to do here. Examples here can be Program Director, Assistant Director, Assistant Professor, and others.
- In the Specialty to which this letter will be assigned, we may select the pertinent one. Remember that this information will be visible only for you, the programs will not see this.
- Select from the options if the author meets the description.
- Finally, in the "I waive my right to view my Letter of Recommendation" section, we will select our choice. It is highly recommended to waive the letter so that the writer feels free to give a sincere and open opinion about us. This is the way that the Program Directors will consider this option. It is a personal decision so please think what is best for you.

The steps are described in the ERAS website like this:

1. Click *Add New* to enter and save LoR information.
2. Confirm the LoR entry by marking the associated check box and selecting *Only checked* in the Confirm drop down list. *Note:* You may only edit and/or delete a LoR entry prior to confirming.
3. Select *Download Letter Request* or *Email Letter Request* in the associated Action column to provide your LoR Author with the form.

Once you have the Letter Request, facilitate it to your potential writer so that he or she can start preparing it and upload it. In case that you do not waive your right to see the letter, you are able to upload it by yourself (not recommended). Remember, **once the letter is uploaded by the Author it takes about two weeks to be available**, so do everything with anticipation to the dates of application to NRMP.

# WHAT TO DO AFTER THE LETTER WAS UPLOADED IN ERAS

Once the author has written the letter for us, we can reach that person for a thank you note through email or a phone call. Again, we should remember that the author may revoke the letter at any time, so we need to make sure that we have their support permanently. Being polite is the best formula.

## J1 vs. H1B Visa for Medical Residency

One of the most discussed topics among International Medical Graduates (IMGs) is the migratory status. Choosing between a J1 and H1B Visa for Medical Residency can be confusing due to the complexity of the topic. Please note that this post is aimed to be educational only. It is highly recommended to consult this issue with an experienced immigration lawyer or any other professional with knowledge in this area. In this post, I will mention the basic features of the two visa options for residency and their respective characteristics.

# DEFINITIONS:

- **International Medical Graduate (IMG):** Any physician who received his or her medical degree from a medical school outside of the United States or Canada, regardless of citizenship. These types of graduates will need a visa for residency (unless U.S. citizen or green-card holder).
- **U.S International Medical Graduate (IMG):** Any U.S. citizen who received his or her medical degree from a medical school outside of the United States. Visa sponsorship is not an obstacle for this group.
- **Immigrant:** Permanent U.S resident visa. Green-card holders are considered part of this group.

- **Non-immigrant:** Temporal visa. The visas offered for U.S. residency training programs are the non-immigrant J1 and H1B visas.
- **J1 visa:** Exchange visa.
- **H1B visa:** Temporary worker visa.
- **Graduate Medical Education (GME):** The education offered after medical school in the United States is termed Graduate Medical Education or GME. Residency programs in the U.S. are considered GME programs.

# BASIC REQUIREMENTS FOR ENTRY INTO A U.S GRADUATE MEDICAL EDUCATION (GME) PROGRAM:

1. **ECFMG Certification:** Obtained after finishing the medical credential verification done by ECFMG and the USMLE Step 1, 2 CK, and 2 CS exams.
2. **Apply for a residency training position:**

   - · Apply through ERAS.
   - · Attend interviews at the programs.
   - · Register with the NRMP MATCH or get an outside-of-the-match offer (pre-match).
   - · Secure a letter of offer or contract from the program.

| Features | J1 Visa | H1B Visa |
|---|---|---|
| Founding source | Multiple: ECFMG, Department of State & Homeland Security | Unique: US employer (Residency program) |
| Requirements | USMLE Step 1, Step 2 CS, Step 2 CK exams, and ECFMG Certificate | USMLE Step 1, Step 2 CK, Step 2 CK, Step 3, and ECFMG Certificate. |

| Features | J1 Visa | H1B Visa |
| --- | --- | --- |
| Type of Visa | Exchange Visa - Non-immigrant (temporary visitor) | Employment Visa - Non-immigrant (temporary worker) |
| Time limit | 7 years | 6 years (may be extended in certain circumstances) |
| Fees | ECFMG fee: $325. SEVIS fee: $180. J1 Visa application and other fees: $160 to $300 approximately. Total: $665 to $805 approx. | From $1500 to 6000 (Family, lawyers, etc.) Usually partially or fully covered by the residency program |
| Processing time | 1-2,5 months approx. | Conventional time: 3-5 months. Premium processing ($1225): 15 days. |
| Requires strong ties to home country? | Yes. | No. |
| Mandatory return to home country after finishing residency? | Yes, a two-year home country return is required. It can be waived by working 3 years in an underserved area. | No. |
| Spouse and family visa sponsorship | Yes, J2 for dependents (spouse and children under 21 years old) | Yes, H4 for dependents (spouse and children under 21 years old) |
| EDA (Employment Authorization Document) for spouse | Yes, the dependent can apply after their entry to the United States | No. Spouses cannot work. |
| Dual intent (Can the visa holder apply for permanent residency such as Green card?) | No. After finishing the applicants must return to their home country for 2 years or do a waiver for 3 years, then apply for a job on an H1b visa, and then transition to Green Card through their employer. | Allowed. |

| Features | J1 Visa | H1B Visa |
|---|---|---|
| Can the employer sponsor for U.S. Permanent Residency? | No. | Yes. After finishing the training period, the applicant would need to get a job on an H1b visa and then transition to Green Card right away. |
| Advantages | Easier process. Faster and cheaper option. The spouse can work by applying for an EAD. The majority of programs accept this type of visa. Most fellowship programs accept J1 visas. | Dual intent allowed to achieve a permanent residency status faster than the J1 visa. No mandatory return to home country after finishing the training program. More job options to apply for after residency/fellowship in the US. |
| Disadvantages | No dual intent allowed. Mandatory two-year home country return. Visa stamps need to be renewed every year at a US consulate outside of the US. Renews every year. | Higher fees for the application. Spouses cannot work. A minority of residency, and even worse, fellowship programs offer an H1b visa. This narrows the options for fellowships although it is still possible to get a position. |

Now, there are several scenarios that can occur for every person and that is why it is important to understand that there are several strategies one can take to select the best visa option for the residency training. Again, I would like to stress the importance of consulting with an experienced professional to make the best migratory strategy depending on one's future aspirations.

There are **two elements** that a residency applicant should consider when creating his or her rank order list (ROL). The first element is the **interest in obtaining a permanent residency status** in the United States and thus live and practice medicine in this country. The second element is the academic goals mostly related to the intention of **pursuing a fellowship after residency.** There are other important aspects to keep in mind, but these two are important determinants in one's future decision in the rank order list.

## 1. Interest in a permanent resident status:

If an applicant is interested in practicing medicine after residency and obtaining a **permanent resident status in the United States, the H1b visa is probably the best option.** (1) An H1b visa is usually issued for 3 years and it can be extended one time for 3 more years – although there are certain circumstances in which it can be extended even further.

Should an applicant be interested in a permanent status after residency but also be aiming to pursue a fellowship, the time limit of the H1b visa should be acknowledged. Since the H1b visa has a theoretical limit of 6 years from which 3 years were used for residency training, there are only three years available for fellowships. If the fellowship of interest is longer than 3 years, it is important to plan in advance with a lawyer the best strategy to accomplish one's goals. One strategy would be applying for a job after residency through an employer and get a green card before applying for a fellowship. A green card can be obtained from an employer willing to sponsor it after finishing residency on an H1b visa and it would be an advantage when applying for a fellowship.

## 2. Fellowship interest:

A fellowship can be pursued with both types of visas (J1 and H1b). In both cases, it is feasible to apply for a fellowship just after residency. The H1b visa has no two-year home residency requirement, and although the J1 visa does have this condition, it can be completed after fellowship – the J1 visa can be extended for 3 more years to complete the fellowship and then the home residency requirement would apply.

As mentioned before, if the fellowship training is longer than 3 years, it is relevant to plan with a lawyer if an H1b visa would be the best option in that case. The **best visa for pursuing a fellowship, in reality, is the J1 visa.** That does not mean a fellowship cannot be done with an H1b visa, because it is possible to do it. However, bear in mind the vast majority of residency programs that do not offer H1b visas but only J1 visas. This fact **limits the options of fellowships for H1b visa holders**.

After residency or a fellowship training has been done, there is the opportunity of doing a waiver to avoid the two-year home residency requirement, after which the physician can apply for an H1b visa with an employer and subsequently apply for a green card or permanent status.

This means that **the permanent residency option is also available with a J1 visa** but is longer and sometimes more difficult to get.

**In a nutshell:**

- The **H1b visa is the best option for seeking a permanent residency status** in the United States (e.g. green card). After finishing residency, a physician can apply for a job under an H1b visa and then apply for a green card (permanent residency status) right away. It is also possible to apply for a fellowship with an H1b visa provided that the program lasts three years or less.

- The **J1 visa is the best option for pursuing a fellowship** if one is interested in having broader options to apply (most programs do not offer H1b visa but do accept J1) and the benefit of getting a permanent residency status is not an important objective – or if the applicant is sure to be willing to pursue a waiver option in an underserved area after the training has been finished to get a permanent resident status.

# TWO-YEAR HOME RESIDENCY REQUIREMENT – 212 (e) WAIVER FOR THE J1 VISA

The J1 visa requires that the Foreign Medical Graduates (FMG's) return to their country of residence for at least two years before returning to the United States. There are legal options that exist for FMGs to remain in the United States after training in a residency program under a J1 visa. The most common ones are:

- The Conrad 30 J 1 Program.
- The U.S. Department of Health and Human Services (HHS).
- Employment in a medically underserved area (MUA).
- Health Professions Shortage Area (HPSA).

There are other options available as well. To learn more about the J1 waivers available for IMG's, please go to the following links:

https://www.shusterman.com//jwaiversfordoctors/internationalmedicalgraduatesimmigration

Check out SGM Law group: https://www.immi-usa.com/j1-visa-waiver/j1-visa-waiver-for-physicians/

## Dealing with Immigration

There is a lot of talk lately that IMGs are having a very hard time dealing with immigration. The truth of the matter is that, although it's not really a fun process, it is definitely possible to get a visa and live in the US working as a resident.

## Here are the most essential steps in this process.

You will need to fill out an I-20 form. This form certifies that you are eligible to apply for a visa as a nonimmigrant student. Once you have this form (lucky you) you can now pay what is called the I-901 SEVIS fee. You will need to bring a receipt of that payment to your visa application appointment.

The ECFMG can sponsor what is known as a J-1 visa for IMGs. This is simply a special type of visa given to students and scholars who wish to travel to the US for educational purposes.

The ECFMG, in turn, will first require you to complete a DS-2019. Of course, you must have a valid passport. Also, they require you to have applicable health and accident insurance. Be sure to visit their website for detailed instructions.

## Final thoughts

The selection of the type of visa is difficult and not totally under our control. Having passed the USMLE Step 3 exam usually before the match day is key for an H1b visa. There is no rule or entirely true statement regarding which visa is the best because the decision depends entirely on an applicant's preferences. The decision of choosing programs offering an H1b or J1 visa for the rank order list (ROL) should be done carefully thinking about one's major goals, the personal and familial circumstances, intention to permanently reside in the United States, the availability of programs offering a candidate both of these types of visas, and others.

## References:

http://www.txmedicallicensinglaw.com/2013/11/articles/texas-medical-board/foreign-medical-graduates-and-the-h1b-visa-a-better-choice/.

## Medical Residency Interview

What to research about a residency program before an interview.

Knowing "what to research about a residency program before an interview" is crucial. The worst mistake that we can make during an interview is not being prepared enough for it. In order to give a good impression and become a strong candidate, we need to demonstrate our interest in the program. Programs use the classic question: "Do you have any questions for me?" as a way to assess two major things in an applicant: how well that person can prepare for a challenging situation, and what their true interest is in that particular program.

After receiving an interview invitation, one should try to investigate as much as one can to be informed about the program's vision. What does the program promote? What are the features that make that program special? It is also good to identify the important authorities like the program director, assistant program director, coordinator, etc. Savvy candidates will even go further and analyze the last publications, books, and any other academic paper published by those professionals so that they can point out their interest to work with them.

## What to research about a residency program before an interview?

Elaborating a table with the programs in which you will interview can help to summarize important information, it can also help to compare between them. A sample table is shown:

Residency programs comparison - Interview process

|  | PROGRAM 1 | PROGRAM 2 | PROGRAM 3 |
|---|---|---|---|
| State |  |  |  |
| City/Location |  |  |  |
| Type of program |  |  |  |

|  | PROGRAM 1 | PROGRAM 2 | PROGRAM 3 |
|---|---|---|---|
| Reputation | | | |
| Diversity of population | | | |
| Most common languages | | | |
| Available positions | | | |
| Interviews held last year | | | |
| Program stability | | | |
| Likely changes for the next several years | | | |
| Type of visa offered. | | | |
| Waiver available at the program or help for obtaining a position (for J1) | | | |
| Participates in the main MATCH | | | |
| Offers pre-match positions | | | |
| Educational activities such as Conferences/ grand rounds/ | | | |
| Faculty teaching/ support | | | |

|  | PROGRAM 1 | PROGRAM 2 | PROGRAM 3 |
|---|---|---|---|
| Teaching opportunities | | | |
| Mentorship opportunities | | | |
| Research opportunities | | | |
| Equilibrium between clinical work, academic activities and research. | | | |
| Resident autonomy | | | |
| Elective diversity | | | |
| Away elective opportunities | | | |
| Medical technology availability and application | | | |
| What do most graduates do? | | | |
| Fellowship opportunities in-house | | | |
| Fellowship MATCH rate | | | |
| Board pass rate | | | |
| Call frequency (hours per week) | | | |

| | PROGRAM 1 | PROGRAM 2 | PROGRAM 3 |
|---|---|---|---|
| Ancillary support (nursing, social workers, etc.) | | | |
| Patient cap (Patients per resident) | | | |
| On call system (admission caps, night float system) | | | |
| Main advantages | | | |
| Main disadvantages | | | |
| Salary | | | |
| Health benefits | | | |
| Non-health benefits | | | |
| Cost of living | | | |
| Vacation/parental leave/sick leave | | | |
| Post interview communication preference. (Yes or not). | | | |

|  | **PROGRAM 1** | **PROGRAM 2** | **PROGRAM 3** |
|---|---|---|---|
| 1-10 scale: How good did you feel about the program after the interview? |  |  |  |
| 1-10 scale: Friendliness of the program with their staff and you? |  |  |  |
| 1-10 scale: Residents' feedback about how good the program is? |  |  |  |
| 1-10 scale: Compatibility between the program and you? 10 is the best. |  |  |  |
| Program's expressed Rank intention. |  |  |  |
| How would you rank the program? High, middle, or low? |  |  |  |

There are other important things to consider such as crime safety, weather, childcare, culture, recreational areas, and others. However, the table contains the features that we believe are the most important to consider. Please, analyze everything that you believe is important. One of the most recommended aspects to consider is how compatible the program is with you, and vice-versa.

Secret: As soon as you complete your residency interview, take 30 minutes to write down all the pros and cons about the program in the table above. Do not wait after you have completed all your interviews before listing this information. You will start to mix them up as you go on more interviews.

In summary, gathering this data will help us to be informed about the most important facts concerning a residency program. It can also help us to decide how to make our rank order list after the interview season is over. The sources that we can use for obtaining information are the residency program website, emails from the programs when they invite one for an interview, and the FREIDA AMA database.

## Residency Interview Questions and Answers

The preparation for the residency interviews is broad, and it encompasses several aspects needed to be shown to the programs. These qualities can help showing to a program how well prepared a candidate is for a residency position. The preparation for the residency interview questions and answers plays a crucial role in the image that an interviewee would like to show during their meetings with the program members.

The questions asked by the interviewers are the major tools they use to analyze and understand an applicant. What you say and do during your interviews is very important because it may get you close to the goal of securing a residency position, or it may decrease your chances to succeed. There are many sources of information about the residency interview process commenting on how to behave during a residency interview. However, being natural during the interviews has the benefit of making you feel more comfortable during the whole process and helping the program to understand if you are compatible with what they are looking for. It is a good idea to show yourself and be selected for who you are, instead of being chosen for who you are not and have a bad time during your residency training.

Preparing the most important residency interview questions and answers will boost your confidence and will allow you to send the right message about yourself to the interviewers. There are several ways to practice for the interview season. Elaborating your own personalized list of questions and answers can help you to get a better idea of what you would like to say, although memorizing your answers may not be the best idea since it can give a "robotic" impression about yourself to the people meeting you. Practicing your answers by saying them out loud to yourself, speaking to a friend or colleague, or doing mock interviews can aid in the adaptation process for interviewing in a relaxed and professional way.

International Medical Graduates (IMGs) for whom English is not their native language, practicing pronunciation and grammar is a good idea as well. Depending on the number of interviews you are granted, you can select the programs that you are less interested in first so that you can practice how an interview day is held and lose the fear of the first interview. If the first interview does not go as well as you expected, continue to prepare yourself and work in the aspects you did not feel well during the previous experiences.

The **academic tools** you can use for preparing your questions and answers for the interviews are:

1. Your own list of questions and answers: It is preferable to write them down so you can review them before every interview.
2. Flashcards.
3. Audio recordings of your responses.
4. Residency preparation courses.

## 1. List of residency interview questions and answers.

It is better to write a list of questions and answers that you may encounter during your interviews. The order of questions should be made by the most common questions asked first, and then the other possible questions so that you do not get surprised by a question during your interview that can make you feel anxious and ruin your performance. Prepare every question with a brief, concise, and complete answer. The duration of the answer in spoken time should not be longer than 90 seconds to avoid fatiguing the interviewer.

## MOST COMMON QUESTIONS ASKED DURING A RESIDENCY INTERVIEW:

1. Tell me about yourself.
2. What are your strengths and weaknesses?
3. What are your hobbies or interests? What do you do to relieve your stress?
4. Why did you choose this program? Why this city? Why did you choose the United States? (For IMGs)
5. Why did you choose this specialty?
6. How do you know the program?
7. What are your future goals? Where do you see yourself in 5 or 10 years?

8. Why should we choose you over the other qualified applicants?
9. Could you tell me about an interesting case you have seen recently?
10. Do you have any questions for me? *

* This is the most important question you should try to prepare. It is not easy to remember what questions you have and the pressure at that moment can be great. Think about this well before the interview.

Next, there will be a description of all the important questions that can be asked during a residency interview. Try to prepare for them as well.

## PERSONAL TYPE OF QUESTIONS ASKED DURING A RESIDENCY INTERVIEW:

1. Tell me about yourself. It is the most important and common question, should be 1-2 minutes in length and medically related.
2. How would your friends describe you? How would you define yourself? Who are you as a person?
3. What do you do in your spare time? What are your hobbies and interests? How do you relieve your stress?
4. Do you see any problem managing a professional and a personal life?
5. What are your goals? What do you see yourself doing in the future? Where do you see yourself in 5 or 10 years from now? What are your long-term goals? What are you planning to do after finishing your residency training? Are you interested in pursuing a fellowship?
6. What is your most important accomplishment? What other accomplishment have you achieved? (the recommendation is to prepare a professional or extra-curricular accomplishment and use it depending on how much have you been able to express so far during the interview)
7. What motivates you?
8. Why did you become a doctor? Why did you choose medicine as your career?
9. If you could not be a physician, what career would you choose?
10. Why should we choose you? What are your strengths? What sets you apart from the crowd? How would your friends describe you? How would you describe yourself? What are your key skills? What can you bring to our residency program? What qualifications do you have that set you apart from other candidates? Why should we choose you over

the other highly qualified applicants? (Personalize it always, depending on the main interest of the program that you are applying to)

11. What are your weaknesses? What is your worst quality? If you could change one thing about your personality, what would it be? What would your friends say is your biggest weakness? What would your last resident or attending physician want you to change with respect to your work habits? (Mention at least 3)

12. How well do you take criticism?

13. What leadership roles have you held? Tell me about a time when you had to be a team player to accomplish a goal. Tell me when you were a leader.

14. Tell us about your research experience. Do you want to do research?

15. What is the greatest sacrifice you have already made to get to where you are?

16. If you could do medical school again, what would you change? How have you done in medical school? What were the major deficiencies during your medical school training?

17. Describe the best/worst attending with whom you have ever worked. What rotation gave you the most difficulty and why? Discuss a particularly meaningful experience in your medical training.

18. What was the course during medical school that you liked the most?

19. What is the worst experience that you had in medical school? Tell me about a difficult time during medical school. What was your most difficult situation in medical school? Tell me about a particularly stressful situation you encountered in medical school and how did you handle it?

20. Where else have you been interviewed? Where else are you interviewing? Where have you applied other than here?

21. Have you always done the best work that you are capable of?

22. Whom do you depend on for support?

23. What kinds of people do you have difficulty working with?

24. What type of patients do you have trouble dealing with?

25. What was your most memorable patient encounter?

26. What if you don't match? What will you do if you don't match?

27. What was the last book you read? Tell me something about the last book you read.

28. Tell me a joke.

29. There is a gap of 2 years in your CV. What did you do during this time?

There are questions that can be answered in the same way, it would be better to prepare a single answer for all of them. In that way, it will be much easier for you to remember them.

## QUESTIONS ABOUT THE SPECIALTY OF CHOICE:

1.  How would you contribute to our residency program?
2.  How would you contribute to our residency program?
3.  Why are you going into this specialty? Why did you choose Internal Medicine? What do you see as the positive features of this specialty?
4.  What have you done to inform yourself about a career in this specialty?
5.  What do you see as the negative features of this specialty? What problems do you think the specialty faces?
6.  What do you consider to be important in a training program? What are you looking for in a program? What is your ideal program?
7.  What are you avoiding in a training program?
8.  Why have you applied to this residency program? Why did you choose this program? This is the most specific question about a program. We will need to answer with facts about that particular program.
9.  Are you applying to any other specialty?
10. What will be the toughest aspect of this specialty for you?
11. What problems will our specialty face in the next 5-10 years?
12. What clinical experiences have you had in this specialty?

## CURRENT EVENTS QUESTIONS ASKED DURING A RESIDENCY INTERVIEW:

1.  What do you think about what is happening now? This question is related to the current events in the United States Healthcare System.
2.  How do you see the delivery of healthcare evolving? This means how will the healthcare coverage in the United States evolve compared to the present time.
3.  How is the healthcare system from your country different from the one applied in the United States? (IMGs)

# QUESTIONS ASKED TO INTERNATIONAL MEDICAL GRADUATES DURING A RESIDENCY INTERVIEW:

1.  Why did you leave your country?
2.  Why did you leave your country?
3.  How is the healthcare system in the United States different compared to your country?
4.  What have you done to familiarize yourself with medicine as it is practiced in the United States? How well do you see yourself adapting to the US healthcare system?
5.  Do you have an ECFMG certificate? What ECFMG requirements remain for you to complete?
6.  How would you rate your oral and written communication skills?

# BEHAVIORAL TYPE OF QUESTIONS ASKED DURING A RESIDENCY INTERVIEW:

1.  Tell me three things that would make you valuable for our residency program.
2.  Tell me three things that would make you valuable for our residency program.
3.  Tell me about a time when you worked effectively under a lot of pressure?
4.  Tell me about the most interesting case that you have been involved with? Tell me about a recent case that you have seen. (Prepare at least two cases, they do not need to be rare or very interesting. Instead, use this opportunity to show how you have been involved in the treatment of patients).
5.  Tell me about a time when you made a mistake and had to admit it to your resident or attending.
6.  How would you deal with a fellow resident who is not doing his share of the work?
7.  Tell me about the time when you were really upset by the words or actions of an attending or resident?

8. Tell me about the time you had to build a relationship with someone you did not like. Tell me about the time when you became really angry over a situation at work.

9. Tell me about the time when you had a personality conflict with another team member. How did you deal with it?

10. Your attending physician asks you a question and you are not sure of the answer. What would you say or do?

11. Your colleague is abusing alcohol or drugs. How would you handle this situation?

12. Tell me about a time when you were disappointed in your performance. Tell me about a situation in which you overcame adversity.

13. Tell me about a time when you disagreed with how an ethical situation was handled. Tell me about the problem you had with a classmate, faculty member, or patient. How did you handle it?

14. Describe a clinical situation you handled well.

15. Tell me about a clinical situation that did not go as well as you would have liked?

16. Tell me about the time when you handled a stressful situation poorly.

17. Was there a time during rotations in which you didn't feel like part of the team? How did you handle the situation?

18. Tell me about the time during rotations in which you went above and beyond.

19. Describe to me a time when you received an evaluation with which you disagreed.

20. Your senior resident insists on a treatment plan you feel may harm the patient. What do you do?

The idea behind the behavioral type of questions is to know about the interviewee's decisions by asking how that person handled a difficult situation in the past. Giving an example is a must for this type of question.

## 2. Flashcards:

Preparing flashcards with the questions and the answers in the back is a very good way to practice. Do a random selection of the flashcards and that will help you to be prepared to answer any question properly. You can use Quizlet. Go to quizlet.com to create your own flashcards.

## 3. Audio recordings:

If you have the available time to do it, try recording your responses on audio sets. Then listen to them when you are preparing for your interviews. That will help you analyze your speech, pronunciation, pacing, the tone of voice, and so on. It is a very important part of the interview. It is also very important to prepare your body language for the interview. Your body language is the most important communication skill needed to be polished for your interviews.

## 4. Residency interview preparation courses:

There are several courses available in different cities and online to improve your interviewing skills. The choice depends on the need for improvement you think is required for you. Most of the people do not use them, but they can improve your skills mostly if you have never had a work interview before.

**5. When you go to your residency interview, dress professionally.** Arrive on time. Be nice to everyone you meet including the secretary, residents, technicians, nurses. Everyone you meet during your interview is important, and if you have one bad interaction with anyone, it can cost you a residency spot.

**6. Bring along with you a pack of thank you cards.** After you complete your interview. Take note of the name of your interviewer; write a personal hand-written thank you note based on your interaction with the interviewers and give it to the residency secretary before you leave. Always give the secretary of the program, program director and assistant program director a thank you for the opportunity to interview with them.

## Basic Work Schedule Terminology During Residency

As an IMG (International Medical Graduate), I had to research and speak with a lot of people to understand different kinds of work schedules during residency. Familiarizing yourself with the basic work schedule terminology during residency is quite important. It will help you to understand how your life as a resident will be and how to compare the workload in the different programs that you are interested in. If you are feeling confused by terms such as on-call, night shift, moonlight, float system, and others, please, read this post that can help you solve all those doubts.

## Basic work terminology during residency to understand:

1. **On-call:** Regardless of the total hours that you will work, being on-call means that you will spend an entire day and night until the next day at the hospital. It can be a short or long call. The short call is usually until 8 pm, 9 pm or close. The long call is usually more than 24 hours. It can also be home -call or house-call (in-house always means at the hospital). Home-call means that you can go home and attend calls and beeper calls from home. In-house-call means that you need to stay at the hospital.

2. **Day or night shift:** It is common during training programs like emergency medicine. What it means is that you will work on a predefined schedule, typically 12-hours long. For example: from 7 am to 7 pm, or 7 pm to 7 am. This can continue for months, depending on the particular schedule of the residency program. However, in most cases, it also demands some daytime duties and it continues like that throughout the total residency length.

3. **Night float:** This is a kind of new work system. In this context, a resident must cover the night shift every night, for example: from 7 pm to 7 am, six days a week, usually for a maximum of 1 month. No daytime work duties are needed. This helps reduce the duty hours of the residents working during the day, maintaining an adequate patient follow-up since night float residents know the patients that they see every day. Consider it to be like a rotation during your residency.

4. **Moonlight:** In simple terms, it means working as an independent physician outside of the residency program. Moonlighting can be external when working outside of the scope of the program, and internal when you work inside the hospital as a provider. Every program has its own regulations, and not all of them will approve moonlighting.

I hope this simple but to the point post has helped you to better understand the basic work terminologies during residency. For acquiring information about a specific program regarding the work schedule during residency, please visit the program's website or research it using the <u>AMA FREIDA Database</u>.

## The NRMP MATCH Process

**Overview:** Learn about the **NRMP MATCH Process.** Tutorial on how to apply for the NRMP Match step by step. Entry and certification of the Rank Order List (ROL). How does the Match algorithm work, and how is the Match week?

The **"NRMP Match Process"** is the magic system that makes the assignment of residency training positions accredited by the Accreditation Council for Graduate Medical Education (ACGME) run smoothly and accurately. The MATCH system is operated by the National Resident Matching Program (NRMP). The Match is a standardized and uniform process held in the same steps and methods for all applicants and participating institutions. This post will be directed more towards the Match process for an IMG (International Medical Graduate).

The Match, as its own name suggests, joins two parts that love each other (the program with the applicant). Furthermore, it is important to understand how it works because this system is actually oriented to favor the applicant's preference, as long as the programs have ranked that participant high enough to match. Almost all the residency training programs participate in the MATCH, with some programs not participating and filling their positions entirely outside of the Match (Pre-Match programs).

There are different types of Match, but this post will cover the NRMP Match with focus on the Main Residency Match. It is very important to familiarize with the NRMP Match process, and for that reason, it is highly recommended to check the NRMP website for the most important and official information. You can go to the NRMP Website by clicking on the following link:

## NRMP National Residency Matching Program

There are educational contents posted on the NRMP website, particularly this videos that are shown here:

**The NRMP Process for Applicants (all applicants in general):**
**The NRMP Match Process for International Medical Graduates:**

However, in this post, I will try to describe the most important aspects of the MATCH. **The Match process can be divided into 3 parts:**

1. Application to the NRMP-Match.
2. Rank Order List (ROL).
3. The MATCH process.

# 1. Application to the NRMP/MATCH Process

The first step before applying consists of the eligibility verification. For IMGs, such verification is mostly dependent and done by ECFMG (Educational Commission for Foreign Medical Graduates). For an IMG to be eligible for applying to the Main Match, the following criteria should be met:

- Get the **ECFMG Certification** by accomplishing the verification of identification (Form 186), medical school credentials verification, and examination requirements set by ECFMG (USMLE Step 1, Step 2 CK, and Step 2 CS exams) before the Rank Order List deadline.

The other important part of the NRMP/MATCH process is related to the application for Residency in the ERAS (Electronic Residency Application Service) system since this will allow an applicant to apply to the programs and get interview invitations that are crucial for getting matched. For information about how to apply for Residency using ERAS, please go to the following link:

## Application for Medical Residency via ERAS

Please note that it is not necessary to hold an ECFMG Certificate by the time of application in ERAS. However, this is the most desirable option since some programs do not grant invitations to applicants without ECFMG Certification. Furthermore, it is vital to understand that the deadline for getting ECFMG certified is the NRMP Rank Order List deadline. You will notice that the deadlines do not necessarily depict the desirable timelines.

If you are eligible or close to being eligible (ECFMG Certified), the next step is to apply for the NRMP/MATCH:

## NRMP Registration – National Resident Matching Program or "MATCH"

Remember, it is NOT mandatory to apply to NRMP for sending the applications through ERAS, it can be done later when the MATCH is opened. The application date for the NRMP Match is open on September 15 at 12 pm EDT. It is very important to follow the calendars for the NRMP and ERAS deadlines. To review the NRMP MATCH calendar, please go to this link:

NRMP – National Resident Matching Program Calendar and Deadlines

For applying to the NRMP MATCH, we can use the R3 system website, so please follow these steps:

1. Go to NRMP – National Resident Matching Program.
2. Select login/register or directly choose to register for the "Main MATCH."
3. You will be directed to the R3 system (the 3 Rs represent the Registration, Ranking, and Results system for the Match). Fill all the required basic information about you and your medical school until NRMP asks you to create a username and password for your account.
4. Continue and enter in your account in the following window with the data just created. You will see the notice for the NRMP policies.
5. After reading everything, click "I accept."
6. In the next window, you will see the fees and payments needed. Select next and you will be asked to provide your payment information.
7. After the payment is made, you will observe a summary of the payment and an option for printing it which is recommended.

That is everything you need to do for registering for the MATCH at NRMP. Now, please don't forget to come back to your ERAS account and go to the personal information part (which is the only part of the application that can be changed after the application has been done). In the "MATCH information" option of the personal information, type your NRMP ID and then click on save my personal information. This is needed because programs need the NRMP ID to rank you after the interviews.

## 2. Rank Order List (ROL):

The Rank Order List (ROL) is a list of the residency programs that you are willing to attend for your training. The list is a key component of your Match, since it will dictate what program you may get matched into depending on your choice. I would like to state that the **Match system works to benefit a candidate's choices.** This gives the applicant the opportunity to dictate his or her own preferences and get the best chance to get their favorite program. It is crucial to understand that once an applicant has agreed to apply for the Match, and has not withdrawn from it at the appropriate deadline, there is a binding agreement that is being accepted. The agreement means that regardless of the program that an applicant gets matched into, that person is mandated to attend that program. Not doing so, is considered irregular behavior and can have severe consequences for that applicant. Be sure to be willing to do this before applying for the Match and follow the deadlines we have provided before.

## The Matching Algorithm

To understand well what an ROL is, first, it is very important to understand how the Matching algorithm works. The Matching Algorithm is a computerized process that uses mathematical calculations and operations to match candidates and programs with their most preferred choices. Please, take a look at this video from NRMP that explains it very well.

The applicant's ROL will dictate where the algorithm starts looking for a Match. The applicant's first choice program will be considered first and then it will continue on and on to the following programs until a definitive Match is reached. It is also important to understand the magnitude of the algorithm, since it works for thousands of applicants every year.

In theory, you could rank programs you did not interview with, but there is virtually no chance for them to rank you. Therefore, one should rank only programs to which one has attended for an interview. The **most important considerations when ranking a program** are the following:

- **Rank programs based on your preference**. This may sound obvious, but there are a lot of applicants that rank the programs they think they have more chances to get matched into, rather than the programs that they like. That is a really big mistake. The misconception sometimes is that if you rank a "safety" program, you have more chances to get matched. That is not the case. Even if you put that safety program on the bottom of the list, if the other programs did not rank you high, but that program did, you will get matched. The order on your list does not affect the order in the program's list. But putting the programs you liked the most first on your list will give you the opportunity of being selected by the programs you love first.

- **Rank all the programs you interviewed with** unless there are programs to which you would never want to attend. Remember that it is dangerous to rank a program that you do not like, since it is possible that you can end up working there and have a really bad time. Avoid having a short ROL list, since that decreases your chances of matching significantly.
- **Do not rank programs that did not grant you an interview**. All the programs rank only applicants they interviewed.
- **Rank as many programs as you can**. The magic number of programs that you may need to rank does not exist because the experience differs from one person to another. Therefore, the best approach would be to rank all the programs you interviewed with, excluding the ones you would not want to get matched into. The decision is hard since it is up to you to decide if getting matched in such programs is better than not getting matched at all. The fee is already paid when you apply for the NRMP Match, and extra fees are in place once you have more than 20 programs (which is a lot and most applicants will not have). For more information, please check this link: http://www.nrmp.org/match-fees/.
- **Create and enter your ROL in the R3 system as soon as possible.** Create a ROL as soon as possible, usually during the interview season and then continue to modify it until you are sure about it. Enter that ROL in the R3 system soon, because during the last days the server may be overloaded or the website may get really slow. There is plenty of time to enter your ROL in the R3 system.
- **Avoid last-minute changes.** Anxiety can trick us sometimes. That is why it is recommended not to make last-minute changes in our ROL. If you have thoughtfully determined your ROL, and it has not changed for a week or more by the time it is close to the

ROL certification deadline, it is better to avoid making changes at that point since stress can alter our reasoning and we could make changes that we may regret later on.

## Rank Order List Certification:

The ranking opens on January 15 or close and the ROL Certification Deadline for every year is circa February 21. It is recommended to certify and send the ROL using the R3 system at least a couple of days before that date.

On the R3 system website, there is a "Certify List" button that when selected asks applicants to enter their unique R3 system password to confirm certification. Please remember that, by certifying an ROL, applicants are registering for a binding commitment to training at any program with which they match.

## Rank order List (ROL) entry and certification using the R3 system:

The NRMP organization has created several tutorials on how to enter your ROL and certify it. It cannot be better and that is why I will provide the link to this tutorial because it explains step by step what to do and contains pictures and illustrative information. Please, check it out:

http://www.nrmp.org/wp-content/uploads/2017/11/Enter_Certify_ROL_MRM-App.pdf

**There are two ways in which applicants can verify that their ROL's were submitted and are active:**

1. Changing the applicant status field in the R3 system from "Ranking" to "Certified."
2. By getting a confirmation email that is sent to the primary email address on file in the R3 system.

## Changing and Re-Certifying an ROL (very important)

This is different than when applying for Residency using ERAS where once you submit the application no changes can be made; it is possible to make changes to an ROL even after it has been certified. Nevertheless, **when a certified ROL is changed in any way, the new version MUST**

**be re-certified to be used in the Match**. This is very important. Do not forget to certify again the changes you have made. Once a change to the ROL is done, there is no way to get the previous versions of our ROL since the R3 system does NOT retain previous information of an ROL, regardless of whether it was certified.

## The Match Week: What is it like?

The Match week begins generally around March 12. There are several things that will occur from there and you can check them on the Match schedule.

http://www.nrmp.org/match-calendars/

The most important things that occur during the Match week are:

- **March 12:** SOAP begins.
- **March 15:** SOAP ends.
- **March 16:** MATCH DAY. The most important date of the season. The official time of results available on the website and by email is 1 pm for the Main Residency Match and SOAP.

The MATCH process can be really confusing and stressful.

## Statement of Need for J1 Visa – Medical Residency

Congratulations! After getting the most fabulous email and result (You have MATCHED), the next step to be taken is the paperwork for residency and visa related matters. The Statement of Need (SON) for the J1 Visa is one of the most important documents required for the application to the visa sponsorship by ECFMG, and thus it is important to know what it is and how to get it.

Please, checkup the ECFMG website for more information about the J1 visa sponsorship program (Exchange Visitor Sponsorship Program – EVSP). To learn more about what ECFMG indicates about the Statement of Need, please go to the following link:

https://www.ecfmg.org/evsp/applicants-regulations-statement-need.html

## What is the Statement of Need?

The statement of need (SON) is a document submitted by the Ministry of Health of the country of most recent legal permanent residence of the applicant. This letter should affirm the need for medical professionals in that country with skills acquired by training on a foreign medical program (specific to the area, for example, Internal Medicine). It works as a written assurance, adequate to the Secretary of the United States Department of Health and Human Services.

## How to get a Statement of Need?

The statement of need (SON) should be obtained from the central office of the Ministry of Health of the country of most recent legal permanent residence (regardless if that country is the applicant's birth country or not). There are several ways of contacting the office of the Ministry of Health of one's country:

1. **By searching the Ministry of Health website:** Most countries issue the Statement of Need frequently and thus they are familiar with the paperwork. Most will publish information on their official websites regarding the requirements and how to contact them to get the letter. For example, Ecuador has posted an article with the requirements and contact information to start the process via email. http://www.salud. gob.ec/declaracion-de-necesidad-de-especializacion-fuera-del-pais/.

2. **By contacting the Ministry of Health directly via phone or email.** Go to the Ministry of Health website and search for the contact information. Call or email them providing your information such as complete name, nationality, national I.D., and other pertinent information. Do not forget to provide them your ECFMG I.D. as well.

3. **By contacting a professional** who did the process before getting the J1 sponsorship from ECFMG: A colleague or friend who is familiar with the required paperwork can become an excellent source of information regarding this process.

It is important to stress that reading the **ECFMG Exchange Visitor Sponsorship Program (EVSP)** information on the ECFMG website is extremely important.

https://www.ecfmg.org/evsp/index.html
**How should the Statement of Need be sent to ECFMG?**
ECFMG requires getting the original statement of need issued by the

Ministry of Health central office. There are several considerations to keep in mind:

*To be admitted by ECFMG, the original SON must be received in the original, sealed envelope of the Ministry of Health. In addition, the Ministry of Health official issuing the letter must place it in a Ministry of Health envelope and stamp the outside flap with the issuing government seal. The document should be forwarded directly to ECFMG; if the sealed envelope is opened, ECFMG will not accept the SON.* **Electronic or scanned copies of the SON will not be accepted by ECFMG.**

The other very important consideration to bear in mind is the wording in the letter. The correct wording can be found on ECFMG by clicking the following link:

https://www.ecfmg.org/evsp/applicants-regulations-statement-need.html

*USMLE®/ECFMG ID Number: __-__-__-__-__-__-__-__*

*Name of Applicant for Visa: _____*

*There currently exists in (country) a need for qualified medical practitioners in the specialty of _____. (Name of Applicant for Visa) has filed a written assurance with the government of this country that he/she will return to this country upon completion of training in the United States, and intends to enter the practice of medicine in the specialty for which training is being sought.*

Finally, the SON must have a certified translation inside the envelope to be sent to ECFMG if it is written in a language other than English. The envelope can be mailed to ECFMG by the Ministry of Health or the applicant. Sending the document using a trusted mailing company is recommended to expedite the process.

## What requirements may be needed for getting the Statement of Need?

- The letter of acceptance or contract for residency or fellowship training.
- The academic coursework (syllabus, curriculum, program of study). Required by some countries (for example, Ecuador).
- Copy of the National I.D. of the applicant.
- Copy of the medical degree.

- Request letter or any other form of solicitation for the Statement of Need that is written and signed by the applicant.

There may be other requirements depending on the country issuing the letter.

## How long does it take to get the Statement of Need?

It depends mostly on the country issuing the document. As mentioned before, most countries are familiar with this process and have structured programs to provide applicants with the document in a fast and efficient manner. Once the SON reaches ECFMG, the processing of the document will start if all the other required documentation was already uploaded by the Training Program Liaison (TPL) or the applicant.

ECFMG has set timeframes for processing the documents depending on the type of program:

- Four to six weeks for ACGME-accredited training programs.
- Six to eight weeks for non-standard training programs.

### IMG-Friendly Internal Medicine Residency Programs

Applying for a U.S. Residency program can be quite challenging and complex. When researching which programs to apply, it is crucial to consider which states and programs are known to be *IMG-Friendly Internal Medicine Residency Programs*. There are several resources one can use to figure this out. Research has helped me determine **my top ten IMG-friendly states** as follows:

1. New York.
2. Connecticut.
3. Pennsylvania.
4. Michigan.
5. Florida.
6. Illinois.
7. Texas.
8. Ohio.
9. New Jersey.
10. Massachusetts.

This list represents the states with better rates of acceptance of IMGs, and largest program size by state. New York is the state with the largest number of internal medicine residency programs that are known to be IMG friendly, though competitive. However, I must say that New York has been shifting this tendency in the last couple of years and is accepting less international applicants than before (my opinion). Connecticut, Pennsylvania, Michigan, Florida, Illinois and the other states on the list are great places to search for residency programs.

To determine this list of programs, I have done my research and used several resources. FREIDA (from AMA – American Medical Association) was the most important tool. You may use this list as a guiding tool and template to begin doing your own research. The names and codes of the programs will be listed so that more information can be found by you when using FREIDA and other resources that you may find appropriate.

| Name | Accreditation ID | State | City |
|---|---|---|---|
| University of Alabama Hospital Program | 1400100893 | AL | Huntsville |
| University of Arkansas for Medical Sciences Program | 1400421030 | AR | Little Rock |
| Bridgeport Hospital/Yale University Program | 1400811074 | CT | Bridgeport |
| Danbury Hospital Program | 1400811076 | CT | Danbury |
| Griffin Hospital Program | 1400831077 | CT | Derby |
| Norwalk Hospital/Yale University Program | 1400831086 | CT | Norwalk |
| St Vincent's Medical Center Program | 1400811075 | CT | Bridgeport |
| University of Connecticut Program | 1400831078 | CT | Farmington |
| Yale-New Haven Hospital Program (Waterbury) | 1400800910 | CT | Waterbury |

| Name | Accredita-tion ID | State | City |
|---|---|---|---|
| Yale-New Haven Medical Center Program | 1400821085 | CT | New Haven |
| George Washington University Program | 1401021093 | DC | Washington |
| Georgetown University Hospital Program | 1401021091 | DC | Washington |
| Howard University Program | 1401021461 | DC | Washington |
| Providence Hospital Program | 1401021095 | DC | Washington |
| Aventura Hospital and Medical Center Program | 1401100924 | FL | Aventura |
| Florida Atlantic University Charles E. Schmidt College of Medicine Program | 1401100923 | FL | Boca Raton |
| Florida Hospital Medical Center Program | 1401131539 | FL | Orlando |
| Florida State University College of Medicine (Sarasota) Program | 1401100947 | FL | Sarasota |
| Florida State University College of Medicine (Tallahassee) Program | 1401100894 | FL | Tallahassee |
| Jackson Memorial Hospital/Jackson Health System Program | 1401121100 | FL | Miami |
| Kendall Regional Medical Center Program | 1401100926 | FL | Miami |
| Mayo Clinic College of Medicine and Science (Jacksonville) Program | 1401121509 | FL | Jacksonville |

| Name | Accreditation ID | State | City |
|------|------------------|-------|------|
| Memorial Healthcare System (Hollywood, Florida) Program | 1401100950 | FL | Pembroke Pines |
| Mount Sinai Medical Center of Florida Program | 1401112101 | FL | Miami Beach |
| Naples Community Hospital, Inc Program | 1401100942 | FL | Naples |
| Orange Park Medical Center Program | 1401100937 | FL | Orange Park |
| University of Central Florida College of Medicine/HCA GME Consortium (Gainesville) Program | 1401100938 | FL | Gainesville |
| University of Central Florida College of Medicine/HCA GME Consortium Program | 1401100909 | FL | Orlando |
| University of Florida College of Medicine Jacksonville Program | 1401121099 | FL | Jacksonville |
| University of Florida Program | 1401121098 | FL | Gainesville |
| University of Miami Miller School of Medicine/Holy Cross Hospital Program | 1401100929 | FL | Fort Lauderdale |
| University of Miami/JFK Medical Center Palm Beach Regional GME Consortium Program | 1401131535 | FL | Atlantis |
| Atlanta Medical Center Program (Wellstar) | 1401212106 | GA | Atlanta |

| Name | Accreditation ID | State | City |
|---|---|---|---|
| Emory University Program | 1401221105 | GA | Atlanta |
| Medical Center of Central Georgia/ Mercer University School of Medicine Program | 1401221491 | GA | Macon |
| Morehouse School of Medicine Program | 1401221502 | GA | Atlanta |
| Piedmont Athens Regional Program (new) | 1401200928 | GA | Athens |
| Advocate Health Care (Advocate Illinois Masonic Medical Center) Program | 1401611114 | IL | Chicago |
| Chicago Medical School at Rosalind Franklin University of Medicine and Science Program | 1401621111 | IL | North Chicago |
| Chicago Medical School/Rosalind Franklin Univ of Med & Sci Program | 1401600543 | IL | McHenry |
| John H Stroger Hospital of Cook County Program | 1401612113 | IL | Chicago |
| Louis A Weiss Memorial Hospital Program | 1401611115 | IL | Chicago |
| McGaw Medical Center of Northwestern University Program | 1401621119 | IL | Chicago |
| Mercy Hospital and Medical Center Program | 1401611116 | IL | Chicago |
| Mount Sinai Hospital Medical Center of Chicago Program | 1401621541 | IL | Chicago |

| Name | Accreditation ID | State | City |
|---|---|---|---|
| Presence Saint Francis Hospital Program | 1401611126 | IL | Evaston |
| Presence Saint Joseph Hospital (Chicago) Program | 1401611122 | IL | Chicago |
| Southern Illinois University Program | 1401621132 | IL | Springfield |
| University of Illinois College of Medicine at Peoria Program | 1401631131 | IL | Peoria |
| University of Illinois College of Medicine at Urbana Program | 1401621456 | IL | Urbana |
| Berkshire Medical Center Program | 1402411179 | MA | 1402411179 |
| Lahey Clinic Program | 1402421511 | MA | Burlington |
| MetroWest Medical Center Program | 1402421177 | MA | Framingham |
| Mount Auburn Hospital Program | 1402411176 | MA | Cambridge |
| Salem Hospital Program | 1402412180 | MA | Salem |
| St Elizabeth's Medical Center Program | 1402421173 | MA | Boston |
| St Vincent Hospital Program | 1402411183 | MA | Worcester |
| Steward Carney Hospital Program | 1402411166 | MA | Dorchester |
| UMMS-Baystate Program | 1402411181 | MA | Springfield |

| Name | Accreditation ID | State | City |
|------|------------------|-------|------|
| University of Massachusetts Program | 1402421184 | MA | Worcester |
| Harbor Hospital Center Program | 1402331158 | MD | Baltimore |
| Prince George's Hospital Center Program | 1402321161 | MD | Cheverly |
| Sinai Hospital of Baltimore Program | 1402312157 | MD | Baltimore |
| St Agnes HealthCare Program | 1402312156 | MD | Baltimore |
| Union Memorial Hospital Program | 1402312159 | MD | Baltimore |
| University of Maryland Medical Center Midtown Campus Program | 1402311154 | MD | Baltimore |
| Allegiance Health Program | 1402500912 | MI | Jackson |
| Detroit Medical Center/Wayne State University Program | 1402521194 | MI | Detroit |
| Hurley Medical Center/Michigan State University Program | 1402531196 | MI | Flint |
| McLaren-Flint/Michigan State University Program | 1402521471 | MI | Flint |
| Mercy Health Saint Mary's Program | 1402500927 | MI | Grand rapids |
| Providence-Providence Park Hospital/MSUCHM Program | 1402511203 | MI | Southfield |
| St John Hospital and Medical Center Program | 1402511191 | MI | Detroit |

| Name | Accreditation ID | State | City |
|------|------------------|-------|------|
| St Joseph Mercy Hospital Program | 1402512186 | MI | Ann Arbor |
| St Joseph Mercy-Oakland Program | 1402511200 | MI | Pontiac |
| Wayne State University School of Medicine Program | 1402500896 | MI | Rochester |
| William Beaumont Hospital Program | 1402512201 | MI | Royal Oak |
| Hennepin County Medical Center Program | 1402631207 | MN | Minneapolis |
| Mayo Clinic College of Medicine and Science (Rochester) Program | 1402621208 | MN | Rochester |
| University of Minnesota Program | 1402621205 | MN | Minneapolis |
| Mercy Hospital (St Louis) Program | 1402831217 | MO | St Louis |
| SSM St Mary's Hospital-St Louis Program | 1402811220 | MO | St Louis |
| St Luke's Hospital Program | 1402821219 | MO | St Louis |
| University of Missouri at Kansas City Program | 1402831214 | MO | Kansas City |
| University of Missouri-Columbia Program | 1402821210 | MO | Columbia |
| Vidant Medical Center/East Carolina University Program | 1403611323 | NC | Greenville |
| Atlantic Health (Morristown) Program | 1403311235 | NJ | Morristown |

| Name | Accreditation ID | State | City |
|------|------------------|-------|------|
| Atlantic Health (Overlook) Program | 1403311245 | NJ | Summit |
| Cooper Medical School of Rowan University/Cooper University Hospital Program | 1403321227 | NJ | Camden |
| Monmouth Medical Center Program | 1403311233 | NJ | Long Branch |
| New York Medical College at St Michael's Medical Center Program | 1403300532 | NJ | Newark |
| Saint Peter's University Hospital/ Rutgers Robert Wood Johnson Medical School Program | 1403321531 | NJ | New Brunswick |
| Seton Hall University School of Health and Medical Sciences (St Francis) Program | 1403313523 | NJ | Trenton |
| Seton Hall University School of Health and Medical Sciences at Englewood Hospital and Medical Center | 1403321228 | NJ | Englewood |
| Seton Hall University School of Health and Medical Sciences Program | 1403321498 | NJ | Elizabeth |
| University of Nevada Reno School of Medicine Program | 1403121483 | NV | Reno |
| Albany Medical Center Program | 1403531248 | NY | Albany |
| Bassett Medical Center Program | 1403511253 | NY | Cooperstown |

| Name | Accreditation ID | State | City |
|---|---|---|---|
| Bronx-Lebanon Hospital Center Program | 1403511263 | NY | Bronx |
| Brookdale University Hospital and Medical Center Program | 1403511264 | NY | Brooklyn |
| Brooklyn Hospital Center Program | 1403512265 | NY | Brooklyn |
| Coney Island Hospital Program | 1403511269 | NY | Brooklyn |
| Harlem Hospital Center Program | 1403511273 | NY | New York |
| Hofstra Northwell School of Medicine at Staten Island University Hospital Program | 1403511304 | NY | Staten Island |
| Icahn School of Medicine at Mount Sinai (Beth Israel) Program | 1403511261 | NY | New York |
| Icahn School of Medicine at Mount Sinai (Bronx) Program | 1403531517 | NY | Bronx |
| Icahn School of Medicine at Mount Sinai (Queens Hospital Center) Program | 1403521510 | NY | Jamaica |
| Icahn School of Medicine at Mount Sinai Program | 1403531288 | NY | New York |
| Icahn School of Medicine at Mount Sinai/St Luke's-Roosevelt Hospital Center Program | 1403521301 | NY | New York |
| Interfaith Medical Center Program | 1403521276 | NY | Brooklyn |
| Jacobi Medical Center/Albert Einstein College of Medicine Program | 1403531521 | NY | Bronx |

| Name | Accreditation ID | State | City |
|------|------------------|-------|------|
| Lincoln Medical and Mental Health Center Program | 1403521470 | NY | Bronx |
| Montefiore Medical Center/Albert Einstein College of Medicine (Moses and Weiler Campuses) Program | 1403521287 | NY | Bronx |
| Montefiore Medical Center/Albert Einstein College of Medicine (New Rochelle) Program | 1403511258 | NY | New Rochelle |
| Montefiore Medical Center/Albert Einstein College of Medicine (Wakefield Campus) Program | 1403521285 | NY | Bronx |
| Nassau University Medical Center Program | 1403521254 | NY | East Meadow |
| New York Medical College (Metropolitan) Program | 1403531290 | NY | New York |
| New York Medical College (Metropolitan) Program | 1403531290 | NY | New York |
| New York Presbyterian Hospital (Cornell Campus) Program | 1403521270 | NY | New York |
| New York-Presbyterian/Queens Program | 1403511262 | NY | New York |
| Rochester General Hospital Program | 1403531314 | NY | Rochester |
| Rochester Regional Health/Unity Hospital (Rochester) Program | 1403531527 | NY | Rochester |

| Name | Accreditation ID | State | City |
|---|---|---|---|
| St Barnabas Hospital Program | 1403521485 | NY | Bronx |
| St John's Episcopal Hospital-South Shore Program | 1403521486 | NY | Far Rockaway |
| Stony Brook Medicine/Mather Hospital Program | 1403500922 | NY | Port Jefferson |
| SUNY Health Science Center at Brooklyn Program | 1403521305 | NY | Brooklyn |
| United Health Services Hospitals Program | 1403531255 | NY | Johnson City |
| University at Buffalo (Catholic Health System--Sisters of Charity) Program | 1403521251 | NY | Buffalo |
| Woodhull Medical and Mental Health Center Program | 1403521487 | NY | Brooklyn |
| Wyckoff Heights Medical Center Program | 1403521520 | NY | Brooklyn |
| Akron General Medical Center/ NEOMED Program | 1403811328 | OH | Akron |
| Canton Medical Education Foundation/NEOMED Program | 1403821330 | OH | Canton |
| Case Western Reserve University (MetroHealth) Program | 1403811336 | OH | Cleveland |
| Case Western Reserve University/ University Hospitals Cleveland Medical Center Program | 1403821335 | OH | Cleveland |

| Name | Accreditation ID | State | City |
|---|---|---|---|
| Cleveland Clinic Foundation Program | 1403812339 | OH | Cleveland |
| Cleveland Clinic Foundation Program | 1403821340 | OH | Cleveland |
| Kettering Health Network Program | 1403821347 | OH | Kettering |
| Mercy St Vincent Medical Center/ Mercy Health Partners Program | 1403812533 | OH | Toledo |
| Ohio State University Hospital Program | 1403811342 | OH | Columbus |
| St Elizabeth Health Center/ NEOMED Program | 1403811349 | OH | Youngstown |
| St Vincent Charity Medical Center/ Case Western Reserve University Program | 1403811338 | OH | Cleveland |
| University of Toledo Program | 1403821348 | OH | Toledo |
| Abington Memorial Hospital Program | 1404112358 | PA | Abington |
| Albert Einstein Healthcare Network Program | 1404111369 | PA | Philadelphia |
| Conemaugh Memorial Medical Center Program | 1404131367 | PA | Johnstown |
| Drexel University College of Medicine/Hahnemann University Hospital Program | 1404121374 | PA | Philadelphia |
| Geisinger Health System Program | 1404111362 | PA | Danville |

| Name | Accreditation ID | State | City |
|---|---|---|---|
| Lehigh Valley Health Network/University of South Florida College of Medicine Program | 1404121359 | PA | Allentown |
| Main Line Health System/Lankenau Medical Center Program | 1404111373 | PA | Wynnewood |
| Mercy Catholic Medical Center Program | 1404111375 | PA | Darby |
| Pennsylvania Hospital of the University of Pennsylvania Health System Program | 1404111376 | PA | Philadelphia |
| PinnacleHealth Hospitals Program | 1404111365 | PA | Harrisburg |
| Reading Hospital Program | 1404121388 | PA | West Reading |
| Robert Packer Hospital/Guthrie Program | 1404112389 | PA | Sayre |
| St Luke's Hospital Program | 1404131360 | PA | Bethlehem |
| Temple University Hospital Program | 1404121378 | PA | Philadelphia |
| UPMC Medical Education (Mercy) Program | 1404111385 | PA | Pittsburgh |
| UPMC Medical Education Program | 1404121504 | PA | Pittsburgh |
| Memorial Hospital of Rhode Island/ Brown University Program | 1404321473 | RI | Pawtucket |

| Name | Accreditation ID | State | City |
| --- | --- | --- | --- |
| Roger Williams Medical Center Program | 1404331401 | RI | Providence |
| Grand Strand Regional Medical Center Program | 1404500406 | SC | Myrtle Beach |
| University of South Dakota Program | 1404621406 | SD | Sioux Falls |
| University of Tennessee College of Medicine at Chattanooga Program | 1404711407 | TN | Chattanooga |
| Methodist Hospital (Houston) Program | 1404813534 | TX | Houston |
| Texas Tech University (Amarillo) Program | 1404821477 | TX | Amarillo |
| Texas Tech University (Lubbock) Program | 1404821459 | TX | Lubbock |
| Texas Tech University (Permian Basin) Program | 1404821519 | TX | Odessa |
| University of Texas Health Science Center at Houston Program | 1404831423 | TX | Houston |
| University of Texas Health Science Center at Tyler/Good Shepherd Medical Center (Longview) Program | 1404800890 | TX | Longview |
| University of Texas Health Science Center School of Medicine at San Antonio Program | 1404821425 | TX | San Antonio |
| University of Texas Medical Branch Hospitals Program | 1404821421 | TX | Galveston |

| Name | Accredita-tion ID | State | City |
|---|---|---|---|
| University of Texas RGV (DHR) Program | 1404800891 | TX | Edinburg |
| University of Texas RGV (VBMC) Program | 1404821524 | TX | Harlingen |
| University of Texas Southwestern Medical School Program | 1404821419 | TX | Dallas |
| Eastern Virginia Medical School Program | 1405121432 | VA | Norfolk |
| Marshfield Clinic Program | 1405631444 | WI | Marshfield |
| Charleston Area Medical Center/ West Virginia University (Charleston Division) Program | 1405511438 | WV | Charleston |
| Marshall University School of Medicine Program | 1405521439 | WV | Huntington |

A well-thought strategy is required to smartly and effectively apply for residency, allowing you to determine a focused group of programs to apply for. I hope this serves as a guide for IMGs like myself struggling to find the best way to get the residency spot of their dreams.

## Basic Work Schedule Terminology During Residency

As an IMG (International Medical Graduate), I had to research and speak with a lot of people to understand different kinds of work schedules during residency. Familiarizing yourself with the basic work schedule terminologies during residency is quite important. It will help you to understand how your life as a resident will be and how to compare the workload in the different programs that you are interested in. If you are feeling confused by terms such as on-call, night shift, moonlight, float system, and others, please read this post that can help you solve all those doubts.

## Basic work terminologies during residency to understand:

1.  **On-call:** Regardless of the total hours that you will work, being on-call means that you will spend an entire day and night until the next day at the hospital. It can be a short or long call. The short call is usually until 8 pm, 9 pm or close. The long call is usually more than 24 hours. It can also be home-call or house-call (in-house always means at the hospital). Home-call means that you can go home and attend calls and beeper calls from home. In-house-call means that you need to stay at the hospital.

2.  **Day or night shift:** It is common during training programs like emergency medicine. What it means is that you will work on a predefined schedule, typically 12-hours long. For example: from 7 am to 7 pm, or 7 pm to 7 am. This can continue for months depending on the particular schedule of the residency program. However, in most cases, it also demands some daytime duties and it continues like that throughout the total residency length.

3.  **Night float:** This is a kind of new work system. In this context, a resident must cover the night shift every night, for example: from 7 pm to 7 am, six days a week, usually for a maximum of 1 month. No daytime work duties are needed. This helps reduce the duty hours of the residents working during the day, maintaining an adequate patient follow-up since night float residents know the patients that they see every day. Consider it to be like a rotation during your residency.

4.  **Moonlight:** In simple terms, it means working as an independent physician outside of the residency program. Moonlighting can be external when working outside of the scope of the program, and internal when you work inside the hospital as a provider. Every program has its own regulations, and not all of them will approve moonlighting.

# International medical graduate success stories

Every year international medical graduates apply from both Carribean medical schools and Non-US IMGs, for residency. The road to residency is very hard for international medical graduates as the process is grueling and expensive. I get calls and emails from thousands of IMGs every year asking if they have a chance of matching. In 2020, after the ACGME/AOA merger, 61% of IMGs matched into residency which is the highest in residency match history. A lot of international graduates get discouraged about lower match rates but I wanted to share some amazing stories of IMGs who have defied the odds and match into residency.

"I graduated from Dow University of Health Sciences in Karachi, Pakistan. I came to the US as IMG from Pakistan. I had completed my step 1 and step 2CK in Pakistan. I struggled when I was studying for USMLE, it was hard, but my grandmother helped me stay motivated. My score was 94 on step 1 back then. I got married when I got to the US, tried to take my Step CS 2 days from landing in the US, but failed. I retook step 2 CS and studied the right way and I passed. I got my ECFMG certification but no clinical experience. One day I found a yellow page book and started calling doctors around. I called 40 doctors and only one person responded. I found a Jewish doctor who agreed to have me shadow him for clinical observership. I applied to family medicine, peds, psych and anesthesia. I did not restrict myself with any locations. English was not my first language, so I practiced my script with my family and husband, for residency so as to get myself prepared and to make a good first impression. I had my personal statement checked by so many people, friends, family and others. I ranked anesthesia first and internal medicine, Family medicine and Peds. I matched into the Anesthesia program at University of Arkansas (UAMS). After residency I completed fellowship at Pediatric Anesthesiology fellowship: UT Houston, later became an Assistant Professor at Memorial Hermann Children's Hospital/LBJ/UT Houston, 3 years before moving to UAE to live close to the family. Working at a Children's Hospital in UAE during my tenure at UT, I coached and mentored medical students, residents and fellows. I was also the anesthesia team lead for the scoliosis repair program in my hospital.

After my move to UAE, I have started calling myself a global physician and started actively motivating and mentoring medical students and physicians struggling in various phases of life.

I am also a member of the board of trustees for an organization that takes care of underprivileged people, especially old people in Pakistan.

Dr. Sabina Ali Khan
Board certified, Pediatric Anesthesiology
IG: @sabina.ali.khan.md

I graduated with as IMG from University of Malta in 2017. I failed USMLE Step 1 in 2015. I initially had no plans of coming to the US. I just studied from First Aid and did not use UWORLD. After graduation, I started working as a foundation doctor in the UK. I have a Masters degree in Genetics. I got married and moved to the US, but I did not have any contacts when I first got to the US. A lot of things I got were from people online. Everything I read online said that if you failed step 1 as an IMG you had no chance. I was studying for USMLE while working 40 hours a week at MD Anderson, Houston doing clinical research and also doing an observership. I took all my USMLE Steps 1, 2CK, CS and 3 in 9 months while working. I was able to organize my time, have a schedule and did UWorld questions. I scored 219 on Step 1 on my second attempt. I took step 2CK and got 253. I almost gave up, because I applied to 140 programs mostly Internal medicine and Family medicine because I was under the impression that those were the only programs that would accept a fail in USMLE, and got no interviews. I had also applied to nine pathology programs as a Hail Mary with the hope that they would overlook my Step 1 fail because I was interested in Pathology. I was working with Dr. Nina Lum, founder of IMG roadmap, and she helped review my personal statement. I got only ONE interview and that was in pathology, my first choice program, so I planned for the interview, putting my best foot forward - and they saw I was interested. I matched into pathology on first attempt. My best advice for all IMGs is to try not to fail any exams but even if you do, never give up, network as much as possible and be humble. You can do it.

Moyosore Awobajo MD, PGY1
UT San Antonio, Department of Pathology
Medical School: University of Malta Medical School, 2017
Graduate School: (MSc, Human Molecular Genetics) Imperial College London, 2011
Undergraduate School: University of Leicester, 2010

I grew up in Lagos, Nigeria and attended medical school at the University of Ibadan, Nigeria. I transitioned to the University of Oklahoma where I got my Masters in Public Health. Despite the odds, I matched into General Surgery at the University of Oklahoma (OU). While at OU, I became the first General Surgery resident in the history of OU Department of Surgery to be inducted into the prestigious Alpha Omega Alpha medical honor society. I am currently a Thoracic surgery resident at the Baylor College of Medicine, Houston.

My advice to all International Medical Graduates is this: do not underestimate the scope of the competition, work hard to get good scores, network as wide as you can, keep dreaming big. Anything is possible.

Ademola A. Adeseye, MD MPH
Cardiothoracic Surgery Resident
Baylor College of Medicine, Houston, Texas
Author, "Making The Match: A practical guide to U.S Residency for International Medical Graduates"

I hope these amazing stories have been able to inspire you that you too can make it. The road to residency is filled with many twists and turns and only the one who is relentless, disciplined and perseverance will make it into residency. You must first believe in yourself and in God that you can make it. Remember, the word IMPOSSIBLE says I'M Possible. Keep working hard, networking, putting in the work and soon, you too will see your dream of becoming a physician in the United States come true.

## Final thoughts

When You Don't Get A Match

Unfortunately, some applicants will not get a match. This may happen because of failure to pass the Steps, but some students won't match even after having passed the three necessary exams.

Most programs receive thousands of applications from many well qualified medical students. In the end, they may opt for students with higher scores or other characteristics they are searching for.

This is an extremely harsh reality, especially for IMGs. Years of dedication and many thousands of dollars are spent trying to get into a residency program. It is normal to feel disappointed and sad, to say the least.

First and foremost, if you are feeling any symptoms of depression, we strongly urge you to seek professional help. Depression and suicide are a real problem in the community of medical students and physicians. Do not be afraid to get the help you need.

Secondly, you can try again next year. Maybe you just need to improve your resumé with some more meaningful clinical experience, for example. Also, there are many rewarding career paths you can take to use your knowledge and passion for healthcare.

Physician assistants (PAs) and nursing careers offer plenty of high-paying opportunities. Another practical option is to pursue a master's degree in public health (MPH). For example, John Hopkins has an MPH program that is popular with IMGs who ended up pursuing a career in education. Another option is to get a Masters in science (MS) in several fields if you are interested in research.

Finally, SmashUSMLE Reviews offers coaching/mentor opportunities for IMGs. You can use your experience to help others navigate the process.

The bottom line is, although it can feel like a disaster, you are not alone and there are plenty of other options.

Reference: Ecuadoctors.com,
https://ecuadoctors.com/u-s-medical-residency/

# CHAPTER 16:
# SmashUSMLE Review
# SMARTMD Program

WELCOME TO THE SmashUSMLE S.M.A.R.T. ™ Program. If this is the first time you are hearing about the program, then congratulations! You have hit the jackpot! My name is Dr. Adeleke Adesina. I am the founder of the program and I am very excited to meet you. The reason I am so excited to tell you about our S.M.A.R.T. ™ Program is because thousands of students have used this simple USMLE / COMLEX algorithm to be able to successfully crush their USMLE / COMLEX exams.

I welcome you on this journey and I am extremely excited to share these simple secrets that took us about 10 years to completely put together, just for you. Pat yourself on the back, and get ready for the ride. Here, we will explain the overview of our S.M.A.R.T. ™ Program. These are the steps you will take to be able to tackle this monster that we call the USMLE or COMLEX exam. We believe in you and trust you will be able to crush this exam. And remember, this exam does not define you, you are more than a test taker. SmashUSMLE reviews mission is to train you to become a better doctor.

## What is the S.M.A.R.T program?

S.M.A.R.T. ™ stands for Strategy, Mastery of Clinical Knowledge, Assess your knowledge, Repeat and review concepts, and Test taking strategies for taking NBME / USMLE and NBOME / COMLEX exams.

## Strategy:

- Practice test strategy (identify your weak areas).
- Create your USMLE/COMLEX schedule.
- Plan your pre-dedicated and intensive mastery period.
- How to use First Aid for the USMLE exam.

Here at SmashUSMLE reviews, we separate ourselves from the competition, like Kaplan, Doctors in Training, USMLERx, and other companies, because they focus on regurgitation of information, which is why many students fail their USMLE / COMLEX exam.

No one takes the time to teach strategy. There is a lot of content out there and many companies are only trying to sell you their content. We don't believe in that. At SmashUSMLE, we believe that to fail to prepare, is to prepare to fail. If you are driving from Florida to California, what are you going to need the most? A GPS. That's what we provide you as a personal coach when you sign up for our SmashUSMLE review program.

Your coach works with you one-on-one to teach you the correct strategies that help you understand the exam inside and out. We found that over the years, - especially if you are an international medical student - that the barrier to success on the USMLE is due to lack of strategy. Especially if you did not go to medical school in the United States. Even for US medical students, the majority of students who perform poorly on the USMLE and COMLEX did so because of lack of personal coaching and structure.

Before you take the USMLE/COMLEX, You need to know how the NBME / NBOME question writers think. You need to start thinking like they do and we help you learn that in our program.

At SmashUSMLE, we focus on a practice test strategy that allows you to identify your weak areas. It is very crucial that you are able to know what you're good at and where you need to improve. How will you tackle an exam if you don't know what you are strong in and which areas you are weak in? Once you identify your weak subjects, then you can know how to create your schedule. Many students I have met over the last 10 years do not know how to create their schedule. They go online and download other people's schedules. That will not work for you since every student is different. You cannot simply replicate someone else's schedule because you don't know their strong and weak areas. They have made their schedule to focus most on their weak areas, and you need to tweak your own schedule so that you focus on your own specific weak subjects. Once we teach you the practice test strategy, you will use that to personalize your own study schedule for the boards.

Then, we can show you how to maximize your intensive mastery period. There is another section that shows you what exactly you should be doing around your intensive mastery period, called the IMP. That is your dedicated study period. Some students have a 6-7 week period of IMP if they are US med students. If you are an IMG, you may need 3 months or even 4-6 months. Every student is different and your IMP needs to be preplanned even before you start studying for board exams.

First aid is the bible for Step 1. You need to know how to use your First Aid. A lot of students don't know how to use the book, and we will also show you how to use it properly.

## Mastery of clinical knowledge:

- Start watching USMLE video lectures (for weak subjects and IMGs must watch all lectures).
- Take notes in the latest edition of First Aid while watching the videos.

How should you watch the video lectures and use them to study? Should you study weak subjects first, or your strong ones?

You should be watching videos for content you are weak in first. You don't have the luxury, especially if you are a US student, to watch every single video. If you just came out fresh from your first two years of medical school, you still have all the knowledge in your mind and you should only be watching videos of subjects you are weak in. For example, if you are weak in biostatistics, you should watch all the biostatistics videos. However, for IMGs, you MUST watch all the videos. Some of you may have been out of medical school for 5 or 10+ years. You have not seen the Krebs cycle in perhaps 3+ years. You should watch all the videos from the beginning. The videos are short, high powered, high review videos that will help you knock this knowledge back into your mind. While watching videos, you should be taking notes in your First Aid. Always buy the latest edition. This is how you master the clinical knowledge portion of the exam.

# How to use video lectures when studying for Mastery of clinical knowledge

1. Start with a list of your weak topics. The first step to using videos when preparing for the boards is to **look at your schedule and highlight the important topics from First Aid that you find difficult.** You should factor in video studying time; watch a lecture and take detailed notes. Follow your list and only use videos when appropriate, and don't use video studying if you are strong in a certain subject area. You should use question banks or read the text for such concepts.

2. Use the speed option. With 6-8 weeks to prepare for the USMLE/ COMLEX, you do not have the luxury of watching every single video at 1.0 speed. **Try speeding up the video to 1.25x or 1.5x or even 2.0x**, if possible. Your brain is very adaptive. Start with 1.25x and after a while, you will adjust your learning speed. If you want to increase the speed more, know that you may lose the ability to take notes and you may need to rewind more. This may slow your studying down and you'll waste precious time.

3. Keep track. Once you have watched a video, check off the list of topics you have already covered on your master schedule until you complete your entire board review.


## Assess your clinical knowledge:

USMLE Q bank – Understand clinical framework

- The EASE method
- The checkpoint system

How do you assess what you have learned? This is where the Q bank comes in. The Q bank is the pathway to assessing what you have truly learned and what you still need to review. A lot of students do not know how to use Q banks in such a way as to siphon out everything they can from it. That is why we have created a section dedicated to explaining how to assess your clinical knowledge. You first have to understand the clinical framework of how question bank writers always write questions. There is always a clinical vignette that is presented on the board exam. That is how Step 1 and Step 2 content is all written. If you do not under-stand the clinical framework, you are setting yourself up for failure. This is what makes us different. We really focus on understanding the clinical framework.

We teach you the EASE method. You will learn a lot about the ease method in one of our mastery series sections in which we teach you how to use that EASE method while answering questions.

Also, there is a checkpoint system. While reading a clinical vignette, there are checkpoints you should be thinking about, while you are reading the question. This will allow you to answer the questions appropriately and without wasting time focusing on irrelevant material.

This is how you assess your clinical knowledge. By reinforcing concepts in question banks over and over and learning the integrative portion of the board exam, you are setting yourself up for success. You are hitting for that 240 or 250 on Step 1 or Step 2 CK.

## Review flashcards:

- Review weak subjects.
- Repeat and integrate concepts in your mind.
- Reinforce with flashcards

When we talk about review, the key is repetition. Review your weak subjects over and over. Always think about reviewing as grabbing the lowest hanging fruit. If I'm trying to take some apples off a tree, will it be wiser for me to be reaching for the apples all the way to the top? Or, the lowest hanging fruit, which is an apple I can actually reach for? This is how you should think about review. Whenever you are weak in a subject, we want you to review specific topics in the subject area that you do not understand well. That is what is going to get you those extra points. That is going to increase your score from a 220 to 227, to 232. That is what separates the good from the great and from the people that fail the exam. While you are reviewing, we want you to be repeating and integrating concepts in your mind. If I say parvovirus, you should be thinking about aplastic anemia. That should be the next topic entering your mind. This is integration. You should always be thinking of an association that is commonly tested on step 1.

Also, you cannot beat flashcards. Flashcards force you to review content very quickly. It especially allows you to recall information you have read in the past and allows you to see if you are able to answer the questions in an easy manner.

# Test taking strategies:

- Take NBME assessment tests at 1 week, 3 weeks, and 5 weeks into dedicated study time.
- Learn test taking strategies. Take the USMLE.

Before you take the real exam, you need to be taking NBME assessments to gauge your performance from week 1, to week 3, to week 5. If you spend 3 months studying, spread the exams further out than weeks 1, 3, and 5. Do the NBME exams at 1 month, 2 months, and then 3 months into your dedicated study time. This will allow you to understand your performance curve to see if you are growing and improving your knowledge.

There is a separate section on test taking strategies. This is a marathon, guys. You need to be prepared. People that run 13 or 26-mile marathons prepare their minds for the many miles, because what happens is that by the 17th mile, your body is locking up on you as it builds up lactic acid. We do not want you to get fatigued like that. By the time you reach the finish line we want you to get ready to hit it head on. So, the key we teach you at SmashUSMLE is test taking strategy; how to overcome anxiety on the exam; eating the right food content for the exam; making sure you answer all the questions. These are all the things we are going to teach you in this program. This is what makes our program awesome! We are going to show you different test taking strategies that help students crush these exams, because we want you to walk into that exam confident, head up, and shoulders back; walk in there and knock this beast out of the park, because this is just one single exam. You are one step closer to crushing Step 1. One step closer to becoming a doctor and matching into residency. That is what you are training for. That is the ultimate goal.

**So, without further ado, remember the S.M.A.R.T. ™ Program.**

- Strategy
- Mastery of clinical content
- Assessing your clinical knowledge
- Review
- Test taking strategy and taking NBMEs.

This is what makes us different here at SmashUSMLE.
I cannot wait to get you on board so you can take this course!
Visit smashusmle.com to get started.

# CHAPTER 17:
## Student concerns

HERE ARE SOME of the common concerns that students face when doing practice questions or taking assessment exams:

1. I am very nervous and anxious about the exam.
2. I am not a good standardized test-taker.
3. I always run out of time on standardized exams.
4. The questions stems are too long.
5. We have to read the question as many times as possible to figure out the answer.
6. We have to answer every question correctly because we are smart and we want to get every question right.
7. I find myself changing the exam answers.

Let's look at some solutions for these worrisome concerns and mistakes medical students often make.

### 1. Test-taker anxiety

Everyone experiences some form of anxiety and stress when it comes to exams. Some have a higher level of anxiety than others. However, if you could choose one day in your entire life when you want to be the least anxious and worried, it would probably be the USMLE or COMLEX exam day—the day for one of the most important exams you will take in your medical career. This is because you only get one shot at it (unless you fail), and if you miss your target, there are no amendments. Once you pass the exam, you cannot retake the test ever again, perhaps sad, but true. *For USMLE Step 1 test takers in 2022, USMLE Step 1 will be reported as pass/or fail but Step 2CK and 3 are reported in three-digit scores.*

There is a difference between stress and anxiety. Anxiety disorder can affect anyone and will negatively influence your studying. This will reflect on your performance during the preparation process and on the actual exam. If you know you have an anxiety disorder, seek help before taking the test. Most schools provide services that help students struggling with anxiety or depression. Those services are there for a reason—use them.

With respect to stress, there are a number of ways to tackle it. While some people tune in their favorite music, or go outside their study place preferably in a natural setting like a garden/park, others prefer to do some breathing exercises, jotting it down or seeking the company of a friend. Always remind yourself that a little bit of stress is a good thing. Remember, it's always about eu**STRESS** and not di**STRESS**.

Honestly, no matter how hard you study or how long you study for the exam, you can never be truly satisfied with the level of your preparation for the test. How much work you put into studying prior to your exam date makes the difference. If you have completed two to three thousand questions, you should have no doubt that you are well prepared. And if you have more questions, then *relax*. Be prepared— it's the best advice we can give you. Anxiety only makes it worse. Allow yourself a relaxed and positive attitude because you have done your best, and accept the fact that you can only prepare so much. Do your part, and leave the rest to God.

## 2 and 3. I am not a good standardized test-taker *and* I have time issues

Many students use this pair as excuses for poor performance on their Boards when the real reason was lack of preparation. **As Benjamin Franklin said, "By failing to prepare, you are preparing to fail."** Consider this: you got through the SATs, undergraduate college exams, the MCAT, graduate school exams (for some of us), and the first two years of medical school, where you took exams every other week. There is no doubt you will make it through this exam, too, unless you work towards failing. Create a different perspective about the test. Think positively about the exam, and realize that you are not the first one to take the test and you will not be the last. When you take the practice tests, time yourself and create an atmosphere to mimic real exam conditions; go to the library or classroom, where you will be less distracted, match the timings and even try to make your diet as you would do the exam day. Practice this way, and you will feel that the exam is just like any other day for you.

# 4 and 5. Issues with the question style

Remember, there is not much time during the exam. Reading each question more than once is wasting time. When you're doing practice questions or taking assessment exams, you should aim at reading each question once and only once. Read it slowly and carefully. Every word counts so be careful! Words can count for you and against you. How? Many of the questions as you will see in SmashUSMLE, UWorld or other question banks include extra information put there to distract you and widen your differential. Try to stay focused and read the question without distractions. If you have read it carefully and still cannot answer the questions, chances are that you simply do not know the answer. Mark it and return to it if you have time at the end of the block. *Do not* panic. Maybe you are overthinking it; maybe it is just a topic you never studied. Move on to score points from questions you *can* answer.

What works for many people is to first read the question statement (usually the last sentence of the question paragraph). This helps you select the relevant clues from the question paragraph and identify the key that opens the answer.

Many questions can be answered based on the information given, combined with a little or sometimes no information beyond the question. You need to read such questions in detail.

Example: "Blah Blah Blah. What is the most likely diagnosis?" or "Blah Blah Blah. What is the most likely cause of this disease?"

With these types of questions, read the whole paragraph and use every hint to rule in and rule out possible answers.

However, some questions describe the disease, tell you what it is, and then ask you about the pathogenesis or mechanism of the underlying process. This completely depends on your knowledge of the fact that the specific question is addressed. Basically, you could have just read the last sentence and answered the question. In that case, reading the whole paragraph wasted time; you could have just skipped to the last sentence and answered the question.

Example. "Blah Blah Blah. The patient was diagnosed with Duchenne Muscular Dystrophy. What is the mode of inheritance of this disease?"

Answer: Autosomal dominant.

The point is clear—save time when you can, read quickly but efficiently, and do not let them trick you with extra information. Key to solving the USMLE exam questions is to know what part of the question is important and ignoring the distractors. Refer to "how to dissect USMLE questions chapter for more details."

## 6. Answering all the questions correctly

Answering all the questions correctly is impossible, simply because these exams test material from many books, and there is no way you can cover everything for the exam. Study hard, do your best, and aim for the best scores, but be realistic. Deciding in advance that you must answer each question correctly will do nothing but hurt you, because every time you can't answer a question, it increases your anxiety and nurtures a pessimistic attitude.

The worst feeling is missing the easy questions, the stuff you felt silly reviewing because you knew it better than your name before you sat for the exam. Now under the influence of anxiety, it completely flies out of your head, and you sit there biting your fingers and hitting your head on the desk. Stop! Tell yourself that USMLE exam questions are about the **intent**, not just **content**. Move on, and come back to it later. There is a high chance that you will remember the answer in a few minutes when you are less anxious.

Please do not take any books (especially your *First Aid* book) with you to the testing center. As soon as you walk out for every break, you are going to check your answers—you know it! Do not do that.

Do not read your *First Aid* during break sessions either! Take the time to relax and walk around the center to get fresh air. The exam is long and requires a positive attitude and rested mind the entire time. Do not get your mind busy with negative thoughts about how or why you missed that one question. It is okay; it is okay; it is okay. It happens to everyone.

## 7. Changing exam answers

This is a huge no-no during the exam. In any MCQ type exams, it's not *strange* to *change* the answers. The probability that you will switch the right answer to a wrong one is very high. Warning! Warning! Except if you are *absolutely* sure that you chose the wrong answer initially, please, *do not change your first answer*. Do you know why they call the wrong answers *distractors*? Because they are wrong; do not fall for them.

Make it a habit, even when you do practice questions, to pick one answer and move on. If you are not sure, mark it and go back if you have extra time. Do not waste your time looking through the answers if you know the right answer. You are almost certainly correct. Leave your answer alone and move on. Trust us—on the actual exam, you will still be tempted to do this! It is almost inevitable, but try your best to avoid this urge.

For example: "A twenty-eight-week primigravida woman presents with painless vaginal bleeding …" The answer is placenta previa! Do not waste your time with other options; move on!

## After the Test

It is important to correlate the feelings and emotions you experience after taking the assessment exams to the scores you get on the assessment exams.

The reason we say that is because you will walk out of the actual test feeling very similar to how you felt after the assessment exam, and that should tell you how you did on the test. Hopefully, it should be good news for you.

For example, after taking every single assessment exam, we felt horrible afterward and thought that we failed. However, the scores were really good. Some of our friends felt that they did really well and ended up getting similar scores to us. On the day of the actual exams, we walked out thinking we failed, while some of our friends walked out thinking they performed really well. It felt just like taking another self-assessment exam, except that we did not get the scores right away. But it was comforting to know that we felt the same way as we did when we were taking our assessment exams, and we probably had done just as well.

Celebrate regardless! No matter how bad you think you did, still celebrate, because you deserve it. You just completed one of the most difficult exams in your life. Most likely, you got the score you expected based on your assessment exams. It takes about four weeks to receive the USMLE scores and six weeks to receive the COMLEX scores. NBME will send an e-mail the morning of the day the scores are to be released, and the scores will be available online. You can print it for up to 120 days. The report includes a three-digit score, the two-digit score, and a breakdown of the topics (pathology, anatomy, et cetera). NBOME will mail a letter with the score report of your COMLEX exam, similar to the USMLE report, and scores will also be available online. Regardless of your scores, keep a positive attitude and be flexible and smart about your choices when it comes to residency.

# CHAPTER 18:
## Summary chapter for Board review

1. Set your goals: Write down your target score before you begin studying for the USMLE or COMLEX. Place your target score in a place where you will see daily and work towards it. You cannot hit a target you do not have.

2. Create a schedule and follow it. Schedules are a road map to guide you to your destination. Adjust your schedule based on your weak areas only.

3. Have a positive mindset: This is a marathon and you must have the most positive attitude to get through long hours of studying. Surround yourself with people who are positive, join a Facebook group, join SmashUSMLE SMARTMD WhatsApp group. You will need a lot of motivation to get through the dark days.

4. Avoid social media and USMLE forums. Most students spend too much time on reddit and USMLE-forums looking for answers, but end up with anxiety and confusion from reading too many people's posts or online advice. Focus on what you can control, study at your pace and work hard, you will see results.

5. Turn off your phone: The biggest distraction when studying for the USMLE/COMLEX is your phone. Turn it off while you study because one peek at one Instagram post can lead to one hour of scrolling on social media. Resist the temptation.

6. Avoid alcohol and drugs. Do not laugh, this is actually serious. Some Students abuse these substances.

7. Check your mental well-being. You cannot perform well if you are depressed—do not take the test; take a leave of absence and seek help through your school or, see a healthcare professional.

8. Select review sources for all topics before you begin; switch sources only for a good reason. Do not let panic drive you to exceed the time and material you had scheduled for a given topic. From the beginning, put **practice question time** on your study schedule. Use them to 1) preview a topic, 2) test knowledge of a topic, and 3) refresh your memory on a topic. Periodic comprehensive exams, which help you practice switching from topic to topic, are also good training, but save these for later in the schedule.

9. Regular routine builds confidence in your progress. Eat well, sleep well, exercise, and protect yourself from negative influences. Take care of yourself like an athlete in training. This COMLEX/USMLE immersion study experience can improve your discipline.

10. Use study groups and partners if they have the right pace and approach for your needs. Coordinate the topics, plan in advance and prepare for the sessions.

11. Does anxiety hinder either your study or your test-taking? The good antidote is to do practice questions and habitually analyze your errors. See if you are capable of predicting your own performance. If anxiety or other factors affect your progress, ask for help in your school or wherever you can receive adequate treatment. They should offer services for students who are having anxiety issues.

12. **Health**– Throughout this study process, don't forget to take care of yourself. Limit social interaction and fun time, as it is in your best interest to focus at this critical time.

13. Limit your caffeine intake and get enough sleep each night. Develop a strict daily routine for yourself, so you can make the most progress out of each day.

## Five Principles for Effective Learning and Test-Taking

- **Keep learning active.** Whether you learn best by preparing written summaries, reciting information aloud, or making diagrams or concept maps, do whatever it takes to *learn it the first time*! This will make your study process much more efficient, since you can spend more time reviewing—which is critical to *retaining* information. Re-read First Aid at least twice before taking the actual exam, check your weakest areas and work to improve your knowledge to maximize your score.

- **"Encode" the information in as many ways as possible.** This is how you can make learning an active process, by making *meaning* from the material, connecting it to other facts you already know, using mnemonics, white boards, sound effects, YouTube, colorful analogies, or metaphors and by categorizing the information in a meaningful way; e.g. Most common cause of cancer in the US, the five cities where a particular microbe is found (Histoplasmosis, Blastomycosis, Coccidiomycosis). Also, incorporating all the senses is best for recall.

- **Attempt to visualize information.** The latest research into long-term memory shows that we store and recall information in terms of images, events, and experiences. So any method you can use to make an image more vivid— e.g., making it multisensory, using color coding—will make facts easier to recall.

- **Repeat reviews.** This is what ultimately shifts information from short-to long-term memory and maintains retention. **Active learning + regular reviews = long-term retention**. If any one part of this equation is missing, you risk not really knowing and recalling the information when needed. Use flashcards that you make to continue to review what you have learned in the past, for quick recall and long term memorization.

- **Practice questions.** The key to mastery is through practicing questions. Using the EASE-checkpoint method discussed in the earlier chapter is the key to using a systematic approach to learning. By the time you do thousands of questions, you will be familiar with how the USMLE and COMLEX are constructed. Use questions to determine where you need to focus your study time. Continually assess what you've learned, go over your correct and incorrect answer choices and clarify any unclear concepts.

# Question Analysis During the Study Process→→ Three Steps

1. ***Identify topics.*** Identify all possible topics that are being covered by the question and the answer choices. Highlight or circle *all* the words that could possibly change the meaning.

2. ***Understand the correct answer …for obvious reasons!***

3. ***Understand the wrong answers and why they're wrong.*** Incorrect answers are plausible or they would not be good distractors. For this reason, it's extremely valuable to go over the wrong answers as well. Ask yourself: "under what circumstances would this answer be correct?" By doing so, you learn *four times* as much about the topic, you learn better test-taking skills, and you also uncover the pattern and subtleties of question construction. Going through this process can prepare you for other questions!

## During the exam, do not …

- Let yourself get mentally down after the first day. Most Board exams win the battle on the second day because people are not mentally prepared and give up at sign of discouragement. Be sure to keep yourself sharp until the very end.

- Try to determine how well you are doing. You won't be able to be objective, and you'll only increase your anxiety.

- Expect to feel like a "master of the medical universe." Chances are that you will probably not achieve the level of competency you are used to. Remember, this is a nationally standardized exam—not a mastery test.

- On the day before test day, DO NOTHING. Give your brain and body a day of rest, as you will need both to be functional the next day. You may do questions if you must, but do not open a book. By now, you've worked hard and it's time to show it. Be confident in yourself and your answer choices.

We hope this summarizes your approach to Board studying.

# CHAPTER 19:
# The Journey to 260

WE WANT TO give you a clearer perspective on what it actually means to score a 260 on the real exam. We chose 260 as a benchmark because this is a very difficult score to get and only 4% of students who take the USMLE attain this goal. However, we believe if you "shoot for the moon, you'll land amongst the stars." If you shoot higher, you increase your chance of scoring higher, and do not beat yourself up if you did not attain the magical 260. This is not the cure for HIV or pancreatic cancer. Let see what the numbers say:

- The mean scores on the USMLE Step 1 among US and Canadian exam takers in 2014, 2015, and 2016 were 229, 229, and 228, respectively. For Step 2CK, the means for 2017, 2018, and 2019 were 242, 243 and 243, respectively. For step 3 the mean was 225, 226,226 (2016-2018) (USMLE score interpretation guidelines)
- Only 9% of all exam takers scored 255 or higher on the USMLE Step 1; **Only 4% scored 260 or higher on the exam**
- Less than 1% scored 270 or higher (see snapshot below)

| Norm Table Based on US/Canadian First Takers* | |
|---|---|
| **USMLE Step 1** | |
| *USMLE Score* | **Percentile** |
| 265 | 99 |
| **260** | **96** |
| 255 | 91 |
| 250 | 84 |
| 245 | 76 |
| 240 | 67 |

What about scoring a "240?" The magical number that guarantees you will not be turned down by most residency programs.

***Only the top 33% of exam takers achieve a 240+ on test day.***

To give you a much better perspective, here are the 2018 USMLE Step 1 scores of U.S. Allopathic Seniors by preferred specialty and Match Status. Note: In 2022, Step 1 scores will be pass/fail.

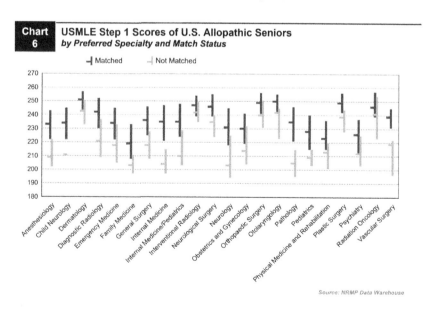

**Chart 6** — USMLE Step 1 Scores of U.S. Allopathic Seniors *by Preferred Specialty and Match Status*

Source: NRMP Data Warehouse

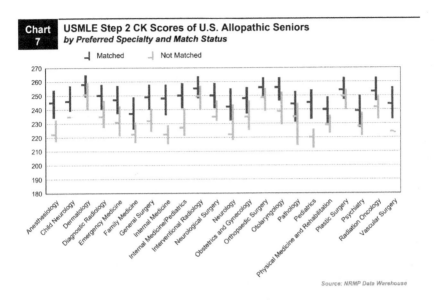

**Chart 7**

**USMLE Step 2 CK Scores of U.S. Allopathic Seniors**
*by Preferred Specialty and Match Status*

Source: NRMP Data Warehouse

*\*Chart 6 from the NRMP Charting the Outcomes in the Match for 2018*

Now that you know the truth, just look at the graph above and select the specialty you want to match into. You can see the scores of the matched and unmatched candidates. As a U.S. graduate, you can match with a 235 in most specialties except Dermatology, Neurosurgery, Otolaryngology (ENT), Plastic Surgery and Radiation Oncology. Because of the extremely competitive nature of these specialties, you must score very high to get a chance to match into them.

If you are an international student, we strongly recommend that you ignore U.S. graduate average scores. They don't apply to you. You should aim for a 240 or higher to increase your chances of getting interviews and matching into residencies.

Remember to work hard to achieve your dream score. You should not close the door to your dreams, but instead, be diligent in your study for the USMLE and know that, in the end, everything will work out. Your USMLE score is not the only thing that will get you into residency.

"Most things will be okay eventually, but not everything will be. Sometimes you'll put up a good fight and lose. Sometimes you'll hold on really hard and realize there is no choice but to let go. Acceptance is a small, quiet room."

*— Cheryl Strayed,*
*Tiny Beautiful Things:*
*Advice on Love and Life from Dear Sugar*

# CHAPTER 20:
## Exam day secrets

IT's GAME DAY! Am I ready? Those are the three words that you will ask yourself, one day before your USMLE exam.

Before I answer this question for you. Let's recap.

You have been studying for the last 7 weeks (if you are a U.S medical student with a dedicated study period) or 12 weeks or more, if you are an international medical graduate. You are ready if you have completed the S.M.A.R.T doctors program - as I call it - at SmashUSMLE reviews.

1. **Strategies**: You set your target USMLE score. You have used the NBME test taking strategy and determined your weak subjects. You created your schedule accordingly and followed it to the letter.

2. **Mastery:** You have mastered the clinical contents in First Aid by watching videos on topics you are weak on, improved your clinical content deficits and you are able to recollect/recognize the information when presented in a clinical vignette.

3. **Assess your knowledge**: You have completed a minimum of 2000 USMLE Step 1 or Step 2 CK question bank and read the correct and incorrect answer choices. You took notes in your first Aid book accordingly. If you completed two question banks, then you are a rockstar! Your NBME scores have been improving with time and you are approaching your target score.

4. **Review**: You have read your First Aid book twice! Fully understand the concepts in a big picture not just minutia. You are able to integrate all the concepts together in your mind. You can think in 2-3 step order processes when questions are presented to you.

5. Take NBME exams 5 days before your actual USMLE scheduled date and score above or near your target USMLE score. For example, if

you were aiming for 235, and your NBME scores are ranging between 233 and 240.

Did you know that you can take your NBME at the Prometric center? Yes. You can do a USMLE Computer based test at the Prometric center, as long you are registered already to take the USMLE and have a permit.

Practice Sessions are available, for a fee of $75 (U.S), for registered examinees who want the opportunity to become familiar with the Prometric test center environment. This is totally optional and the questions are the same as the NBME question online. It just allows you to imitate the look and feel of taking the NBME questions at the Prometric center.

If you have done the step above, then, you are ready to take the test. But if you have not, or your NBME score is low or barely passing, **YOU SHALL NOT TAKE THE TEST**. Do not take the USMLE, you will fail or get a low score, I guarantee you that.

Reschedule your test and re-evaluate what you are doing wrong, or get a coach to help you identify your weak areas.

Here is the truth, no matter how hard and long you study, you will never be able to memorize every single concept in First Aid. If you can recollect 85-90% of the concepts in FA, you will crush the test.

## Here are 10 Rituals you must do before taking your USMLE.

1.  Day before the test:

    *DO NOT STUDY: STOP! STOP!! STOP!!! I mean don't study anything. Place your First Aid and all review books in a closet where you will not see them. Your mind will play games on you, telling you to read more at loeffler's endocarditis or amino acid pathway, there is a little disease you forgot to read, start studying last minute. No! Do not do it. Stay away from online forums and social media.*

    Do the USMLE exam orientation: visit http://orientation.nbme.org/Launch/USMLE/STPF1

    Use the Google chrome browser to navigate through USMLE exam tutorials. This will save you 15 minutes on your test day that you can use for your exam. I strongly recommend you do this tutorial!

2.  Collect all your identification. You will need to present any of the following: Driver's license with photograph, National **Identity** Card, or some other form of unexpired, government-issued **identification**.

3.  Print your paper or electronic copy of your **scheduling permit from the NBME website.** I forgot mine on the exam day. That was the worst feeling, I panicked and freaked out when I realized this. Do not be like me, print at least 2-3 copies just in case. Thank God, my friend brought it for me.

    **If you do not bring your scheduling permit on paper or electronically (e.g., via smartphone) and acceptable identification on each day of your exam, you will not be allowed to take the test** and will be required to pay a fee to reschedule your test. Your rescheduled test date(s) must fall within your eligibility period. Check out: https://www.usmle.org/apply/rescheduling-fees.html for rescheduling fees.

4.  Go shopping: Go to the food store and buy some fruits or protein bars. Cook or buy the lunch meal you will be eating when you take your main break. Use the snacks to increase your energy when you take your mini breaks. It's a long exam, you do not want to be hungry taking this test.

5.  Clothing: Select your most comfortable clothing, clean it, fold it and get it ready. Bring a sweater, in case the exam center is too cold for you.

6.  Visit the Prometric center. Drive to the Prometric center to see how far it is and go in to ask questions from the proctors. Get a feel for the place, check traffic to prepare for congestion in the morning.

7.  Check your mode of transportation: Fill your car with gas, check to make sure it is running well. If you plan to take uber/lyft, download the app and set it up in advance.

8.  Exercise: Go for a brief workout. Listen to good calming music. Do not get injured playing basketball or football. Wrong sport to choose. Just running is fine.

9.  Watch Netflix or go to the movies: This is perfect. Watch your favorite movie on Netflix or go to the movies with friends, but do not stay out late drinking. This is not the day to get a hangover.

10. Get a good night rest. Go to bed early and sleep for at least 8 hours. Get up and shower. Wake up at least 2 hours early, eat breakfast, pray and check to make sure you have all your IDs before leaving the house.

## For Step 1, Step 2 CK, Step 3

You should arrive at the test center approximately 30 minutes prior to your scheduled testing appointment. If you arrive after your appointment time, you may not be admitted. If you arrive more than 30 minutes after your scheduled testing appointment, you will **not** be admitted and must pay a fee to reschedule your test. Your rescheduled test date(s) must fall within your eligibility period.

## Step 2 CS

You should arrive at the test center at the time listed on the confirmation notice you will have printed after scheduling your appointment. There will be an on-site orientation to demonstrate the equipment available for you to use in the examination rooms and to review examination rules and procedures.

If you arrive during the on-site orientation, you may be allowed to test after signing a Late Admission Form. If you arrive after the on-site orientation, you will not be allowed to test and must pay a fee to reschedule your test. Your rescheduled test date must fall within your eligibility period.

## Security Procedures
## For Step 1, Step 2 CK, and Step 3 ONLY

During check-in, the test center staff will scan you with a metal detector (handheld or walk-through) and ask you to empty your pockets and turn them inside out before entering the testing room to confirm that you have no prohibited items. You will be asked to repeat this process each time you return to the testing room after a break. Additionally, your photo ID and fingerprint may be scanned electronically, and you must sign the test center log each time you enter or exit the test room.

Before you enter the test room, test center staff will give you laminated writing surfaces and markers to use for making notes and/or calculations during the testing session. You will be instructed to write your name and

CIN, as shown on your scheduling permit, on one of the laminated writing surfaces provided.

Writing surfaces and markers should be used only at your assigned testing station, and only after you have entered your CIN in the computer to start your test session. If you have filled the laminated writing surfaces and need additional space for making notes, raise your hand to ask test center staff for a replacement. You must return laminated writing surfaces to test center staff at the end of the testing session.

**Do NOT write on anything (e.g., skin, clothing, tissue) other than the laminated writing surface. Failure to comply may result in a finding that you engaged in irregular behavior.**

Test center staff will escort you to your assigned testing station and provide brief instructions on use of the computer equipment. You must enter your CIN to start the examination. A brief tutorial is available before each examination. You must run the sound check for the audio headphones either before the examination begins or during the tutorial, so that problems can be resolved before you start the examination.

## For Step 2 CS ONLY

During check-in, in addition to having your photo ID scanned electronically, you will be asked to place your personal belongings (e.g., pens, study materials, cell phones) in small bins, which are inaccessible for the duration of the examination day. Any personal belongings that you may need during breaks or during the examination, including your lab coat and stethoscope, can be placed at your seat in the orientation room. Please note that every area of the testing center is under video surveillance at all times; examinees are escorted by proctors at all times, with the exception of restroom breaks.

## During the test

BEFORE STARTING YOUR EXAM, TAKE 10 DEEP BREATHS AND THEN START.

Wait...

**Let me show you my secret hack to biostatistics on the USMLE exam**

Biostatistics and behavioral science are one of the least favorite subjects of medical students taking the USMLE step 1, 2 CK and Step 3 exam.

I totally get it, but listen, the NBME questions writers are not trying to make your life miserable, but are preparing you for your future as a clinical.

In medical school you learn anatomy, physiology, pathology, Pharm and so on but as important as these subjects are in understanding basic sciences, the practice of clinical medicine is based on evidence-based guidelines.

You must be able to read and analyze journal articles, randomized control trials, and meta-analysis publications, and you must be able to use these recommended guidelines to practice medicine to safely take care of your patients.

So, whether you hate doing math or memorizing formulas, you MUST learn biostatistics for the USMLE and COMLEX exam.

**Here are the top 6 things you must know about the biostat section on the USMLE/COMLEX;**

1. It's a word problem section on the USMLE – get used to it.
2. Know how to solve fractions, percentages, decimals.
3. Know how to convert words into 2x2 tables!
4. Memorize ALL statistical formulas!
5. Know definitions of statistical terminologies
6. Practice, practice, practice!!!

On your test day, you will be given a piece of white board and maker. **The first thing is to write down all the biostatistics formulas.** This will help you tremendously throughout the test. Here are the formulas below.

**The Truth**

| Test Score: | Has the disease | Does not have the disease | |
|---|---|---|---|
| Positive | True Positives (TP) a | False Positives (FP) b | $PPV = \dfrac{TP}{TP + FP}$ |
| Negative | c False Negatives (FN) | d True Negatives (TN) | $NPV = \dfrac{TN}{TN + FN}$ |

| Sensitivity | Specificity |
|---|---|
| $\dfrac{TP}{TP + FN}$ | $\dfrac{TN}{TN + FP}$ |
| Or, $\dfrac{a}{a+c}$ | $\dfrac{d}{d+b}$ |

Odds ratio: **(AD)/(BC)**

Relative risk: **[A/(A+B)] / [C/(C+D)]**

Relative risk reduction: **1-RR**

**Attributable risk (AR)** = risk in exposed - unexposed patients = **[A/(A+B)] - [C/(C+D)]**

**Absolute Risk Reduction (ARR)= [C/(C+D)] / [A/(A+B)]**

**Number needed to treat: 1/ARR**

**Number needed to harm= 1/AR**

**Positive Likelihood Ratio** = Sensitivity/1- specificity

Reality

| | H1 | H0 |
|---|---|---|
| Study rejects H0 | Power $(1 - \beta)$ | $\alpha$ Type I error |
| Study does not reject H0 | $\beta$ Type II error | Correct |

# Now let's begin the exam,

Stick to your plan. You will be anxious but calm your nerves. You are prepared. Ignore the people around you, just concentrate on yourself. It's time to smash the USMLE exam. Follow the same strategies you have used to answer over 2000 questions, and do not change your plan.

If you are unsure of the answer to a question, do not waste your time on it, cross out the incorrect answers, narrow it down to 2 possible best answers and mark the question and skip it. Your ultimate goal is to answer every question: there are no penalties for getting questions wrong. Remember, TIME IS NOT YOUR ENEMY, WRONG ANSWERS ARE YOUR ENEMY.

Once you have attempted all questions, now go back to the marked questions and try to answer them again. You will notice that you omitted some important information when reading the question, the first time that will help guide you to answer it the second time. If you just cannot figure out the answer, take your best educated guess and move on.

As you move from one block to another, here is a word of advice for you; DO NOT KEEP THINKING ABOUT THE QUESTIONS FROM THE LAST BLOCK THAT YOU DID NOT KNOW OR COULD NOT ANSWER. This will affect your focus on the exam and affect your overall performance. It's a common pitfall students' fall into on the test.

You cannot go back to the block anyways and there is absolutely nothing you can do now, so cut your losses and move on.

You have an option to take breaks. Take them. If you start to feel tired, take a quick bathroom break, eat your snacks in between breaks to rejuvenate yourself.

Then look at yourself in the mirror and talk to yourself with energy. Say "hey listen man/woman, I have come so far on this journey, I am here to crush it, I am crushing it, and I am still in the game. Today I am crushing this test and getting closer to becoming a doctor. I will not let my family down, I will not let my friends down, and I will not let my mentors down. If there is someone who can do it and pull it off, that is me. I am here for a reason, I am here to fulfill my dream, I am here to start a new chapter of my life, I will, I will, I will have my hand raised by the end of this day.

You will get a 30-minute break in between your 4th and 5th block. Take it. Go outside, get some fresh air, eat your lunch and relax. Do not take your First Aid or review book with you to the testing center; you will be tempted to look at it and get more anxiety as you realized you may have picked the wrong answer on one or more questions.

Remember, you will not get every question right on the test. There will be experimental questions that you will see that are not graded. Do not be frazzled about these questions, every student feels the same way. You will say things like wtf, FML, I never read anything about this. Do not worry yourself. Just take your best guess and move on.

## After the test

Celebrate. You have done what very few people in life will never experience; Conquer step 1 or 2 or 3 and on your way to becoming a doctor. Be proud of yourself. You did it! Wait patiently for your score report and I hope you get the dream score you aimed for at the beginning. I am really proud of you as I conclude this chapter. You are a SMARTDOC.

Best of luck.

## Reference

*Admission to the test: https://www.usmle.org/bulletin/testing/#Admission*

# CHAPTER 21:
## The 10 unwritten rules about clinical rotations

WE TOOK THE boards after second year and celebrated our achievements. Overnight, we became third-year medical students. The beginning of a new world awaited us as we wore our white coats and strode through the doors of the hospital. Excitement, mixed with a sense of uncertainty, lingered in our minds. We were unfamiliar with the hospital environment.

There are many reasons to celebrate being a third-year medical student. Medicine becomes more practical and hands-on; there are no more endless lectures packed with information. You get to "play doctor" and meet the patients you read about in the books. You apply what you've studied -- or at least see it applied practically to real patients. You experience different aspects of medicine that will help you decide what you want to do for the rest of your life.

Unfortunately, there are also reasons to feel anxious about third year. You will miss having a flexible schedule. As a second-year medical student, your attendance was not mandatory, and you had the luxury of listening and re-listening to lectures in the convenience of your own home. In third year, however, rotations are more like work: You *never* want to be late. If you are on surgery rotation, you have no option but to be there at 6 AM or earlier for the entire rotation. And because you're not in a classroom you no longer have a structured schedule. In addition, you and your class-mates will get different experiences and learn different things. You will be tired after rotations and you won't feel like studying at the end of the day. Many third-year students will tell you it is vacation time. Should you believe them? No!

As an International medical graduate, it's different. Getting clinical rotations can be difficult. You have options for observerships, externships and clinical rotations. Check the IMG survival guide chapter for more details.

There are many unwritten rules that we are all supposed to know, and sometimes we must learn them through our mistakes. The simple rule in medicine is that if you fail once, you must learn never to repeat that mistake. As third-year students, we learned some guidelines that have helped us excel in our clinical rotations and impress our residents and attending physicians. We hope that these tips will also help you move seamlessly from the classroom to both in-patient and out-patient clinical settings.

1.  Do not take anything that happens in the hospital personally. The hospital is a high-stress environment. Many situations that arise as you rotate -- for example, issues with unhappy patients, doctors who disagree with other doctors, nurses with attitudes -- will be completely new to you, and you will not be sure how to handle them. No matter the situation, make sure you act professionally at all times. In particular, a common problem for students is learning to accept criticism from interns, residents, and attendings. Try to focus on the reason why you are on the rotation: to learn! Try to accept constructive criticism with a smile because it will ultimately make you a better doctor.

2.  Read! Read! Read! We cannot overemphasize the extreme importance of keeping up with information. *This is the only way to impress your attending - with what you know!* We realized how easy it was to neglect our studies, but we made it a priority to read constantly on our rotations. It quickly becomes apparent when you do not read on clinical rotations, and you quickly realize how much you do not know. You cannot afford the luxury of *not* studying.

3.  Do not expect every attending physician to be a teacher. Although we know it is our attending's responsibility to teach, we also came to realize that we will meet only a few *good* teachers. Let's face it: Many of us are going to become attending physicians someday, and we cannot assume that everyone knows how to teach well. It is a skill, and the attending must be willing and able to do it. As for us, we learned a lot from the doctors who taught us and we read up on the rest.

4.  Be on time to every rotation. In fact, getting there early is safer and better. You can spend some time reading the charts until your intern/ resident arrives.

5. Be professional in your attire and in the way you carry yourself. Remember, these physicians will fill out your evaluations and possibly write you a letter of recommendation for your residency application. They will remember you, so always leave a good impression.

6. Ask for letters of recommendation early. Doctors are busy and can take months to write a letter.

7. Read up on your patients' conditions, especially if they have a diagnosis that you are not familiar with. You should be able to understand what the doctors are discussing.

8. Do not ask questions if you can look up the answers. Jot down your questions somewhere so that you don't forget them, and look them up when you get home. It looks bad if you ask simple questions that you should know or can easily research.

9. Study early. Remember, you have a shelf exam or school exam at the end of each rotation. This test usually counts as a big portion of your rotation grade. These clinical grades are important for when you apply to residency, so you want to do really well on them. Also, you have 2 board examinations at the end of third year: the clinical knowledge and the clinical skills exams. Thus, studying early is crucial.

10. Strengthen your residency applications (and don't put this off). Keep up with the work; we started working on our curriculum vitae right after taking the boards. You will need this to request a letter of recommendation from your attending physicians. It is also important that you find tangible projects or research to pursue which will help strengthen your residency application.

The third year is all about what you decide to make it, in terms of both academic learning and clinical experience. Most hospitals have few lectures for each rotation, if any. That leaves learning in your hands, to a certain extent. The best advice we can give is to read as much as you can during third year. Seek advice from upper classmates and find out what resources are the best to use for each rotation. Read books, journals, and exam questions every night. Even if you are tired after a grueling 12-hour surgery shift, make it a point to read for at least 1 hour every night and catch up more on weekends. Also, keep a pocket-sized review book with you at all times. There will be a lot of time to kill that you can use wisely to read.

Each person's experience is different as a third-year student. We are not saying that we had a blast on every rotation, but we made the best out of each one. Try to maintain your self-confidence and believe in yourself. Do not be ashamed of being wrong! You have earned the right to be part of this elite group. Use every opportunity as a chance to learn and keep your eyes on the prize. Then you will be well on your way to becoming a good physician.

*Original article was published on Medscape*

# CHAPTER 22:
## Surviving medical school

THIS BOOK WAS written to provide you the secrets and "ins and outs" of how to get high scores on the USMLE and COMLEX, and how to match into top residency. This short chapter is designed to give you some tips and basic rules that you should always keep in mind throughout your journey as a medical student. It is all about studying smart and studying hard. Notice: studying smart comes before studying hard, because time is the most invaluable treasure and your closest friend during medical school. If you can manage your time successfully, you can still enjoy your life to a certain extent (do not get too excited). We put this chapter at the end of the book because we did not want to deviate from the big picture of the book, which, in a nutshell, is studying effectively for the Boards.

The following are the most common "big" mistakes that students commit from day one in medical school. Unfortunately, many students eventually realize that they caused more damage than good to their minds and bodies. Some of these damages are short-term, while others are long-term. For example, students experience quick burnout after their first year of medical school due to intense and continuous studying. Many students sacrifice their health for medical school. Imagine your cholesterol level at 250 mg/dl from all the hamburgers and free pizzas that you ate at the club meetings or presentations you attended. This is all avoidable; at least recognize what the mistakes are, so you can minimize the damage early on.

The rule is simple; you do not need to sacrifice much besides time to get through medical school. Sacrificing other things, like your health, should be a warning sign to you that you are not being efficient with your time. So read the following carefully …

## Number Zero: Realizing what you got yourself into

The study of medicine is a long process and demands a great amount of discipline and sacrifice. Yet the reward is priceless. Many physicians say that it is not the same as it used to be, that things have changed quite a bit. Although this might be true, they are strictly talking about money. The financial reward might have decreased, but as a first-year or second-year student, you should not be thinking about medicine only in terms of money. We are hoping that you picked medicine for the amazing field that it is, the rich opportunities it provides for helping humans, and the avenues it opens for making a difference in the world. Think of the bright side—you will be providing people with medical care and a better life until you decide to retire; something as simple as giving sample medication to someone whose co-pay is high can ease the suffering of that patient. So, think of every long night of studying as an opportunity to learn to become a great physician one day. Think of all the people who did not get into medical school who wish they were in your spot.

Medicine is rewarding in many aspects besides money, and it will all come once you graduate and finish residency. So be patient—the path of medical school is long, but it has an end - a bright and happy one. Yet this end is the beginning of another journey, where you harvest the products of your hard work and continue getting rewards on a daily basis with every patient you help as a practicing physician.

## Number One: Depriving yourself of healthy, fresh food and buying fast food, junk, and processed foods

This very common and very serious mistake is usually committed for the sake of saving time to study. Imagine what you put your body through, just so you can gain an extra ten or fifteen minutes for studying. Over a two-year period, there might be long-term consequences to your health. Your brain needs fresh food, water, fruits, and vegetables. Please try to graduate medical school without ulcers, hypertension, diabetes, and high cholesterol. There is no reason you should not be able to cook (if you know how to) or buy veggies and fruits. Your brain works better on bananas and strawberries than on French fries and popcorn. We guarantee you, not only will you save money, but you will save something far more important—your health from deteriorating.

## Number Two: Ruining your health by not exercising

"Oh, why should I waste thirty minutes on exercise when I can read a few more pages about the obesity, heart attacks, and strokes that happen to people with sedentary lifestyles?" Sounds like a contradiction to anyone?

Again, this is a very common mistake, and it affects more students than those who used to avidly work out and exercise before medical school started. You will be sad, with low self-esteem and less energy than you can potentially experience if you do exercise. You should be able to maintain at least a thirty-minute workout four times a week up until the day of your Boards. It is not wasted time; you can listen to lectures at the same time and hit two birds with one stone. Your body deserves to stay healthy and be in great shape. Work exercise into your schedule; make it a mandatory part of your day. Most medical schools have a gym on campus, which should be sufficient for a quick thirty-minute power workout—so no excuses.

## Number Three: Pulling all-nighters and depriving your body and brain of sleep

Neglecting sleep is such a bad idea. As grandma says; healthy body, healthy mind. We guarantee you if you pull an all-nighter and go to class the next day: one, you will not absorb much; two, you will be wasting time because you will probably end up having to listen to the lecture again; and three, you will probably need a nap when you come back from school, which means you will sleep later and wake up the next day sleep-deprived … and the cycle continues. If you plan your time well, you should be able to get the seven or eight hours that you were used to before medical school. Your classmates may hate you, because their sleep cycles will be all messed up, and they'll be exhausted all the time. But that's okay; it is about being smart with your time.

Caffeine addiction is common among medical students. Beware of this! Not only will you develop side effects and withdrawal symptoms, it might reflect negatively on your studies. Caffeine might wake you up the night before the test, but it might not get you through the test. We cannot tell you not to drink coffee, but everything should be done in moderation. **Needless to say, please stay away from alcohol and drugs!**

## Number Four: Competing with your classmates and comparing your grades with others

We all know we had to be competitive to get into the field of medicine. By now, we believe you are aware of that. However, medical school is a leveling ground for all of us. We all came from various backgrounds and different undergraduate schools, where enduring the pressure of getting good grades to enter medical school was about the survival of the fittest.

But once you are accepted to medical school, it becomes a level playing field, where the best of the best students are assembled to learn medicine.

Most medical students are still engulfed in the mentality of competing with other students, for numerous reasons: satisfaction, to measure their progress, a superiority complex, or because it simply feels good. These attributes will clearly not make you a better physician, and you scoring a 95 percent on your pathology exam has no bearing on whether you will be a great pathologist or clinician.

As soon as you walk out of your first exam, look around. You will see people screaming at each other, pulling their hair, and gambling their lives away on what answer was right for question number thirteen. It is easy to spot them; they will ask you if you chose option C for question 84. Seriously? Do they think you'll remember that? Avoid everyone after the exam, and be friends with those who share this philosophy, because the moment the exam is over, you should be ready to move on to the next task. When the grade is released, you can review the test on your own and see where your mistakes are so you can avoid them in the future. The best advice we received during our career as undergraduate year was from an organic chemistry teacher, Dr. Maria Vogt, PhD, from Bloomfield College, who warned us, "You love to compete with other students because you make them your yardstick for measuring your progress and how smart you think you are, but what you do not know is that there are a lot of smarter people than you out there. The best way to be your best is to compete only with yourself, because you will never outcompete yourself, and you will become a better person every time you try again."

We listened to this advice, and we can testify that it helped us tremendously to succeed in medical school. We never wanted to know what people's grades were; neither did we discuss exam questions or share grades with others. Comparing grades will create a hostile competitive environment that is absolutely unnecessary; you need to be with people who are calm and happy and not bragging about their 93 percent on the physiology quiz.

## Number Five: Spending time with negative people

It is easy to spot them. They walk around looking angry, depressed, and constipated ☺☺. They always talk about how they hate their lives, and they regret getting into medical school because they never sleep enough. School is too hard; they do not have time to go to the gym, et cetera. Their Facebook status is updated at least three times a day with derogatory statements about medical school. Stay away from such students, because they will drag you into their pessimism and convert you into one of the miserable people. Instead, be a positive person. Smile! You are lucky you got into medical school; why aren't you thankful? Most medical schools in the United States accept one to two hundred applicants out of five to six thousand. Day by day, it is getting more difficult to get into medical school, and many people wish they had your spot. No one said it would be easy, but success is definitely achievable. You should appreciate the gift of being a medical student—be happy that your journey began. Although it is hard now, it will get better after you take your Boards and start clinical rotations.

## Number Six: "Studying my notes ten times is probably the best way to prepare for exams."

Wrong! Do questions from day one. The only way to test your learning is to do questions. For example, after studying your BRS physiology textbook, make sure you complete the questions at the end of each chapter. This will help solidify the concepts you just read. **Studying the same thing over and over does not make you smarter, but getting a question wrong will teach you quite a bit**. Even regarding the Boards, professional educators will tell you that it is statistically proven that students who do more questions perform better on Boards, and that the only time you should go back to the big books is when you constantly miss questions on a certain topic and find that the explanations from the questions are not doing the job.

## Number Seven: "I will study for the Boards in March before my exam in June."

Not a very good idea. People will tell you that their fifth cousin did that and got 260 on USMLE or 740 on COMLEX. Please do not believe them—unless NBME sent them the wrong report, it is impossible to get such a score without hard work. Studying for the Boards begins day one of medical school. Preparing is a tough process that only a few people complete in the correct fashion. We think we've made this point very clear throughout the book.

## Number Eight: "Studying ten books on one subject is the best way to cover all the possible material they might test on the Boards."

The fact is you will never know it all, and it is impossible to predict what new topics the Board questions will cover. The high-yield material is in the review books, but even the review books will not have it all. That being said, pick a good review book that students' reviews recommend. Reading an entire pathology text before the Boards is probably not the smartest idea, but you can use one as a reference. Stick to one book you like for each subject, and do questions, the more the merrier. Again, use *First Aid for the USMLE Step 1* wisely.

## Number Nine: "I am going to be a machine and memorize it all, just memorize, memorize, memorize."

Depending on your school and the curriculum it follows, you will start your first day in school with some level of biochemistry, anatomy, physiology, histology, et cetera. On day one, columnar cells, impulse transmission, and glycolysis are probably covered. The next day, you learn about brachial plexus and cardiac output. This is an enormous amount of information overload, and students are often not prepared for it, so we all memorize, right?

Let us share a short story with you. Being told that we'd better be memorizing machines, we got our coffee, Red Bull, and power snacks and started memorizing like there was no tomorrow. Even on day one, we said to ourselves we were going to memorize the book from cover to cover, including the ISBN number and the author's name ☺☺. We memorized a tremendous amount of information. After talking to some people the next day, we realized, however, that we only retained about 50 percent of the material, and that we did not really have a solid understanding of what was going on. We realized that we packed the info in little Ziploc bags in our brains; it was all isolated—nothing was integrated. Biochemistry notes about diabetes were just biochemistry notes to us; we did not know how we could possibly link it to physiology, and we blamed it on the school curriculum, which of course is not true. We did not have the big picture in mind. Big picture?

If the material is not integrated in your mind and organized for your understanding, you will not retain the information in your long-term memory. More Details will be discussed later, but the main idea is to think of medical school as one class; it is your job to integrate it all and make it flow.

## Number Ten: "I cannot wait to be done with the Boards so I can forget all this useless information."

Oh, you did *not* just say that, did you? You will be surprised that most of what you learn in the first two years of medical school will return during residency. Attending physicians and residents like to pimp on material they are comfortable with. Some of them like microbiology, and they will make your life miserable if you do not know your bugs, while others like pharmacology and will torture you if you do not know your drugs. One day you may be doing rounds with a GI fellow who knows everything about the GI system—yes, everything, including histology, anatomy, and physiology. The next day you are with the endocrine doctor who loves hormones. Notice, this is what you learned in the first two years. So learn the material; do not just memorize it. Know it for life. **The best way to evaluate your understanding of a topic is your ability to explain it to others**; if you can do that, then you learned it well.

## Number Eleven: "I am going to study on my own because I do not need anyone's help."

Medicine is all about teamwork and sharing information. You have to be able to cooperate and work with others in groups. Even when you apply for residency, it is very important to keep this concept in mind. The moment the medical team feels that you will not be a good team player and you may have "issues" with your colleagues in the hospital, is the moment your application goes in the shredder.

Although it may be true that you *can* study on your own, it will benefit you to find yourself a small group of people (two or three maximum) who share the same principles—they like to exercise, do not like to share grades, and have a positive attitude. Once you find the right group of people, arrange to meet for two or three hours weekly for a very efficient session. Ask each other questions about concepts you do not understand, or even better, "pimp" each other on little details you think your friends might have understood. Also, arrange for a review session the night before the exam for last minute "pimping." It works great. We cannot tell you how many times friends pimped us on stuff that we didn't know, even things we had underlined six times and highlighted seven times but still did not know. Most importantly is to have a clique leader to keep people on track if the topics being discussed shift from glycolysis to football or shoes. The group leader should be the most anxious of you all, the one who is always stressed out and shaking his or her leg (restless leg syndrome ☺☺).

## Number Twelve: "I do not have time to study for the physiology quiz. Let me just do last year's exam—I heard they repeat questions."

Although it is important to do questions, it is more important to do them after you learn the material. Many people try to take the easy way out and just memorize the answers to questions from last year's material instead of studying. Please don't do it. All the material is on the Boards, and anything you do not study now is something extra you have to study before the Boards. Do not procrastinate! Use your time efficiently to avoid this situation; study and then do questions.

Remember, studying for physiology is studying for the Boards! Learn it now.

## Number Thirteen: "I am so stressed out."

Stress is normal; everyone in your class is facing similar amounts of stress, some more than others. But you will notice some people walking around with a frown on their face, while some wear a huge smile. How is that difference possible, if they are all in the same class, under the same pressure? The key is time. If you have some extra time, you are able to reduce stress. First, your friends will play a very important role—that's what friends are for, especially if they are your classmates. They can help you calm down when you are freaking out. Secondly, do something on your own that makes you feel better, whether that is exercise, yoga, listening to calm music, talking to your parents, or praying. Something out there that makes you feel better. Find it and do it. Do not let the stress affect your studies, relationships, or, most importantly, health. No one said medical school was easy; it is very stressful and demanding. However, managing stress will become very important; otherwise you will realize it is taking a toll on your life.

To Recap ...

You are going to be a doctor—step up to the prestige of the profession. Think of yourself as two entities; your body and your brain. Your brain needs to be happy in order for you to succeed in medical school. Therefore, eat healthy, exercise, sleep enough, keep your grades to yourself, stay positive and avoid negative people, study smart from day one, do questions, and study for the Boards as early as possible. Get the big picture of any topic you are covering and relate it back to the Boards. Notice all the items above share one common factor: *time.* We think time is very sacred and that it deserves a discussion here.

We all agree that managing your time is the key factor to success in medical school. So how do you study in an efficient way and make time for other activities besides studying? Everyone studies differently, but find a way that works for you, and keep adjusting it as you go along to perfect it. You will know you are doing the right thing when you have time for yourself outside of studying. Yes, it is possible to find extra time for non-school activities such as exercise, a social life, piano, soccer ... whatever you like to do, you can do it. The key points are to always plan ahead, always make a schedule, and stick to it. Studying smart, as mentioned earlier, includes studying the right material in a way so that you retain it in the shortest amount of time. For some people, this may mean talking out loud; others write on a whiteboard or make note cards; others draw, and others just read. Try all the methods and stick to your chosen method. Our clique was like a mafia; people in school knew we were walking dynamos. We were efficient to the point that we always managed to end our review session around 11 pm the night before the test and still get our eight hours of sleep. We excelled on the exams. Looking at other people who studied all night, it was very obvious that what they were doing was wrong, and there was no reason why they needed to deprive themselves of sleep to survive medical school.

Finally - we cannot emphasize this enough - we are all in a great profession. Be passionate about what you are learning! Medicine is a treasure, medicine is an art. As Henri Amiel said: *"To me the ideal doctor would be a man endowed with profound knowledge of life and of the soul, intuitively divining any suffering or disorder of whatever kind, and restoring peace by his mere presence."*

# Author's advice

WE HOPE THIS book has been an invaluable tool to you as a reader, and that the contents have shed some light on how to prepare for the Board examinations and survive medical school and match into residency. We understand your concerns and are fully aware of how deeply you want to succeed, because we were once in your shoes.

Learning to become a doctor is one of the most challenging paths you will ever take in your life, but it is the most rewarding career. You will have ups and down, good days and bad days, but in the end, it will be worth it.

Your ability to succeed on the USMLE® or COMLEX®, and in life, depends on how much effort you are willing to invest. You have the potential to do whatever you set your mind to, including achieving your USMLE dream score be it over 250+ or 700+ (COMLEX). You also possess the key to your potential freedom and success in matching into the residency you decide to choose. You are the captain of your own ship. We implore you to maintain a positive attitude throughout this USMLE preparation process and focus on your goal.

It is important for you to know that one of life's lessons is, "Success does not go to those who have a genius and a natural talent for knowledge, but to those who are willing to put enough time and work to realize their goal." ˜Anonymous˜

Remember, do not let your USMLE or COMLEX score define you. You are more than a test taker. The process is to make you a better physician. Every year some US medical students and international medical graduates fail the USMLE and COMLEX exam and want to give up because they are told they cannot match into residency. Remember, if you fail the USMLE or COMLEX the road will be tougher for you, but if you have to re-apply to residency two or three times, do it, improve your application and network to try and match again.

In conclusion,

*"There are no secrets to success. It is the result of perseverance, hard work, and learning from failure."*

Colin Powell

If this book has helped you, we would love for you to share it with your classmates and colleagues who are also preparing for the USMLE/COMLEX. We want you to share the word on social media - Facebook, Twitter, and Instagram!

If you are frustrated or struggling to study for the USMLE, we are here to help you. You should join our smashusmle reviews online USMLE prep course. We have been training international medical graduates and medical students for over 10 years. Our mission is to train 150,000 doctors over the next 30 years. Our vision is to train you to become a better physician, not a test taker.

Visit smashusmle.com to get started now.

Dr. Adeleke Adesina

CEO, Smashusmle Reviews

Smashusmle.com

admin@smashusmle.com

IG: @smashusmle

Facebook: facebook.com/smashusmle

Thank you for purchasing this book. We wish you all the best on your exams. Good luck!

# Read More!

IF YOU ARE using First Aid for the USMLE Step 1 book and you are struggling to understand the concepts in the book, do not worry anymore. Dr. Adesina has published SmashUSMLE Step 1 High Yield Review book.

This book is a comprehensive review book with over 1400 pages of detailed concepts tested on the USMLE Step 1 exam. This is the book you need. Buy it now.

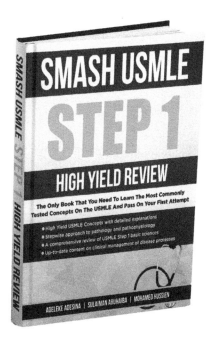

**Buy your copy on amazon.com.**
**https://www.amazon.com/dp/B08FC437PD**

# About the Authors

## Dr. Adeleke T. Adesina

DR. ADESINA is a native indigene from Nigeria. He completed high school in Nigeria before moving to the United States. He earned his Bachelor of Science in biochemistry and general biology (summa cum laude) from Bloomfield College in 2008. After college, he did research at the National Institute of Health, in Bethesda, MD.

He graduated from Rowan School of Osteopathic Medicine, New Jersey. He is currently an emergency medicine physician at Houston Methodist hospital, Texas.

Dr. Farook W. Taha

Dr. Taha graduated from Rowan School of Osteopathic Medicine, New Jersey. After graduating early from high school, he earned an associate degree in liberal arts and science before transferring to Stony Brook University in New York and completed his bachelor's degree (summa cum laude) in chemistry.

He is currently an emergency medicine physician at Dallas medical center, Dallas, Texas.

Both authors have fulfilled their dream of studying medicine, and hope that others will be inspired by the tips we share in this publication.

# Dr. Juan Jose Chango Azanza

DR. JUAN JOSE CHANGO AZANZA born and raised in Cuenca, Ecuador. He graduated as a physician at the Catholic University of Cuenca – School of Medicine, Ecuador. He completed the USMLE Step 1, Step 2 CK, Step 2 CS, and Step 3 examinations in 2017. He is currently a second-year Internal Medicine resident at the University of Connecticut (UCONN)

He is passionate about medicine in general and Internal Medicine. His future career interests are Hematology/Oncology and Academic Medicine.

His aim is to serve patients from different social and cultural backgrounds with dedication and professionalism, ensuring to provide patient-centered care with quality and compassion. He provides bilingual service to the English and Spanish-speaking patients. He is founder of ecuadoctors.com and online blog where he documents his journey to match into US residency as an international medical graduate.

# Acknowledgments

WE WOULD LIKE to thank the following people for their advice and contributions to the completion of this project.

Juan Chango, MD, Internal medicine resident, contributor of the International medical graduate ultimate survival guide to residency, ecuadoctors.com

Robert G. Savarese, DO. Author OMTReview book

Jacqueline Giacobbe, MS. Ed Rowan School of Osteopathic Medicine, Center for Teaching and Learning Academic Center, New Jersey

James White, PhD, Rowan School of Osteopathic Medicine, Neuroscience professor, author of USMLE Road Map Neuroscience and Gross Anatomy

John Barone, MD Kaplan Pathology Instructor

Olufunmilayo Johnson, Pharm. D, B.C.P.S, Clinical pharmacist

Steven Agabeji, MD, Orthopedic Surgeon, Cincinnati Children's Hospital Medical Center, Assistant Professor at University of Cincinnati, Cincinnati, OH. Author, Step-Up to Medicine

Sulaiman I S Abuhaiba, MD, PhD, Clinical Neuroelectrophysiologist and Neuroscience Researcher and publisher of many high-impact original peer-reviewed articles in the fields of epilepsy and clinical neurosciences

Zach Musa, MD, Matcharesident, matcharesident.com

# Resources

The following are high-yield, A+ rated resources that are recommended by students who took the USMLE and COMLEX.

## Review Courses

SmashUSMLE Reviews Online USMLE course by Dr. Adeleke Adesina, DO, CEO and founder, https://www.smashusmle.com/

USMLERx, https://www.usmle-rx.com/

Osmosis, osmosis.org

Physeo, www.physeo.com

Boards and Beyond: www.boardsbeyond.com

SketchyMedical: www.sketchymedical.com

Lecturio, https://www.lecturio.com/

Onlinemeded for USMLE Step 2CK, https://onlinemeded.org/

PASS Program by Dr. Francis Ihejirika, founder and CEO of PASS Program https://www.pass-program.com/

Doctors in Training http://www.doctorsintraining.com/

USMLE Success academy: https://www.usmlesuccess.net/

Cramfighter, www.cramfighter.com

Picmonic, www.picmonic.com

Boards Boot Camp for COMLEX http://www.Boardsbootcamp.com/level1.php

## Flashcards

Anki decks: www.ankisrs.net

First Aid Step 1 Flash Facts, https://www.usmle-rx.com/

Memorang, http://www.memorangapp.com/

## Question Banks

UWorld Question Bank: www.uworld.com

Amboss Qbank: https://www.amboss.com/

Kaplan Question Bank (2,400 questions): www.kaplanmedical.com

USMLERx Qmax(3,000 questions): https://www.usmle-rx.com/

OMTREVIEW COMLEX Qbank, OMTReview.com (5200 COMLEX questions)

COMBANK- for COMLEX: http://www.combankmed.com

## Assessment Tests

NBOME COMSAE (Comprehensive Osteopathic Medical Self-Assessment Examination: http://www.nbome.org

NBME Self-Assessment Exam: https://www.nbme.org/taking-assessment/self-assessments

## Free Online Resources

Medbullets Free Review, www.medbullets.com

Medschool pathology: http://www.medicalschoolpathology.com/

WebPath: The Internet Pathology Laboratory Free (online version): https://webpath.med.utah.edu/

Pathology website: John Barone, MD: www.baronerocks.com

Comprehensive Review Books

First Aid for the USMLE Step 1 2020: A Student to Student Guide,

Tao Le, Vikas Bhushan(Author), McGraw-Hill Medical; 30th edition (January 2, 2020) ISBN: 978-1260462043

SMASH USMLE STEP 1 High Yield Review Adeleke Adesina ASIN B08FC437PD

First Aid Cases for the USMLE Step 1 Tao LE Fourth edition ISBN 978-1260143133

Crush Step 1: The Ultimate USMLE Step 1 Review 2nd Edition ISBN 978-0323481632

USMLE Step 1 Secrets in Color BROWN ISBN 978-0323396790

## By Subject
### Anatomy and Embryology

High-Yield Gross Anatomy, DUDEK, Lippincott Williams & Wilkins, 2014, 320 pages, ISBN 978-1451190236

Clinical Anatomy Made Ridiculously Simple, GOLDBERG MedMaster, 2016, 175 pages, ISBN 978-0940780972

High-Yield Neuroanatomy, FIX Lippincott Williams and Wilkins, ISBN 978-1451193435

High-Yield Embryology, DUDEK ISBN 978-1451176100

USMLE Road Map: Gross Anatomy, WHITE ISBN 978-0071445160

### Behavioral science

BRS Behavioral Science (Board Review Series) 2016 Edition Barbara Fadem PhD ISBN: 978-1496310477

High-Yield Biostatistics, Epidemiology, and Public Health (High-Yield Series) Fourth Edition ISBN-13: 978-1451130171

### Biochemistry

Pixorize www.pixorize.com

Lippincott's Illustrated Reviews: Biochemistry, FERRIER, Lippincott Williams and Wilkins. 2017, ISBN 978-1496344496

## Immunology and Microbiology

Basic Immunology, ABBAS, Elsevier, 2019, 336 pages, ISBN 978-0323549431

Clinical Microbiology Made Ridiculously Simple, GLADWIN MedMaster. 2019, ISBN 978-1935660330

Medical Microbiology and Immunology Flash Cards ROSENTHAL Elsevier, 2016, 192 flash cards, ISBN 978-0323462242

Microcards Flashcards, HARPAVAT Lippincott Williams and Wilkins. 2015. ISBN 978-1451192353

## Pathology

Pathoma, www.pathoma.com

Pathoma: Fundamentals of Pathology, SATTAR, Pathoma, 2019, 218 pages, ISBN 9780983224631

The pathology guy, www.pathguy.com

Rapid Review: Pathology, GOLJAN Mosby 2018 edition ISBN 978-0323476683

BRS Pathology, SCHNEIDER Lippincott Williams and Wilkins, 2009, ISBN 978-1451115871

Robbins and Cotran Review of Pathology, KLATT, Elsevier, 2014, 504 pages, ISBN 978-1455751556

Crash Course: Pathology, XIU, Elsevier, 2019, 438 pages, ISBN 978-0702073540

## Pharmacology

Lange Pharmacology Flash Cards, BARON McGraw-Hill, 2017,189 flash cards, ISBN 978-1259837241

Lippincott's Illustrated Reviews: Pharmacology, HARVEY Lippincott Williams and Wilkins, 2018. 564 pages, ISBN 978-1496384133

## Physiology

BRS Physiology, COSTANZO Lippincott Williams and Wilkins, (2018) ISBN: 978-1496367617

Pathophysiology of Heart Disease, LILLY, Lippincott Williams & Williams, 2015, 480 pages, ISBN 978-1451192759

Osteopathic Manipulative Medicine OMT Review 4th Edition, Robert G. Savarese, ISBN 978-0692157565

PreTest Physiology, METTING, McGraw-Hill, 2013, 528 pages, ISBN 978-0071791427

Color Atlas of Physiology, SILBERNAGL, Thieme, 2015, 472 pages, ISBN 978-3135450070

## References

*First Aid for the USMLE Step 1 2020: A Student to Student Guide, Tao Le, Vikas Bhushan(Author), McGraw-Hill Medical; 30th edition (January 2, 2020) ISBN: 978-1260462043*

Made in the USA
Columbia, SC
21 September 2020